Inspired Excellence

Purpose

Worthwhile Work

Making a Difference

Rich Bluni, RN

DEDICATION

"The circle is a reminder that each moment is not just the present but is inclusive of our gratitude to the past and our responsibility to the future."

Kazuaki Tanahashi

This book is heartfully dedicated to those who have built the foundations upon which we all stand. The thought leaders and pioneers who we look back upon with admiration, awe, and respect. Thank you for your legacy.

This book is dedicated to those who, at this very moment in time, are both the architects and builders of what we presently experience as "healthcare," and who every day—through their minds, hands, and spirit—tirelessly give so very much to make this world a better place with grace, tenacity, and soul.

This book is dedicated to those who will someday be the thinkers, leaders, innovators, and creators who will take the wheel of healthcare and steer us into a future of promise, hope, and light that today we can only dream of.

May all of us—past, present, and future—remember that we are all part of this circle and that as it turns, we are doing work that is purposeful, worthwhile, and makes a difference.

Hold close to your heart a deep knowing that what we do is also inspiring, beautiful, and truly sacred.

TABLE OF CONTENTS

FOREWORD

"The greatest danger for most of us lies not in setting our aim too high and falling short, but in setting our aim too low and achieving our mark."

Michelangelo

"Inspired Excellence."

Congratulations. By opening this book and learning the Nine Principles® Framework set forth and how to apply them, you've started on an exciting journey toward leadership excellence. Leadership is the single most important difference maker enabling good organizations to become extraordinary to successfully achieve their mission and goals while making a greater impact in the world. *Inspired Excellence* captures the "how" to become excellent as a leader and, in living these principles, brings inspiration and leadership together in a powerful combination.

Leadership excellence is at the heart of every extraordinary organization, and leadership is a set of skills that can be learned and mastered. Great leaders are indeed made, not just born. And leadership goes well beyond a role, job, or title. The Nine Principles® Framework in *Inspired Excellence* is a true north to aspire to for every person in every organizational role and level. How to become an excellent healthcare worker, an excellent health-care leader, and perhaps most importantly, an excellent human being. After reading this book, I renewed my commitment to becoming a better leader for the thousands of amazing people who make up our company. But it also inspired me to be excellent in other personal aspects of my life.

The principles set forth in this book have encouraged me to continually revitalize my connection to purpose and integrate my deeply held values into my leadership of Huron. Together, applying evidence-based principles with a full heart and awakened spirit that is connected to purpose is an unstoppable combination of bringing my whole self to our company's journey.

The tried-and-true methods to drive Excellence, founded on years of research, have been instrumental for my own leadership at Huron and have supported the transformation of our company over the past decade. We've seen amazing results from the old and new methods shared on these pages.

But more than telling the story or sharing the journey of one person and what they did to move a single organization, this book takes a wider perspective and does a deeper dive. This isn't a textbook or an autobiography but rather a guidebook, a map, or a beacon to help you to tell your story and take your journey. It is about YOU.

And you could not be in better hands for this journey than with Rich Bluni. He is someone who has been where you are—experiencing both the agonies and triumphs of healthcare and leadership. Rich is also an accomplished coach and a gifted storyteller who brings the lessons and tactics throughout this book to life with practical examples that will get you thinking.

However, if I may be so bold, this book isn't just here to engage your mind (most bookshelves, real and virtual, are full of those). As I closed this book on my first reading, I felt it expanded my spirit. My spirit for leadership, mentoring, encouraging, motivating, accomplishing, and, yes, inspiring.

A smart leader is expected in all good organizations, and an excellent leader is certainly found in all great organizations. However, if you want your organization to be extraordinary, seek to be an inspired leader. They are increasingly rare and exactly what we need more of these days. It is certainly what I want my leaders to strive for at Huron. It is what I sincerely and humbly strive for in my own personal leadership journey. And I believe it is what we all truly hope to be.

On behalf of our entire team at Huron, thank you for what you do and how you serve. The mere fact that you're reading this book says a lot about you. I hope you are a different leader by the time you get to the last page than you were when you opened to the first page.

I know I was.

Sincerely,

Mark Hussey
Chief Executive Officer and President
Huron Consulting Group Inc.

HOW TO GET THE MOST OUT OF THIS BOOK

Welcome to *Inspired Excellence*!

This book is about leadership. It is for anyone who practices leadership regardless of their position in an organization, and we're thrilled to share it with you.

The Nine Principles® Framework— What Is It?

You will find the content of this book is organized around the Nine Principles® Framework, which is the foundation of our leadership work here at Huron. We firmly believe—and organizations have shown—that this framework is the key to creating, inspiring, and sustaining excellence.

The Nine Principles® Framework is both TIMELY and TIMELESS. It is timely because we need it now more than ever, and it is timeless because these principles stand the test of time and continue to be even more significant today to drive positive change. Since their creation in 1999, they have provided an important foundation and inspiration for countless organizations and leaders in creating and sustaining a culture of excellence.

Each principle of the Nine Principles® Framework (Figure 1) is unique and contains powerful tools and tactics that guide and support leadership behaviors that produce positive results. As we review each principle, you will discover how they can be applied to your own leadership journey.

NINE PRINCIPLES® FRAMEWORK

Principle 1:
Commit to Excellence

Set high expectations to achieve results while still living out your mission and values.

Principle 2:
Measure the
Important Things

Continuously track progress to achieve results with an improvement mindset.

Principle 3:
Build a Culture
Around Service

Serve others with great care and concern.

Principle 4:
Develop Leaders to
Develop People

Coach people to be their best at work.

Principle 5:
Focus on
Employee Engagement

Attend to aspirations and desires in the workplace.

Principle 6:
Be Accountable

Commit to individual accountability to achieve organizational goals.

Principle 7:
Align Behaviors with
Goals and Values

Apply consistent practices to move the organization in a positive direction.

Principle 8:
Communicate
at All Levels

Help people understand how and why what they do matters.

Principle 9:
Recognize and
Reward Success

Value and appreciate people working together to get results.

Figure 1: Nine Principles' Framework

These principles also set behaviors and expectations to create and sustain a culture of excellence—the kind of place where individuals choose to work and achieve great things. By enabling an environment where high performers thrive, the principles provide a way for organizations, leaders, and teams to attract and retain the best people, who in turn help everyone find their way to inspired excellence.

Tips to Maximize Your Learning

We know that improvement is essential to organizational excellence, and we're excited to help you get there.

Within each chapter and principle, you will discover valuable tools, tactics, and illustrations to help you develop your leadership skills and elevate every aspect of your work. As you dive into each chapter and principle, please take a moment to reflect on how they relate to you and your unique circumstances. Regardless of your role, discipline, or type of organization, your unwavering commitment to applying these principles will drive results.

Our aim is to make each chapter easy to read and reference, designed for leaders at all levels. We've packed them with relatable stories to guide you along the way. These practical approaches and real-life examples demonstrate how to implement leadership principles in a way that will deeply impact how and whom you lead. Share our stories and add your and your team's personal ones to make the teachings come alive.

While we draw numerous examples from the healthcare profession, we recognize that some of you reading this may work in other fields. Fear not—the Nine Principles® Framework described in this book is timely, timeless, and transcendent—it can apply to you and your organization, no matter who you are. A good practice while reading is to "relate and not compare."

And don't worry about the order of each principle. Great leadership involves both linear and non-linear thinking, so these principles don't follow a proscriptive order, nor is any one more or less important than any other. But don't forget. When all nine principles are present, excellence is not far away.

Think about it like rungs on a ladder—all of them together help you climb higher.

Let the Journey Begin!

So let's get started. While we encourage you to read every page, we also want this content to serve as a valuable reference as you navigate your daily leadership responsibilities. Perhaps one chapter, in particular, calls out to you. Answer that call and read that chapter! Make this voyage your own. Keep this book close by and use it to enhance your work and efforts at achieving excellence.

Look at this book as a roadmap. In that spirit, feel free to journey as you like and make whatever stops along the way make the most sense for where you are and what you hope to accomplish. We are confident this guide will inspire and empower you to take your leadership skills, team, and organization to the next level.

Thank you for investing your time in reading this book. Our utmost desire is that it has equipped you with invaluable insights and knowledge to propel you toward becoming an exceptional leader.

Best wishes to you in all your future endeavors. We have faith that the lessons gleaned from these pages will serve you well. May you continue to strive for excellence—inspired excellence. Thank you!

INTRODUCTION

Journey to Leadership

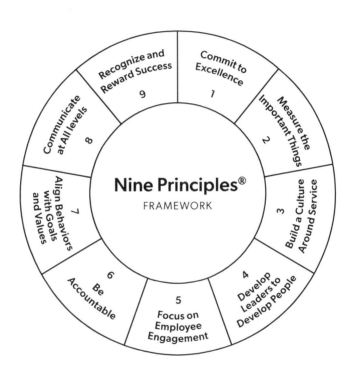

"The secret of change is to focus all of your energy not on fighting the old, but on building the new."

Socrates

Hello. My name is Rich Bluni. I am an R.N., and I've been in healthcare for more than 30 years. I wasn't one of those people who always knew they wanted to be in healthcare. I know of them, these unicorns of mythology. You know of them as well. Some of you may even be one of them.

You probably remember how it went. In second grade, or thereabouts, the teacher would go around the class and ask the age-old question, "What do you want to be when you grow up?" Among all the kids wanting to be astronauts, ballerinas, quarterbacks, race-car drivers, and movie stars, there were the sincere ones who wanted to be nurses, physicians, physical therapists, and all of the types of people my favorite 20th-century human, Mr. Rogers, called "the helpers."

My wife was one of those. When asked, she told Sister Eugenia, her kindergarten teacher, "I'm going be a nurse someday!" She has been a nurse now for more than twenty years.

She knew at five!

Not me. Nope. I was asked the same question sometime around 1972, and my answer was, "Batman." Pinky-swear, that's what I said. My answer must not have amused my teacher because she promptly relocated my chair to the corner. This location became a familiar spot for me throughout my academic career, and I even nicknamed it "The Batcave." I chose this name because it sounded much cooler than simply calling it "The Corner."

Why didn't she like my answer? I'll never know. I mean, who wouldn't want to be Batman? For most of my life, being Batman was as likely a career choice as healthcare.

But truly, healthcare wasn't on my radar. At least not that I was aware of. But like many of us who have come to find our place in healthcare, I had an "influence;" a driver or exemplar working behind the scenes opening that door.

Meet Jack, AKA My Dad.

When I was younger, my dad was the most influential person in my life. His name was Jack. He was known then as a "maintenance foreman" at Jackson Memorial Hospital in Miami. These days those jobs are called facilities management or something similar, but he started working there in 1968.

He was a leader and had several workers who reported to him. If you ever asked my dad back in the day, "What do you do?" he always responded, "I work in healthcare." (More on that later.)

My impression of my dad was that he loved his job. He was supposed to be there at 8 a.m. but was usually there around 6 a.m.

As I got older, I thought my dad was a bit ridiculous. Who goes to their job early and for free? But then, when I went to the hospital with my dad a few times as a kid, I started to see why. He wasn't arriving early to be first in line for the fried eggs and biscuits in the hospital cafeteria. He was going for the people.

He met with his off-going night-shift team to see how they were doing and ensure they were well-supplied and felt safe, listened to, and heard. We call it "rounding" these days. My dad would have simply called it "Caring about my people."

He had breakfast with the oncoming day shift, including environmental services, nurses, pharmacists, administrators, and security. He found the issues that needed fixing before they even made it into the "request system." He had them fixed, often before the sun rose. He also knew the people, and they knew him.

I remember being with my dad and marveling at that. They all looked different, spoke different languages, and wore different uniforms and scrubs. Some worked in offices, some worked with patients, and some did both. Some fixed things or cooked or cleaned. My dad had a connection to all of them. He wanted to know more than what tasks to complete. He also asked about their kids, their health, and their lives.

He was interested in them as people.

Isn't that ultimately what separates the "good" leaders from the "great" ones? If you knew my dad, you would know this wasn't an ego trip. His actions weren't about making him look good, impressing people, moving up the food chain, or achieving some impressive title. That wasn't his driving force. It just wasn't. So, where did this come from?

And then it hit me, like the Batmobile at full speed. It wasn't so much that my dad loved his "job." I mean, he was great at it—he mastered it, he could fix anything. But it wasn't his "job" that he loved...

He once said to me, "I love my work. My job, sometimes, well, that's a different story..."

Think about a great human, a Nelson Mandela or a Mother Theresa. We never say, "They were about their 'Life's JOB.'" We use the phrase "Life's WORK" instead. Now that comes from a much deeper reservoir.

Your job is the education, skills, experiences, and tasks you need to be able to do daily. Don't get me wrong, that's super important. But your work, that comes from a deeper place. If "job" lives symbolically in the brain, "work" lives in the heart… or, if you will, the soul.

My dad truly saw what he did as his "life's work." He lived and breathed something that I didn't even come to learn about until much later.

Huron Flywheel®

Many of you may be familiar with Huron's Flywheel. This Flywheel demonstrates how organizations can create momentum by engaging the PASSION of their employees to apply ACTIONS AND BEHAVIORS, guided by the Nine Principles® Framework to achieve RESULTS.

Historically, a flywheel is a heavy wheel that regulates the speed of machinery. It takes a while to get started, but it turns smoothly and efficiently once it starts. Momentum takes over, and the wheel turns almost effortlessly. You hear the engine, you hear the push that starts it purring, and as the engine moves, momentum gains until the momentum is so great it is difficult to stop. In fact, did you know a train going 55 mph can take over a mile to stop? It's like that!

The Flywheel symbolizes and illustrates the power that purpose, passion, actions, and results generate to create momentum in an organization. Once the Flywheel gets to spinning, it is hard to stop!

Purpose, Worthwhile Work, and Making a Difference

At the center of the Flywheel, the hub, we see Purpose, Worthwhile Work, and Making a Difference. It always struck me that when looking at the Flywheel and reflecting about my dad, it doesn't say "Worthwhile JOB."

Say that out loud. Now, replace "job" with "work." See what I mean? No comparison.

Passion

The first part of the Flywheel is passion. Passion fuels self-motivation through a personal commitment to beliefs, values, and community to drive our actions and set the Flywheel in motion. Passion motivates us to do what we do. It's what gets us up in the morning. For example, healthcare professionals' values and passion for healing and service drive them. Education professionals have a passion for learning that drives them. Pilots are passionate about customer safety. Passion is a high bar for all employees in all industries. The passion people bring to their work sets the Flywheel in motion by connecting the dots to the hub of purpose, worthwhile work, and making a difference so that people see and know how they can make a difference.

Fuel the passion that brings people to work by rewarding and recognizing the behaviors that help your organization achieve the desired results, celebrate successes, and focus on what's working well. Self-motivation born of passion is what sets the Flywheel spinning and in motion.

Action

The next part of the Flywheel is Action. This part represents the actions, behaviors, skills, and principles that guide employees' passion toward desired outcomes and results. At Huron, we use the Nine Principles® Framework captured in this book. This framework helps leaders identify and put into practice the behaviors that will make the greatest impact and bring focus to what's most important. Connect these behaviors back to the core value of making a difference, and your employees will feel motivated to hardwire them and will understand the difference they truly make.

For example, when a nurse identifies an early stroke during Hourly Rounding® and saves a patient's life, they understand the why of Hourly Rounding® and will repeat it. When a leader rounds on an employee, makes a personal connection, and learns someone is struggling and how they can help, they understand the why of a leader rounding with employees and will repeat it. Their passion reignites, their behaviors are reinforced, and they will continue their meaningful work toward achieving their goals and fueling the Flywheel.

Results

The third part of the Flywheel is Results. Results accelerate momentum for sustained success by achieving goals, key performance indicators (KPIs), and outcomes. Without tangible results, the Flywheel slows, and leaders become disheartened and lose momentum.

However, when an organization and its employees see results, the Flywheel sets in motion a positive, upward spiral of success. When organizations start to see their desired results, they focus on what is getting done instead of what isn't. When organizations focus on the positive impact of their employee's actions, they feel more motivated to repeat the behaviors that lead to achieving those desired results. So, the Flywheel begins to spin even faster.

No "Just-A's"

When I think of the Flywheel, especially the center and the hub, I can't help but think of my dad.

I recall at a gathering when someone asked my dad, "What do you do?" and he answered, "I work in healthcare."

A distant family member said mockingly, "Aren't you just a maintenance guy?" My dad was never easily ruffled. He just calmly turned to this man and said, "Oh no. There's no such thing as a "just-a" in healthcare!"

Not to be outdone, the sneering relative replied, "Oh, are you so worthwhile? Do you save anyone's life? Will anyone die if the maintenance guy doesn't show up to work? What are you now, some kinda brain surgeon?"

Everyone went silent in that circle. Especially me. Dad grew up on the streets of Brooklyn during the Great Depression, and was tough. I was nervous about his response. But my dad kept his calm and smiled. "No, I don't do brain surgery. But one of the things I do is maintain and test the hospital generators."

The grumpy relative stared at my dad with a confused look. My dad continued, "If I see myself as 'just-a' maintenance man, then maybe I wouldn't take that task seriously. After all, as you said, it isn't brain surgery. But suppose I shrugged off that task, and the generators weren't properly maintained, fueled, and tested. Those generators wouldn't do their work when the power goes off unexpectedly. The people doing that brain surgery you just mentioned might have some trouble using their ventilators, equipment, and tools. Maybe someone could die."

The room was silent. Dad continued, "Yes. I take what I do seriously. There's no 'just-a's' in healthcare. We are all different rungs on the same ladder. The fifth rung isn't more important or less so than the fourth rung. No one can climb if any of us are missing in action."

There was no microphone during this conversation, but if there had been, it would have dropped. I often share this story in the presentations I give. It was pivotal in my life and a reminder for all of us. There's no such thing as a "Just-A" in healthcare. All of us do this great work because we want our experiences to be of purpose. By its very nature, all that is done in healthcare is worthwhile; at the end of the day, human beings have a deep need to make a difference.

Way before it was so eloquently worded as "Purpose, Worthwhile Work, and Making a Difference," my dad was already living it, as were so many others before and since. After all, a model rarely invents anything. It usually just creates a visual of what many of us already knew to be true in our hearts.

My dad was so passionate about healthcare that he and several colleagues from across the organization formed "The Image Committee." Its purpose was to represent employees diversely and collaboratively through charitable work and engagement. They had employee fairs, picnics, and fundraisers to help those in need.

To address a significant nursing shortage, this committee created a scholarship fund for employees or their direct family members to attend nursing school, with the agreement they would work for the hospital after graduation. My dad was one of the primary movers of this initiative. In between construction projects, painting, plumbing work, generator maintenance, and leading his team, my dad, the maintenance foreman, was helping to address a nursing shortage.

In late 1989, my dad was diagnosed with terminal cancer. They said he had a year, maybe two, to live.

Some of us have had to hear those words about a loved one. It's never easy, and you're never ready. I was 22 years old at the time, and the "Batman" career, let's say, hadn't panned out. After returning from NYC (I'd moved there after graduating high school), I worked as a waiter, painting houses, and in nightclubs as a bartender.

I spent most of my evenings working and most of my days helping to take care of my dad. My dad took care of everyone and had only called out sick three times since 1968. That person, my dad, now needed me to take care of him. I had never done that before, and while I've worked since I was 10 years old with my first job mowing neighbors' lawns for $3, I had never felt so good as when I was helping with my dad. I felt like I was doing something real, significant, and genuinely purposeful.

I fed him and bathed him. Sometimes I read to him, and other times I just sat with him at his bedside. All in the very hospital he loved so much.

They had to put a sign on the door because visitors were nonstop. Everyone came to see Jack. The hospital president came daily, as did the CNO and the CFO. EVS, facility operations, food service, nurses, and security staff also came. All the people I saw growing up, familiar faces and new ones. They were as diverse as you can imagine in many ways. But they were all there for the same reason.

Love.

They loved my dad. How could you not? This man who lived purpose, who made everyone feel that their work was worthwhile, and who made a difference. After all, when you think of it, the whole center of the Flywheel could just say one word:

"Love." And we'd all still "get it."

One day one of his nurses came in while I was cleaning up my dad, and she helped me finish. She paused as she looked me in the eyes and said, "I've been watching you these past weeks. You'd make an excellent nurse, you know!"

Without missing a beat, my dad looked up and said, "Maybe he'll listen to you. I've been telling him for years!" And he had. But I never thought that would be possible. After all, I was the kid who spent most of my life in "the corner" (aka "The Batcave"). Nursing? Me? No, that's never going to happen.

But my dad and I talked long into that night about my future, and he assured me if I wanted it bad enough, I could do it. Not only that, I could even go to nursing school for free because of the program he helped put into place many decades before. So I began that journey.

The nursing school even named a scholarship after my dad, which they graciously made me the first recipient of, and that offset the cost of books and scrubs, and even my first stethoscope. He got to see that happen. The academic part of nursing school didn't come easily to me. Especially the math. But my dad used to tell me, and as I sit here typing these words, I can almost hear his voice, "If you want it bad enough, you'll find a way to get the skills, then you'll start making progress which is going to make you want it even more."

So many years later, when I came to work for Huron, I realized that that's the outside of the Flywheel. It starts with Passion (You want it!), then it moves to Action (You learn what to do and how to do it. You take action). Then you start making progress (Results) which excites you and makes you want it even more (Passion)! This Flywheel keeps spinning because you want it, you learn how to do it, you start seeing results, and you want it even more!

On October 11, 1990, the hospice nurse caring for my dad called me as I walked into my apartment. I had just left his bedside at home after having bathed him. She simply said, "Come back, honey. Your dad is going."

On the drive there, I turned the radio on. The Elton John song "Rocketman" came on, and the refrain repeated, "...and I think it's gonna' be a long, long time" as I pulled into the driveway. I opened the front door to my parents' house and could hear my mom crying. My oldest brother stood like a sentinel at my dad's door, waiting. When he saw me, he quietly shook his head.

Dad was gone. He was 59. I just missed his last moment. The hospice nurse would later tell me how often they wait until someone leaves to finish their journey. And now, I've seen it many times in my career, caring for those about to transition. Perhaps you have, as well. I sat with him. He looked so peaceful. I took my time. This time was sacred.

Sacred. That's a word to sit with, isn't it? It's a good one to describe who and what we are in healthcare. What we do is truly sacred. After all, it is usually a person in healthcare who is the first to touch you as you enter this world, and it is often a person in healthcare who is the last to touch you as you leave this world. Our hands touch the sacred.

So much heart goes into healthcare. Sometimes our hearts are full. Other times our hearts are broken. But "heart;" that's another word to sit with. There's a lot of heart that goes into this work.

On the drive home the next day, I sat in silence, and then, needing some distraction, I turned on the radio. "Rocketman" came on again. I pulled over as I listened to Elton John's beautiful voice sing to me, reminding me, as I decided to take it, that I would see my dad again someday, a long, long time from then. And I finally allowed myself to cry. He wasn't "just-a" dad. He was my hero.

My dad's funeral was standing room only. I saw so many familiar faces and so many new ones. They say over 500 people came that day. They all told me stories about "Jack." They loved him.

I gave his eulogy. At 22, it was the first public speech I ever gave, and I had my dad's name badge in my pocket. Funnily enough, I speak for a living now and often still carry that name badge. It's sitting with me as I type these words. It's the only thing I asked my mom for after Dad passed away.

They named a street after my dad at the hospital he loved so much. I got to be there when they unveiled it. I was at work that day as an R.N. at the very place my dad had worked so many years before.

I've been a nurse since 1993. I've worked in pediatric oncology, PICU, and trauma ICU. Then I became a healthcare leader as a clinical manager of an ER. I then became a director of risk management and patient safety before coming to Huron as a coach in 2007. Now I speak full-time all over North America at conferences, hospitals, and health-care organizations. I've written three books related to healthcare leadership, engagement, and nursing.

I learned a lot about being a leader from my dad. I've continued to learn and grow as I've had the absolute privilege of coaching and working with healthcare leaders and executives for the last 16 years. While they are all unique, I found one commonality in every leader I've encountered. They all have a story. They all have something that drove them, or as I say, called them, to healthcare.

Sacred Work

We get into healthcare for big reasons because we know that what we do is more than "just-a" job. It is worthwhile work. It is truly SACRED. I hope you'll keep your "big reason" front and center as you read. I do not doubt that you've already thought about it by now, probably before you even opened this book. After all, you wouldn't even be here if you didn't already feel a calling, a pull, a deep desire to be better, to be more, to be excellent.

There will be some ideas in these following chapters you've heard before, and there will be some new ones. We are striving for both timeless and timely. Underline, circle, and write notes to yourself. See yourself in each word and page; if you feel so moved, share this book with another leader. Maybe a newer one. It might help them. That's what we are all on this journey for anyway, to help. Let this book answer questions and create more conversations and dialogue.

Hopefully, you'll get some great results from what you learn here. Hopefully, you'll become a better leader and, dare I say, maybe even a better person.

Right now, as you finish this page, you are two leaders. The leader you are now and the one you are becoming. My sincere hope is that we help you a little on that journey of "becoming."

I am reminded of these very wise words:

> "Each of us has that right, that possibility, to invent ourselves daily. If a person does not invent herself, she will be invented. So, to be bodacious enough to invent ourselves is wise."
>
> *Maya Angelou*

May your journey of invention be a bodacious one.

Rich Bluni, RN

Rich Bluni, R.N.
Huron Senior Director, Author, and Speaker

PRINCIPLE 1:
COMMIT TO EXCELLENCE

Set high expectations to achieve results
while living your mission and values.

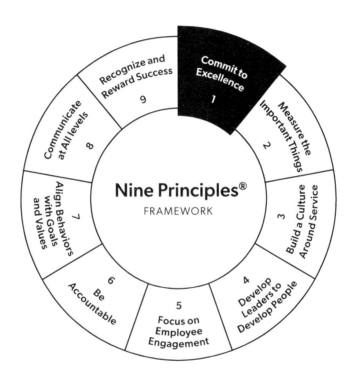

"Commitment is what transforms
a promise into a reality."

Abraham Lincoln

Let's start Principle 1 by reflecting on two stories that are likely familiar to you.

First, we have the parable about building your house on a rock foundation. You know the one—when the storms hit, the house built on rock stands strong while the one on sand crumbles.

Second, we have the story about "The Three Little Pigs." Remember that one? That wolf huffed and puffed, but he couldn't blow down that house made of bricks no matter how hard he tried. No, that thing was solid. That wolf needed his inhaler after that visit.

These truths aren't just wise advice for building a sturdy house. The same holds when you are building an excellent organization.

This is why "Commit to Excellence" is the first principle. It is all about creating a strong foundation that can withstand the challenges that come your way.

Using the symbolism of these two stories, whether it's "winds, rains, and floods" that bear down upon your "house" or a "big bad wolf" huffing and puffing at you, a commitment to excellence is vital for success. Your mission, vision, unbreakable pillars, and the bedrock of culture provide the structure that stands the test of time regardless of the weather or packs of wolves roaming wild.

As Abraham Lincoln reminded us in the opening quote of this chapter, it turns a promise into a reality.

Defining Excellence

What defines excellence?

The dictionary says that excellence means, among other things, "the fact or state of excelling, superiority or eminence." The funny thing about the word "excellence" is even without the fancy definition, we all know it when we see or experience it, don't we?

When you are in an "excellent healthcare setting," whether it be a facilities management, an operating room, a physical therapy gym, an emergency department, or a cafeteria, you'd probably feel it before you could verbally describe it. It's energy. It's how the place looks and shines. It's how people speak to you and treat you. It's in the air and so tangible you can almost grasp it. It's the culture of excellence. It just "feels right."

Just the same, you also know the opposite of excellence in a heartbeat.

Have you ever gone house/apartment shopping and walked into one with your realtor or potential landlord and, within seconds, thought to yourself, "Nope!" It just felt "wrong."

On the other hand, sometimes you walk in somewhere, and it just feels EXCELLENT. It is "home." It might've been hard to speak in granular terms about why it was excellent at that moment, but you just knew. In your heart, you knew you were going to live there. You might've even said aloud, "This is the one! I am home!"

Excellence makes its song heard over the noise of mediocrity and makes itself glow over the dullness of the mundane because it is in its nature to do so. An excellent healthcare organization is no different in its song or glow which is written with a compelling vision, and polished through aspirational goals.

Your teams and your patients look around and, in their way, say: "This is the one! I am home!"

Building the Structure for Success

What do we believe are the essential elements for defining and achieving excellence?

Committing to excellence is all about bringing clarity—and that's what people need and want. It brings the elements of excellence together so that people know what the organization is about and what is expected of them. It allows people more control and simplifies getting teams on board. Plus, it's easier to see who's doing well, who needs some help, and who deserves recognition.

First, the bedrock foundation for your organization is its culture (Values and Standards of Behavior). The pillars represent what excellence looks like across the organization (Goals). It is put into place to support and achieve your vision (future) and mission (purpose).

Here is a tip. Your organization may use different terms to describe these structural elements. You may use strategic focus or KPIs (key performance indicators) instead of pillars. Don't let that distract you. Use this framework to again "relate" and "not compare" and help define or redefine what excellence means in your organization.

VISION

MISSION

SERVICE   **QUALITY**   **FINANCE**   **PEOPLE**   **GROWTH**

DESIRED RESULTS

CULTURE OF EXCELLENCE
Values and Standards of Behavior

Figure 1.1: Commit to Excellence Structural Elements

Mission and Vision— Start With a Compelling Why

Let's start at the top. Mission and Vision. Both work hand in hand to define and drive excellence.

Your **vision** is what you want to accomplish. A vision statement should answer questions like: Where do you want to be in the future? What problem are you solving for the greater good?

For example, one large health system developed a vision to be the "best healthcare system in the universe," not just the "best healthcare system within a five-block radius." Another's vision is to provide "world-class care." Not just "care you'd feel most comfortable with." Other healthcare organizations commit to "zero harm," not just "let's only harm people on Tuesdays and Thursdays if we can." These visions create energy and excitement and help us build our goals.

Your **mission**, on the other hand, is how you get there. It's like your roadmap for achieving your vision. A mission statement should answer questions like: Why does your organization exist? What do you want to accomplish? Who do you serve?

> "Never be limited by other people's limited imaginations."
>
> *Dr. Mae Jemison*

> **"** Junkyard or playground. Mission and vision brought to life.

"What are you staring at? It's just a bunch of garbage!" said the neighborhood pessimist Joseph.

"Nah. It's got potential," I said, looking at the abandoned lot.

It was the seventies, and gas lines and the recession were the main topics of conversation among adults. We kids just wanted to ride our bikes until the streetlights came on and jump over homemade ramps like we were Evil Knievel. And we needed a place that our parents thought was safe enough for us to do that but we wanted something more than a single ramp here or there in a backyard.

This strange triangular lot in our neighborhood was supposed to have a house built on it. But, for some reason, that never happened. No one was sure who owned it, but a fence magically went up around it one day. Then, after a few months, people just started dumping junk in it. Old tires, broken bikes, and even a refrigerator graced the lot with its faded avocado-green majesty.

Standing before that lot this day, I said, "What if?"

Staring at me from his orange bike, Joseph said, "What if what?"

"This would be an awesome bike track!" I replied.

Joseph started laughing. "Dude, it's a mini junkyard. Look at it!"

But I saw something more. Myself, Joseph, Amy, Jimmy, Reggie, David, and Dawn could have a place just for us where the grownups wouldn't bother us. I already knew exactly in my mind what it would look like.

But we needed some help. Joseph's brother had a van, and I suggested we load it up and take it to the dump. Joseph was skeptical, but I was already popping a wheelie and headed toward his house to ask.

After some convincing, Joseph's brother agreed to take us to the dump if we provided gas money. I headed to my house to ask my dad for $5, but he had a better idea. Mr. Bales had broken his arm and needed someone to mow his yard. I could earn the money instead.

So, I got my crew together—Joseph and the gang. I told them about my vision for the lot. At first, they were skeptical. But then, the idea began to make sense, and they joined in on the excitement. They saw it too!

I had my team.

Between us, we gathered $7 for gas money, and Joseph's brother came through with his van. My dad even joined in on the action, helping us knock down the fence and load the van. It took us three trips to clear out all the junk, but we did it.

After clearing away the junk, we still had an overgrown mess of grass and weeds. My group was hesitant, but Joseph and the other kids sprang into action, gathering all the wood and concrete blocks they could find from old ramps we had built together. Meanwhile, I approached Mr. Bales and asked him to borrow his mower. He was thrilled to help, as he lived across the street from the eyesore we were clearing. We got to work, mowing, pulling weeds, and hacking through the overgrown shrubs. It was a messy job but also a little fun.

Just before dark, the lot was clear. With the streetlights flickering on, it was finally time to make our vision a reality.

Before we knew it, there it was. The most awesome bike park ever built by 9- and 10-year-old kids! We constructed five ramps, an obstacle course made of basketball-sized rocks, and even dug a ditch that we filled with water to create mud.

Our parents and neighbors came to see what all the excitement was about. Amy's dad quickly shut down our idea to light a small hole filled with gasoline and drive through it (you couldn't blame a kid for trying). We rode late into the night until only me, Joseph, Amy, and Reggie were left.

Joseph spoke up as we sat on our bikes, staring in awe at what we had created. "This was a good day," he said.

In her quiet voice, Amy said, "No, I would say it was an excellent day."

"Nice work, Rich! You nailed it with that crazy idea of yours," Joseph exclaimed.

I soaked up the praise and felt pretty good about myself. Looking back now, I realize it wasn't just me who made our awesome bike park a reality.

Sure, I had the initial vision, but it wasn't me who made it happen. It was a borrowed van and a bunch of kids with a passion for making that vision a reality. Well, yes, and maybe a little luck too. But the result was truly amazing.

As we were leaving, Amy suggested we try out a fire pit once her dad went on a work trip. We all cheered at the idea, thinking nothing could go wrong. (I won't spill the beans on whether or not we ended up with a "flaming pit of doom," but let's say bike tires don't fare well in extreme heat.)

As the quote from astronaut Dr. Mae Jemison at the start of this story reminds us, we should never allow our imaginations, our vision, if you will, to be limited because others have accepted things as they are.

One person's junkyard is another person's playground.

Excellence begins in the mind—our thoughts, what we see as possible. Then a vision is born. From there, it is defined, shared, and brought to light with a team compelled to make it a reality.

Let's be real. We all want to be part of something grand and special. The bigger the reach, the more exciting the work is and the more invested the team becomes. That's why having a clear mission and vision is so important. Mission and vision are not just words on a sign, they're rallying cries that bring us together and give us a sense of purpose.

Together, mission and vision guide an organization's operations and future goals. They help us understand why we do what we do and connect us to a sense of meaning and purpose. And let's face it, in healthcare, that's what we're all about—making a difference and doing our best to help others.

Vision and missions make dreams become a reality.

The Aligning Structure—The Pillars

Now that we have talked about the capstones of vision and mission, and before we move to culture, let's move to define what excellence looks like across the organization. Committing to excellence also requires setting measurable goals—or desired results—under each pillar or strategic focus of an organization.

As you think of creating excellence, imagine baking a cake. There's a recipe, a list of specific ingredients that have proven successful and effective. Excellence has ingredients. And as with a cake, leave one out, overdo one at the expense of the other, or fail to measure correctly and you have a mess. Don't believe me? Grab a cake recipe and substitute sugar for salt, double the baking soda, or wing it for how many eggs to add, and watch what happens. The baker knows they need the right ingredients in the right amounts to produce the best outcome.

You can't just "wing it" with organizational excellence, either. The pillars provide the ingredients or elements that drive the outcome you desire.

This is why we focus on the ingredients when we coach organizations to excellence.

At Huron, we call this structure "Pillars" or "Pillars of Excellence"— service, quality, finance, people, and growth. Some organizations also choose to add a Community Pillar. Some organizations use strategic priorities or key performance indicators (KPIs) as their framework. Every organization is unique and different, so goal focus also can change from one organization to another. But this book will focus on five common and core pillars now and in the Principles to come.

It takes out the guesswork. This pillar format allows goal setting customized to an organization's specific needs. It gets you directly on target. As they say, "Close only counts in horseshoes and hand grenades." Pillar goals are like GPS-guided missiles.

SERVICE	QUALITY	FINANCE	PEOPLE	GROWTH
Efficient, effective, and meaningful connections, care and engagement with all customers, patients, families, physicians and visitors.	Provide the best quality and safe clinical care and outcomes for each individual we serve.	Ensure equitable allocation and optimal utilization of our facilities, systems, and funding.	Maximize the human potential of each individual in our organization to engage and connect.	Commit to expanding the capacity to serve and meet the needs of our communities.

Figure 1.2: Organizational Pillars

Defining the Pillars

By definition, the pillars are the structures that stand firm on culture's foundation and underpin and support the vision and mission. In short, this is where excellence is defined, stabilized, and measured in each organization. The pillars provide the foundation for setting organizational goals and direction.

Often individuals ask what each pillar intends to do. Let's dive a bit deeper into each pillar and the definition and meaning of each (See Figure 1.2).

SERVICE: *Efficient, effective, and friendly interactions and engagement with all internal and external customers, patients, family, physicians, and visitors.*

When organizations implement tested and proven tactics such as leader rounding, the AIDET® Communication Framework, Bedside Shift Report℠, and other actions and tools outlined in this book, the patient's and family's perception of service increases. Here's a guarantee: either you or someone you care about will be a patient sometime in the future. This guarantee is one we all can understand.

QUALITY: *Provide the best clinical care for each individual we serve.*

Why is the quality pillar so important? As the people pillar tells us, "The best wants to work with the best," and you know what "the best" do? Give the best possible care. Not because they "have to" but because they truly want to. They're not going anywhere!

Once the organization enjoys high employee retention, clinical indicators begin to improve. We all can agree that tenured staff are more effective and efficient. They know where things are, they get the flow, they are part of driving the high standards, they don't accept low/sub-par performers, they understand the processes and protocols, they encourage and uplift each other, and they have present and empathetic leaders.

Not only that, the organization invests in them, and they are invested in the organization's success and work more effectively as a team. They communicate clearly and efficiently, and this reduces sentinel events, bad outcomes, and all the things that cause healthcare leaders to sit straight up in bed from a dead sleep at 2 a.m., screaming in a panicked cold sweat. (We've all been there. It's not fun. Plus, if you are sleeping next to anyone, have thin walls with neighbors on the other side, or have a dog, it scares the heck out of them too!)

FINANCE: *Ensure equitable allocation and optimal utilization of our facilities, systems, and funding.*

Often, as an organization experiences gains in the People, Service, Quality, and Growth pillars, the "Finance" pillar reaps the rewards all along the way. From reduced claims and lower agency costs to a lower length of stay and improved access, organizations will see these gains transfer directly to the bottom line. That bottom line allows better benefits and salaries, updated and improved equipment, and even the occasional new tile on the second floor that brings out the green in our scrubs. (There's no shame in the occasional makeover!)

PEOPLE: *Maximize the human potential of each individual in our organization to engage and connect.*

Because much of our work around the pillars begins with leadership and culture change, organizations often focus on goals in the "People" pillar first. This focus isn't accidental at all. *It all hinges on our people.*

Read that again.

The rest will fall if our teams don't feel valued, seen, and listened to. We see brand new hospitals with shiny floors, pretty art on the walls, HGTV-level physical makeovers, and fancy coffee shops that are an absolute mess because their leaders focused more on "paint" than people. I've also seen hospitals that probably admitted their first patients during the War of 1812 who haven't had a physical makeover since and stand as the absolute "organization of choice" for people to spend their careers at because the culture there was one where the team was valuable.

When we get "People" right, we have the space to align everything else. When we create an enduring culture where people want to stay, we also create a magnetic culture that draws in the best and the brightest. Do you know who best recruits high performers for your organization? Your present high performers! They tell their friends, family, neighbors, and classmates, "Hey! You need to come to my organization! They care about you here, it's an awesome place to work, and we have the best people!"

No one says, "Hey! You should see the tile on the second floor—it brings out the green in our scrubs! You need to transfer here!" You retain and recruit the best people because the best wants to work with the best.

GROWTH: *Commit to expanding the capacity to serve and meet the needs of our communities.*

No one wants to be stagnant. There are new services, new opportunities for your team, new things to learn, and new technologies to play with. When we grow, we also become an attractor for high performers, young people beginning their careers, and providers who would otherwise take their patients and services elsewhere.

One could say that growth creates energy and excitement. Watch as a department gets new equipment, expands its space, or can do new and stimulating things. You will see something we all want in our personal and professional lives: Joy! As William Butler Yeats once said,

"Happiness is neither virtue nor pleasure nor this thing nor that but simply growth. We are happy when we are growing."

Tips for Success

Here are some quick tips for success:

- Senior Leadership Team: When Huron works with hospitals directly, we begin the goal-setting process with the senior leadership team and suggest they limit the number of organization-wide goals to a maximum of 10-12 across all pillars. We all know how we are in healthcare. Most of us want to do it all and have it done yesterday or the day before. We are used to "code blues" and "stat orders." We are wired to save lives and operate on quick turnarounds. But this is a different territory. To succeed with these pillar goals, we need to be wise stewards of the two things we don't have an unending supply of: our time and energy.

- Collaboration: After organizational goals are set, leaders should collaborate to set goals for the facility, division, and department based on all the pillars. The pillars function as a blueprint, a guiding star, and an accountability tool that helps leaders organize and clarify their journey. (And know this, it is a journey!)

- Lasting: We caution you not to think of these like you would those "New Year's Resolutions" that most people give up on after a few weeks! That's the beauty of the process of the pillars. It isn't random, and it isn't simply "hopeful." It is collaborative, measured, transparent, and constantly kept in front of the organization. Imagine if those often-neglected resolutions were treated the same.

  For example, imagine if your goal was to lose 20 pounds, run two miles, or read one book a month. Instead of just thinking about it to yourself or scribbling it on a napkin at a New Year's party, you share that goal with your family and friends in a blog, social media update, or monthly email.

  And imagine they could see your progress as you updated it. You posted your weight, the distance you ran, the book you read that month, and a summary. Imagine what that would do. It sure would create that "accountability discipline" that so often is missing from those little life goals. It'd be embarrassing if Cousin Beatrice rang you up after seeing your last weigh-in, skipped run, or zero books read that month, and called you out in the comment section as a "reply all."

- Customize by Department: While every facility will set goals across all pillars, some units or departments may not have goals under a particular pillar. That is okay and should be something the whole team is clear about and comfortable with. Goals written at a departmental level should reflect the most significant contributions they must make to the organization's success. For example, a department with only three tenured and high-performing employees may not need to set a People goal for the year.

 ## Beyond "Pretty Good."

I used to dread quarterly evaluations. The feedback seemed so vague and subjective. It was like, "You're doing pretty good, Rich!" or "Things are looking better around here." I mean, what does that even mean? Is that a B+ or an A-? I was always left feeling confused and frustrated.

But then my organization introduced the pillar structure. All the other managers and I were initially skeptical as it felt like more work. But after just one quarter, I was a believer. I felt more confident knowing how my unit fit the larger organizational goals. I could see what we needed to prioritize and where we could ease up a bit.

My conversations with leadership became more focused, too. I knew what was expected of me, so I didn't waste time on things that might not work. For example, when our patient experience ratings took a dip, we focused on rounding on all patients, and it made a huge difference. We saw consistent improvement, and it felt like we had a solid strategy in place. On the flip side, we focused on specific fall reduction tactics as a team when our Quality Pillar took a hit. It wasn't easy, but we worked together and made progress. Our monthly conversations felt better and more concise too.

Wow, it's hard to believe it's been 20 years since that experience. Back then, I never would have guessed that I would coach and believe in this so passionately.

You may have heard it said, "Hope isn't a strategy." Good hardworking people can put in effort and hope for success. This is where the pillar structure comes into play and is proven through the test of time across organizations to provide a solid foundation for implementing a successful strategy and driving positive change.

Hardwiring the Pillars

These pillars are a tried-and-true framework or structure that should be integrated into your organization's daily operations. We will provide examples of ways to do this throughout the coming chapters.

Let's start with three critical things you should do to hardwire your organization's strategic direction.

1. Meeting agendas: Set all meeting agendas by pillar to provide focus. Use the pillar framework to guide your agenda, whether it's a staff huddle, a meeting with your direct report, or a staff meeting. *(See more in Principle 7 – Align Behaviors with Goals and Values and Principle 8 – Communicate at all Levels)*

2. Evaluations: Establish your leader evaluation work process by pillar to create accountability. This will help to bring urgency and alignment of work and priorities. *(See Principle 7 – Align Behaviors with Goals and Values)*

3. Communications: Create strong communication mechanisms. For example, use department communication boards by pillar to update staff on measurable progress. This provides a visible way to communicate how the organization is doing across all pillars. Many organizations will also create communication boards in the foyer or other central locations. *(See Principle 8 – Communicate at all Levels)*

Goals that Matter

We've talked about how the pillars can align and be used to set goals. But what do goals look like under the pillars? We will discuss creating SMART goals in Principle 2: Measure the Important Things. However, we will start by understanding each pillar's framework and economic linkages. When done right, your pillar goals will pass our three tests.

TEST 1: UNDERSTANDABLE	TEST 2: MEMORABLE	TEST 3: MEASURABLE
Can everyone understand the goals, what they mean, and how they, as individuals contribute to achieving them?	Are the goals easy to remember and explained in a few words?	Does each goal provide an objective way to know what success looks like when it is achieved?

Test 1: Understandable Goals

Everyone deserves to know how their work aligns with the larger organization's goals. When people "get this, " they are much more likely to be connected to the outcomes and invested in them. It is poor and, you might even say, neglectful leadership to expect people to "move a goal" if they don't see their place in it. They need their own "why," if you will. If we had a goal to decrease infections and didn't shared that with an environmental services (EVS) team, they may not see their part. Everyone benefits from understanding their personal "why."

Test 2: Memorable Goals

Goals should be easy to remember and easily explained in a few words. We like long explanations in healthcare because we often worry we miss or leave out important information. It's like we have informational FOMO (Fear. Of. Missing. Out.). But keep the goals as streamlined and clear as possible. Have FOODI (Fear. Of. Overdoing. It.) instead!

Test 3: Measurable Goals

The measures allow everyone to understand what success looks like when it is achieved. Keep it clear. "Here's where we were. Here's where we are now. Here's where we want to be. Here's what' excellent' looks like." And communicate it. Even incremental progress can boost people, just as knowing that you've slipped back can help people regroup. Always remember, it is truly about progress over perfection!

That is one thing to remember as we talk about measuring excellence. We can sometimes confuse "excellence" with "perfection," but they're not the same thing. Perfection is an unrealized ideal. Excellence is an achievable goal. It's a culture in which employees at every level take certain risks, make mistakes without dire consequences, and are competent in making changes that will help elevate and move the entire organization forward.

> **❝ Saving Lives.**

I remember coaching this environmental service leader who was struggling with his team. They felt like they weren't making a difference and weren't appreciated by the organization. Having a dad work in this same role hit home to me. So, I asked the leader what his team did.

He thought for a moment and said, "Well, we clean the place and try to make it look presentable."

Hmmm. "Presentable." See if that word inspires anything. "How do I look in this, Honey?" "Very presentable."

So, I asked the leader, "Sure, that may be their job, but what happens if they don't disinfect surfaces, clean the floors, and take out the trash?"

He replied, "Well, the place would look bad."

"And then what?" I asked.

"People would complain," he said.

"And then what?" I prodded.

"The place would be filthy!" he admitted.

I continued, "And if the place is 'filthy,' what would happen to the patients, visitors, and staff if they came into contact with those 'filthy' doorknobs, floors, and bathrooms?"

Suddenly, his eyes lit up, and he said, "They'd get exposed to germs!"

"And then what?" I asked again.

"They'd get sick!" he realized.

I paused and asked, "So, are they just 'making the place presentable' or creating a safe environment and preventing the spread of infections and disease?"

The leader got it.

We met with his team and had this same conversation. We talked about how premature babies, cancer patients, immune-compromised, and the elderly are affected by nosocomial infections. We emphasized that they were saving lives and protecting the vulnerable. We shared the infection control data transparently, and the team members began attending infection control meetings.

Do you know what happened? The team's "why" awakened. The infection rates went down.

Striving for "reducing infections and saving lives" will get you way more excited than striving for "presentable" any day. Once they saw beyond their "job"—taking out the trash, mopping the floor, and wiping things down—to their "work" of being the tip of the spear for infection reduction, they saw themselves as more valuable. They were an integral part of a meaningful and essential purpose. The team may have known about the company's goal of reducing infections but didn't realize how they fit into that goal and why they were so important.

Yes, getting people the right skill set is important. But when leaders can connect people to purpose and understand the "why," people become invested in their work. This connection is where the magic happens and when true commitment to excellence happens.

Sample Goals

What do goals look like under the pillars? Let's first look at various economic linkages under each pillar.

Bottom Line Results

SERVICE	QUALITY	FINANCE	PEOPLE	GROWTH
Reduced Claims	Improved Clinical Outcomes	Improved Operating Income	Reduced Annual Turnover	Higher Volume
Reduced Legal Expenses	Decreased Nosocomial Infections	Decreased Cost Per Adjusted Discharge	Reduced First Year Turnover	Increased Capital
Reduced Malpractice Expense	Reduced Length of Stay	Improved Collections	Reduced Vacancies	Increased Revenue
Improved Patient Experience	Reduced Medication Errors	Reduced Accounts Receivable	Reduced Agency Costs	Decreased Left Without Treatment
Improved Support Service Outcomes	Decreased Preventable Readmissions	Reduced Advertising Costs	Reduced PRNs	Reduced Outpatient No-Shows
	Reduced Falls	Improved Staff Productivity	Reduced Overtime	Increased Physician Activity
	Increased Core Measures		Improved Employee Engagement	Increased Outpatient Visits
			Improved Physician Engagement	

Figure 1.3: Sample economic linkages under each pillar

Sample Pillar Goals

As discussed, your pillar goals should be understandable, memorable, and measurable. Also note that as an organization matures, the goals mature. For instance, early on, patient experience goals are valuable and needed under the Service Pillar. But eventually, as the organization matures and behaviors are hardwired, that goal might transition to measures that result from higher patient experience and percentiles, such as reduced claims, lower legal fees, and reduced malpractice expenses.

SERVICE	QUALITY	FINANCE	PEOPLE	GROWTH
Achieve 90th percentile ranking on patient experience surveys in all areas.	Reduce the incidence of Hospital Acquired Pressure Injuries (HAPI) to 3% or less.	Increase annual operating income (margin) to 4% or greater.	Reduce the total employee turnover rate to 12% or less overall, with RN turnover at 11% or lower.	Increase total outpatient visits by 10% or greater over the prior year.
Improve Star ratings from 3 to 4 stars.	Reduce ED Left Without Being Seen to 3% or less.	Reduce staffing agency spending by 50%.	Achieve employee and physician engagement results of the 80th percentile.	Reduce the medical patient visit no-show rate from 16% to 13%.
		Maintain non-federal grant funding.		Reduce the clinic patient visit no-show rate from 16% to 12%.
				Reduce out-migration by 10%.

Figure 1.4: Startup – Goal Samples

We will be talking more about how to set goals in Principle 2, but let's look at the impact different goals have on each other.

The Synergy of the Pillars

One of the best things about aligning goals under the pillars is how they achieve results together. It's kind of like chocolate and peanut butter. Good as stand-alones, but pretty great together!

You can't discuss service without discussing people, quality, finance, and growth. It's tough to achieve excellence with patients when turnover is high. When turnover does go down, so will agency costs, and patients move through the organization more efficiently to reduce medically unnecessary days and increase capacity. Physicians will refer more of their patients to the hospital because they appreciate the value of standardization and fewer delays that a retained staff will provide for them. As a result, you will increase your organization's capacity to help more people.

For example, preventing Hospital Acquired Pressure Injuries (HAPIs) is an important goal under the Quality Pillar, but let's keep in mind what that means. Quality isn't just a measurement or math equation. Reducing HAPIs also means helping patients by preventing something terrible from happening to them. HAPIs can be not only life-altering but life-threatening.

Beloved actor Christopher Reeve, best known for his iconic role as Superman, tragically suffered a life-altering injury in 1995 while horseback riding. He was not only an inspiring warrior and advocate for people who have had to face a similar challenge, but also for those of us who watched him thrive and live his life. However, in 2004 Christopher Reeve died from sepsis caused by a HAPI. His loss was heartbreaking to those closest to him and those who marveled at his strength, resiliency, and authenticity as he shared his journey with us.

So, any talk of "reducing pressure injuries" speaks to the nature of healthcare; healing, protecting, and serving human beings when they are sick, vulnerable, and dependent upon us to care for them. "Quality" isn't just owned by the "Quality Department" but by us all. It is the heart of our work.

But what else happens? Let's walk this reduction of HAPIs through the impact it can have on the other pillars; the synergy among them. Look at the example below.

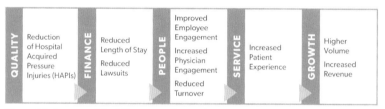

Figure 1.5: Synergy of the Pillar Example – Reduced Hospital-Acquired Pressure Injuries (HAPIs).

- Finance Pillar: Better prevention of HAPIs helps decrease the length of stay because patients can return home sooner. Prevention also affects the potential for lawsuits, which financially drain an organization and emotionally drain well-meaning healthcare workers. If you've ever been through depositions and court dates, you understand. Regardless of the outcome, dollars spent or lost on lawsuits represent real costs and pain beyond the finances for all involved.

- People Pillar: When HAPIs decrease and you start progressing with this goal, you can reward and recognize your teams for their accomplishments and success. What gets rewarded gets repeated. Imagine being able to walk into your medical-surgical department, emergency department, or long-term care or rehabilitation area with an armful of thank you notes, a tray of cupcakes, and true heartfelt recognition because there were no HAPIs that quarter. As a leader, you need those moments; as exceptional caregivers, your team also needs them! Healthcare workers do what they do for "big reasons." They are in this work because it is meaningful. For them, a metric or score doesn't fill souls or awaken inspiration. But when they know their efforts have made a real difference, people feel proud of where they work and like they are on a winning team. Everyone wants to be on that team. So, you not only retain high performers, but they, and your culture, become a magnet to draw the best of the best to your doors, improving employee engagement and reducing turnover.

- Physicians and providers also benefit. They want the best for their patients, too. Their reputation closely ties to the outcomes of the organization. Improved quality outcomes lead to increased physician engagement and buy-in.

- Service Pillar: A patient who develops a HAPI can understandably associate this with a negative experience. It may be interpreted as a lack of care or caring on the part of staff. Patient experience measures will reflect this, and Service Pillar results will suffer.

- Growth Pillar: Physicians refer more patients to organizations where they feel confident the care will be the best, creating greater volume and higher revenues. More patients feel safe and come back when care is needed again. They also consider other parts of the organization for all facets of their care.

You can see from the above example how preventing hospital-acquired pressure injuries affects other pillars. This example is only one, but think of the "domino" effect that one pillar result can have on another. The way they work together is powerful and demonstrates how pillars hold up a structure and drive excellence across all parts of the organization.

Your organization may feel an acute and urgent need to improve a specific area or pillar. It gets our attention. With a comprehensive, pillar-based approach to excellence, you can be sure that improving in one area does not harm achieving desired outcomes in another pillar. And even better, improvement in one can be managed in such a manner that collateral improvement occurs across multiple focus areas.

Culture—The Foundation and Behaviors

We've talked about the top of the structure. Now let's talk about the rock foundation that holds everything in place. Culture.

Let's face it, the most compelling and poetically written mission and vision and masterful goals will fall flat unless leaders and their organizations consciously decide to create the conditions to thrive. This foundation is your values and your standards of behavior. You are building a culture that grants "permission" to take certain risks and make changes that help move the entire organization toward excellence.

A great culture doesn't just happen. Oh sure, you might be fortunate enough to have great people, but like building a world-champion team, it takes intentional work.

Define what you want to achieve as an organization intentionally and the values and behaviors everyone should display. The Nine Principles® Framework helps provide the roadmap to achieving goals under each pillar and defining the behaviors for success. The culture brings it alive.

> "If you want to go fast, go alone; if
> you want to go far, go together."
>
> *African Proverb*

What a beautiful proverb. And look, while "fast" can certainly be a great thing, especially as it relates to getting your morning double-shot espresso caramel latte into your hand at a coffee shop drive-through on the way to work, truly, at the end of the day (or the quarter, or the revenue cycle) we are striving for "far" over "fast."

In other words, you can have the healthiest and most perfect flower seeds, be sincere about being the best gardener ever, and work hard to dig the perfect hole to plant these perfect seeds. Still, if the soil is poor, it never rains, and no sun shines that way, don't expect a beautiful bouquet.

> Culture is the manifestation of our shared values and principles.
>
> It is what **we see and say.**
>
> What we **do and don't do.**
>
> What we **think and believe.**

Now it may sound a bit different from organization to organization. "Culture," especially a great one, could soak up a lot of adjectives such as engaging, inspiring, supportive, fun, and positive. But while you can define some things with words, some you can only experience and feel.

For example, we can describe a beautiful beach day, the stunning majesty of a mountaintop experience, or a beautiful canyon hike. We can use all the flowery and dramatic words available to do so. But it won't begin to compete with **bringing you there**.

Bringing you to the place where you can feel the warm water on your legs and hear the waves crash on the shore and the seagulls sing above you or where you can experience the crisp cold mountain air and the smell of the pine trees and see the majestic view. Walking the canyon and hearing the rocks crunch beneath your boots as you feel the desert heat and walk on that red clay. Which would win that competition?

Culture, while simple to define, is more meaningfully felt. You know it when you're in it. It is unmistakable.

What kind of culture do you have in your organization?

What would be the adjectives you'd use to define your culture? Be honest. Maybe pause and write them down. Ask yourself how you feel about the words staring back at you. Walk the hallways of your organization, hospital, or clinic, and pay attention to what you see and hear. Pretend you're a visitor or a patient. Be as objective as you can be. Now go deeper after you've taken in what you've seen and heard.

What does it feel like there? We all know that is the ultimate test. Have you ever walked somewhere and it just felt off? Have you felt unwelcome or uncomfortable, not because anyone specifically said or did anything, but just the energy you got from there? We all have.

By contrast, have you ever walked somewhere and felt instantly welcome? For sure, you have. You may not have been able to initially "define" it at first, but if you had to, you would probably say things like, "It just felt good there!" or "I feel like part of the family," or "It was just this loving and warm environment."

So, how do people "feel" walking your hallways? How do you feel? That's the quickest and most direct way to "define" your culture.

The great thing is once you start, it begins to take on a life of its own. Leaders certainly need to drive it—they're the ones initially pushing the car down the hill and are needed along the ride—but the momentum will be the team and the culture. You know you have a great culture when team members hold each other accountable before the leaders even get there.

We have seen this in many years of helping to build high-performing healthcare teams and organizations: Culture and meaningful and aspirational goals are an unstoppable force.

Some organizations seeking to understand their culture and how to achieve the culture they want use Huron's Cultural Health Assessment to start them on the journey.

66 Commit to Excellence—Why it Matters.

When my wife, Dawn, was told she had cancer, it was not what we expected. What we were expecting at the time was to have our second child. What we ended up with was her surgery and radiation.

Dawn is also in healthcare and has been an RN for over 20 years. Now she was the one in need of care.

It was quite a pivot from looking at baby furniture and picking out paint colors for a nursery to figuring out surgery scheduling, oncology appointments, and child care since I still had to work and be on the road. Still, because of the radiation treatments, she had to be away from our three-year-old son Luke for a period of time because he was little, and it would be unsafe for him to be around her.

I had the struggle that all of us in healthcare have, trying to find the space in my head to be the "loved one" and the "healthcare worker." It's a tricky balance. Sometimes those two voices in your head conflict. It's rarely a peaceful coexistence, plus you're also the "Chief Information Officer" in that everyone looks to you for updates and when to visit. It's a lot.

But let me ask you, have you ever been in a healthcare situation as a patient or a loved one that maybe was not so great, where the care or the caregivers were not "excellent" but because of who you were and what you know, you were able to get things done right? I have. You wonder, "How do the 'civilians' handle this?" What would've happened if you didn't know what you knew and had the expertise and experience in healthcare that you have in those moments?

Luckily for Dawn and me, the care was terrific. I remember that. But as I write these words, I'm trying to recall the name of a single medication she was on or her radiation dates. I can't, and I was an oncology nurse for many years! Do you know what I do remember? Vividly?

Well, first, I was scared that I would lose the love of my life and my sweet little boy would lose the best mommy ever. But after being reassured by her amazing oncologist that she would do well, the second strongest memories I have of that period were of the people.

The surgeon who sat with me said, "I won't leave your side until you feel confident and comfortable with the plan and have every question answered. Here's my cell phone number. Text me if you're feeling anxious or worried or if you think of any other questions."

The food and nutritional services employee knew I drank a lot of coffee and showed up at my wife's hospital room with a pot of coffee without me asking. (You know you're in healthcare when you measure your coffee intake by the pot, not the cup!)

I remember the nurse managers of every area who rounded on us daily and reduced my anxiety and my wife's. I remember that the staff communicated well, which incredibly impacted me.

I saw the excellence of these teams, and I saw, not as a nurse or as someone who coaches this, but as the person on the other side, how using these tactics wasn't "another thing to do" but made everything they did easier, better, and more efficient. Because of that, they could focus on the stuff that matters to the people on the "other side of the bed"—compassion, listening, answering questions, and reducing anxiety.

I remember watching this team flow with all they did. They had this stuff down! I also remember that last appointment where the oncologist said, "You are officially cancer free!" Her office and clinical staff came in with balloons and flowers and cheered.

I also remember my wife turning to the oncologist. She asked, "So when is it safe for me to get pregnant?" I remember everyone laughed as I said, "Wait! What? We're still doing that?" My wife dried her happy tears and said, "Yes, we are! We were just taking a break." Everyone laughed at the shocked but happy look on my face.

Service is more than a rating on a survey. It is a testament to the excellence and sacredness that is healthcare. It is what people remember above all else. It is the core of our "why" and the reason that many of us choose this as our life's path.

Oh, and after we got the all-clear, after a year or so, I remember holding our daughter Ava in my arms at the hospital as some of the very same nurses who, a year before, had been there for Dawn's cancer journey came by to visit and were now telling me how strong, healthy, and beautiful Ava was.

Yeah, she takes after her mommy, for sure.

Principle 1 Summary

Principle 1: Commit to Excellence, is the foundation for making ourselves, each other, and our organization the best possible. It's powerful when we strive for excellence in everything we do.

Recall the Flywheel we talked about in the Introduction starts with "Passion," which is the core of this principle. Think of all the beauty we encounter and benefit from because a fellow human heart and mind commit and take action with passion.

I know many people may not equate everything in this chapter with "beautiful." It's not just about creating something beautiful; it's about creating something that genuinely makes a difference.

Think about all the amazing things created because someone was passionate about excellence—from life-saving medicines to mind-blowing technologies. None of it would have been possible without commitment.

This commitment is our stepping stone, leap of faith, and line in the sand. It is where this all begins, this incredible journey to excellence. The spark ignites our passion and pushes us to do more and be more.

So, what are you waiting for? Turn the page. This is going to be amazing!

PRINCIPLE 2: MEASURE THE IMPORTANT THINGS

Continuously track progress to achieve results with an improvement mindset.

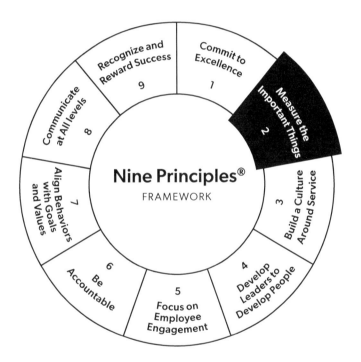

"Measurement is fabulous unless you're busy measuring what's easy to measure as opposed to what's important."

Seth Godin

" Ten Steps.

Lissette (Liz, as she insisted on being called) stood, shaking and white-knuckling her walker as she tried to take some painful first steps. Her daughter Justina was by her side whispering, "Just 10 steps, mom... you got this... just 10."

Liz, an athlete with several marathons and one amateur bodybuilding title, had no idea that one 10-mile bike ride would ultimately change her life. One foggy morning, Liz was struck by a vehicle. In the blink of an eye, 10 miles became almost an unimaginable dream, and 10 steps became her reality.

Her trauma, orthopedic, and physical therapy teams adored her. She was one of those patients you never forget. She was a powerful force, and you felt it in her presence. She had amazed her team by getting out of bed after many weeks of therapy and standing. They said that alone was a miracle. But she warned us all that she was just getting started.

So, it's no surprise that one of Liz's favorite words was "epic." Anytime she made progress, or if you asked her how her day was, it was almost always "epic."

This day, Liz had the "eye of the tiger" as she began to step. Liz nodded to her daughter, and we all held our breath as she started to move. It had been a long journey to just three steps last week, and she had collapsed, weak after that effort.

But this didn't discourage Liz. She asked us to measure approximately 10 steps from her bed to a spot on her hospital room wall. Liz said she chose 10 to symbolize the 10 miles she never completed on the day of her accident. At each step hung a colorful piece of paper with a picture taped to it that signified "epic milestones" in her life: holding her daughter Justina as a baby, holding up a medal from her first marathon, and in her doctoral cap and gown, to name a few.

The picture at the last marker of her 10-step journey was a picture of her dream bike. The exact one Liz said she would one day ride again. "If I can get to 10 steps, I can get to 20. If I can get to 20, I can get to 100. If I can get to 100, I can get on that bike. That will be an epic day!"

Perhaps the athlete in her or her degree in finance drove her, but she was a stickler for measuring things. Liz kept personal logs of her treatment. She recorded how many lifts she could do with her legs, her improvements on her incentive spirometer, and her protein intake. She was obsessed with tracking her progress.

"Come on, Mom! You can do it," urged Justina. "One step down... let's get to 10!"

You could see the sweat and determination on Liz's brow. She took two more steps as her gaze set on milestone four. This picture was of Liz and her husband standing on the beach, smiling brightly at the camera on a hot summer day.

Liz paused to gain strength, never letting her gaze drift from that picture. And then, just like that, it happened. Liz took her fourth step! Everyone in the room burst into excitement as we celebrated step number four together!

But it stopped there. Step five didn't happen, at least that day. Justina and our care team were there to secure Liz safely into her wheelchair when she began to collapse.

There were some quiet moments as we kept our eyes on Liz. She looked at us, pointed to the beach picture, and quietly said, "We saw a turtle as big as a car that day. It was epic!" She went on to say, "Justina, hand me my journal. I need to write that I broke a record today. I took four steps."

Justina knelt by her mom lovingly, saying, "Mom, I'm sorry. You'll get to 10. I know you will."

Liz looked up. "Don't be sorry, Justina. I made progress. I moved from 30% to 40% of my goal! I just made a 10% improvement. This is epic!"

Wow.

How many of us would feel that way, especially in healthcare? Moving from 30% to 40% for many of us would be a disaster! Emergency meetings would be called. PowerPoint presentations would be created. Committees would be hastily formed. "We're supposed to hit 100%!!!" we'd all scream as we hung our heads in shame, drawing the blinds in the boardroom where we all gathered to lament our failure.

Not Liz. She got it. 10% up was good. Wait, to Liz; it was epic. Later, when talking to Liz, she explained her relentlessness with measurement.

"If I've learned anything, it's this. If you truly care and something is important and valued by you, you measure it. Anything of value in this world is measured. A jeweler knows the number of carats in a diamond. A landowner knows how many acres they own. An investor knows the price of the stock they're buying. When you love someone, you know how many years you've been together. If you have kids, you mark their height with a pencil on the door frame to watch them grow. We measure these things because they matter, and we want to keep watch over them."

"Look," she continued, "knowing I took a fourth step today shows I made progress. I put those pictures on the wall to hold myself accountable. Also, if I start to feel sorry for myself and want to stop, I want you all to look me in the eye and say, 'No way, Liz, your goal is 10 steps!' I want people that care about me and my progress to hold me accountable. That's why those numbered papers are there. Not to make me feel less than, but to call me to be greater than."

Many weeks later, we saw Liz reach five, six, seven, eight, nine, and then 10! The one with the picture of the beautiful bike. What a celebration it was that day!

But it didn't stop there. Liz looked at the picture of the bike and then at us. She said, almost in a whisper, "This is a milestone day. Can someone get a picture of me? I want to put a picture of this moment on my 20th step."

She allowed herself to rest and slowly sat down in her wheelchair. She looked and said, "What are you all waiting for? Someone hand me my wallet and phone. I have a bike to order!"

And she did. It was sky blue, and it was EPIC!

I love what I learned from this incredible woman. Anything of value in this world is measured, and being authentic, transparent, and accountable even when the numbers aren't "epic" shouldn't make you feel "less than" but should call you to be "greater than." There is so much truth in this philosophy. It hit me hard, to be honest.

To be even more honest, I don't care for math. So, for me, "measurement" had always had a negative vibe. Who gets excited about numbers anyway? (Inspiring people who change the world is the answer, but it took me a while to get that until I met Liz.)

We can't achieve our "10 steps" toward excellence, much less 10 miles, if we don't measure, reassess, put in the work, and measure again. But not everything needs to be measured, and measurement for the sake of measurement may just be a number play. It's not about making pretty graphs and grids and flashy formulas. To paraphrase the Seth Godin quote we opened this chapter with, it's more about not measuring what's easy but what's important.

Key Concepts of Measurement

Measurement has gotten a bad reputation, mostly because of people like me who were told somewhere in grade school, "Oh… you're not good with numbers!" Hence, I am grateful for calculators, tutors, and grade curves!

What I've learned from my Huron colleagues and my life as a nurse, nurse leader, risk and quality manager, and healthcare coach is that measurement isn't only a way to document numbers but a tool to help us narrow our scope, define the work to be done, and help us be more effective and efficient. It helps align the entire organization toward the actions needed to drive results. It also helps us, if needed, to reorient our direction so that one of the most valuable resources we have and measure—time—isn't wasted.

Ultimately it is all about meaningful growth. You can't achieve growth by thinking small. You need the right mindset. A "growth mindset," if you will. We measure to create a growth mindset.

With any change comes discomfort. Growth, excellence, and improvement all come with a side of "uncomfortable." It's uncomfortable to measure something you've always assumed was "perfect" only to find it's not. It's uncomfortable to be transparent about a measured goal that isn't particularly "brag-worthy." It's uncomfortable when the numbers tell us a different story than we've told ourselves. But we've learned that excellence is on the other side of that discomfort.

Connect to Individual Purpose

When all we see is a number, we can easily disconnect from the deeper "why." Pushback is common in life, especially when you are trying to create serious change. And pushback will be stronger if people aren't engaged with their minds and heart. People who are invested in creating change are probably not doing it purely to move a "number" but because of what that number represents, who it represents, and the true meaning of that number.

As healthcare workers, we care about keeping people safe. So, when we see measurements around fall prevention or infection reduction, we become more invested when that number is connected to the lives saved.

Even when the numbers aren't great—maybe especially then—we put a higher value on what that number represents.

It becomes real and personal. We get it when we hear the story of that person falling and needing surgery and having their life shaken, or how a bad outcome because of a hospital-acquired infection affected a family. It is also real and personal when we improve and protect. Even small wins need to be celebrated.

Healthcare is personal, intimate, and sacred. Measurement helps us tap into all of that. The more connected our teams are to the human impact behind the numbers, the more enthusiastic they will be about moving those numbers.

Clarity of Priorities

It is essential to set expectations so that individuals know what's at stake. When leaders clearly understand the purpose and connection of the measure to the organization's greater mission, they begin to align their tactics and values to support the organization's success. Effective goals help prioritize where and how we leverage our financial and human capital.

The CEO of one organization we worked with shared his perspective on prioritizing goals.

> "Not every great idea is the RIGHT idea for this moment in time."

What did he mean by this?

If everything is a priority, then nothing truly is. We may have many great ideas, but what is the RIGHT idea that will significantly impact our mission? How does the data tell us where (and where not) to invest our resources? How can we use data to create enthusiasm around pursuing a new endeavor?

For example, while all areas of the patient experience survey are important and connected, which one is the most important right now? Based on your current results, it may be most important to focus your organization on the "communication" questions to get the greatest lift in your results. Or it may be a different area entirely. It's similar to caring for a patient with multiple diagnoses or injuries. While they all may be "connected," rapidly dropping oxygen saturation with shortness of breath and chest pain may be what we prioritize over a small laceration.

When we care for complicated patient cases, we are measuring many things. Heart rate, blood pressure, mentation, urinary output, temperature, lab results, and radiology findings. And we use all of that to guide the care we deliver; certainly the priority of care. We must make quick and decisive decisions in some patient scenarios, especially when multiple measurements require our focus. Sometimes those choices are tough, and the priorities may shift as the day progresses. We still make those decisions out of a keen desire to make our patients healthier. It's no different regarding all the measures connected to organizational health.

Cadence of Measurement

How often have you heard individuals say, "But how do you know the data is accurate?" Denial is the number one point of resistance when increasing data transparency. When faced with questions about data validity, consider it good news. Having questions about the data means people are looking at it! When they are looking at it, that means they care about it. And when they care about it, that's when progress can be made. It almost always comes back to that connection to "why."

When considering the frequency of publishing updates for your goals, the important thing to focus on is how you can create data reliability by following a consistent cadence. For some goals, a weekly or monthly measurement is essential. For others, results move more slowly or are only available quarterly or annually. There is no single answer to "What is the best frequency?" The universal answer is that a consistent or predictable cadence matters most. Continuous heart rate monitoring might make sense, whereas monitoring the heart rate once a month might be dangerous. Certain labs need to be evaluated daily, whereas some make sense to do weekly. We determine that through priority, experience, logic, and common sense.

Each goal must be assessed individually, and you should establish a shared understanding of the measurement cadence. Developing a standard cadence helps team members create reliability in the data, ensuring they have ample time to ask questions and test whether their actions are having the expected impact on results.

Remember, questions are good. This data may challenge long-held assumptions or change the story they've been telling themselves about "how things are." It may take some adjustment. Once precedent is set and people can wrap their minds around "this is how it is," the inquiries should settle down.

As the saying goes, the truth shall set you free. Shedding some light on things that may have been "in the dark" can be quite liberating for the people closest to the issue and the organization as a whole.

Leading and Lagging Indicators

When considering all the data we could measure, it's important to monitor both the leading and lagging indicators. As a simple refresh on what those mean: a leading indicator is a predictive measurement; for example, the percentage of people washing their hands before walking into a patient room, while a lagging indicator is an output measurement; for example, a department's number of hospital-acquired infections.

Or, to break it down even more: leading indicators point toward future events, and lagging indicators confirm a pattern that is in progress. Leading indicators reflect those actions or activities that strongly influence improvement in the lagging measure. As we develop the organizational scorecard, we recommend measuring the organization's success against the lagging measures. However, monitoring leading measures is just as important and likely tracked outside of the organizational scorecard. Leading measures are the key performance indicators that inform the health of an organization and can be used to understand what is impacting the current performance (lagging measure). Lagging measures are relatively easy to measure but can be difficult to change because they are often the result of upstream changes in multiple leading indicators.

Suppose an organization is looking to develop a strategy around being the employer of choice in the community. In that case, it may choose to track progress on the lagging measures of "employee engagement" and "employee turnover." These are the ultimate outcomes that suggest how well employees are retained as valued members of the team. In Principle 5, we discuss the topic of employee engagement in more detail, however, we know that "rounding for outcomes" is an evidence-based practice that helps engage team members and is key to driving these measures forward.

Let's say we set a goal of connecting with at least 95% of employees in purposeful rounding each month. The percentage of rounds completed would be the leading measure. Measuring this investment can help predict the outcome of the other two measures. Leading indicators are dynamic and can change rapidly, making it critical to measure regularly and act early when trends are unfavorable and to reward and recognize when we see trends going in the right direction. When people know that what they're doing is making a difference, it feeds their "why" and fuels their passion.

Think of it like running a race. As you start to pick up speed and the crowd starts chanting your name and cheering you on, you get more excited, dig deep, maybe chug some Gatorade and pick up your stride! Same here. Measurement helps guide us when we need to coach and when we need to cheer.

Several questions arise when there is a misalignment between leading and lagging measures:

- What other factors may be influencing the lagging indicators? (Are there any changes in the external environment or new and unpredictable factors that have popped up?)

- Where do we have performance gaps not reflected in the current measurement report?

- What actions or training must occur to create a more favorable outcome?

- Where is the misalignment risk the greatest within the organization?

- How committed are leaders across the organization to the success of the results?

- Do leaders have consistent urgency to implement the leading measures across the organization?

It may be challenging to understand where misalignment exists. Leaving it to "guesswork" or how we "feel" might not help with making the right pivot. It's like picking who you think will win a football game based on the fact you "feel good" about the color of their uniforms. It may work, but it's more likely knowing some stats about the teams would be more helpful. But always know that unpredictable things like the weather changing, an injury, or a sudden sinkhole in the field swallowing up the star quarterback could change the whole outcome! While we can never know the unpredictable because it's unpredictable, we can at least have the most solid foundation possible.

A comprehensive cultural health assessment can help eliminate some of the guesswork and aid in the process of identifying where your organization needs to invest additional support to improve results. Fact-based plans informed by assessment results will provide a more solid foundation from which to address the unpredictable events that arise.

Putting it All Together— The Scorecard

An organizational scorecard brings the strategic plan to life and provides direction to the organization.

> An effective scorecard serves as the road map for how an organization will accomplish its strategic priorities. It drives progress by moving all team members in the same direction. It helps team members understand the meaning and value of their contributions. It takes the invisible and theoretical and makes it visible and tangible.

A scorecard is a dynamic tool that supports both communication and alignment. The thing about anything labeled "communication" is that it is a two-way conversation. When used as a communication tool, the scorecard clearly and concisely provides the most relevant and important information about goals and progress. When reviewed proactively (typically monthly), it creates conversation and stirs creative input. Teams engage in the organization's success, intentionally course-correct actions, and celebrate successes to accelerate performance.

When used as an alignment tool, a scorecard connects goals, measures, and behaviors throughout the organization as team members are activated to drive results. A sample scorecard is provided below, and we will walk through the stages necessary to build and optimize the scorecard effectively for your organization.

Figure 2.1: Organizational Scorecard Sample

Optimizing the Organizational Scorecard—3 Essential Stages

Figure 2.2: Optimizing the Organizational Scorecard – 3 Essential Stages

Stage 1: Build the Scorecard

In Principle 1, we covered the concept of organizational pillars. An effective scorecard will contain goals in each pillar, creating balance across the organization's priorities. The balance is necessary to ensure a proper understanding of what is important and urgent throughout the year.

Typically you identify 1-3 measures per pillar, connect them directly to the strategic plan, and use them to guide the organization's operational priorities over the next 12 months.

You've heard me say this a lot by now, and I will continue to gently remind you, "Don't try to do too much at once!" If you fill up a 2,000-gallon barrel of paint, attach it by a chain to a helicopter, and dump all the paint on the house from above, intending to get it all done at once, you won't have a nicely painted house. You'll have a mess and probably some very ticked-off neighbors!

When identifying the measures to include, ensure the measurement is available for the priorities and that you consistently track and communicate progress. If data is delayed, be upfront about that so the team knows what's going on. It shows integrity and sets the precedent of "keeping it real." People will give you more respect for being honest about not having information ready than for being silent about it and then suddenly sharing it later. Transparency is key here, so be sure the measures you select are appropriate to share internally and externally with stakeholders.

Stage 2: Cascade

In Principle 7, we discuss the topic of alignment and goal cascading in more detail. The organizational scorecard is the starting point for the annual goal-setting process, engaging all team members in the conversation and helping organizations achieve meaningful results. In this phase, you will cascade the organizational results scorecard to division and unit leaders.

Stage 3: Monitor Progress

As the work across the organization begins, it is important to monitor progress and communicate updates in multiple forums. For some of us, this may feel like "TMI" (too much information), especially if our culture has been a little less communicative in the past. Move through this discomfort. On the other side of it is a sense of accomplishment and renewal.

Share progress during leadership meetings, during staff town halls, and during staff huddles. The most effective organizations optimize all communication channels to cascade progress through the organization. Keep it consistent. Human nature is such that if you tell me one number and share a different one with someone else, I wonder, "'What are they hiding?"

Share stories to help bring data to life. People connect to stories with graphs. Share best practices and action plans across teams to coordinate efforts. Brainstorm strategies to break through barriers and uncover those struggling or needing support, guidance, and mentorship.

I recall an organization I coached that was struggling with fall reduction, except in one department. Over many months, the third floor was doing amazing with its fall reduction work. As we all know, one month isn't a trend, but if you see results over many, we are in "the trend zone."

I was meeting with the department head on the second floor. She knew I worked with many high-performing organizations around the U.S. and wondered if I had anyone at any of these organizations to help her with best practices. I shared the third floor's results. Her jaw dropped. I told her that we didn't have to go to the airport. We could just get in the elevator (or take the stairs) one flight to learn from an "in-house rockstar!"

We did that and uncovered opportunities to be more deliberate about sharing best practices across departments. After three meetings with her colleague and making some changes that had worked on that unit, she began to see a fall reduction, which continued for many months.

Often the best practice we need is right in front of our eyes. You'd be surprised to learn that the answers to our questions are usually closer than we suppose.

Engaging External Stakeholders

My two friends and I were on the way to the beach, and in our excitement and teenage exuberance, I took my eye off the gas gauge. Then, on a bridge, my 1970 Oldsmobile 442 sputtered and stalled. Of course, my friends got out and started pushing. They were very invested in the progress we needed to make to get to the beach (well, the gas station first).

But guess who else helped? Passengers from other cars yelled out to us to ask what was wrong, and then they got out and helped push my battleship of a car. Why? They were also invested in getting us on the road so they, too, could get to the beach. They didn't see this as "their problem." They saw it as "our problem."

Think of my friends and me as the "internal influencers" of our progress and the people stuck behind us on the bridge as the "external influencers." They saw the issue and knew their "push" would be helpful to us all. We made it to the gas station near the end of the bridge, got some gas, and were on our way in part because of the help of those "external influencers."

Who are the external influencers of your organization's success? Do they clearly understand the organization's priorities and where you are performing? When external influencers like board members, physicians, community members, etc., ask questions about leadership decisions, it is often the result of not being consistently informed about the organization's direction and progress toward the goals. If they don't know where the gas gauge is, they can't get out and help you push!

When posting the scorecard publicly, on the website, in a community report, or on the communication board (more on communication boards in Principle 8), you establish trust with these influencers. You provide the information they need without them having to ask the question. It might even get you over a bridge and into sunshine!

Converting Data into Information— Telling a Story

To gain buy-in, enable change, and effectively explain progress depends on how we convey the data we've been collecting and the **story** we tell about it.

Listen, we can all agree that data can be complex. It can be downright confusing. Excellent leaders are vigilant about taking data, looking at how it can inspire and encourage it, and allowing it to tell a story. Data without connection, without definition, without purpose is just numbers, lines, and pie charts. Nothing wrong with those, but unless people see themselves in the numbers—see the story of who they are and what they're doing and how it touches the people they are doing this all for—they won't be invested in it.

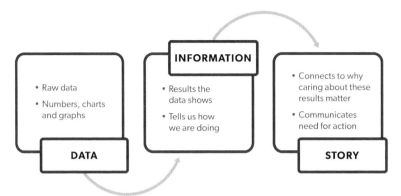

Figure 2.3: Converting Data into Information

Goal Setting—The SMART Way

One of the greatest advantages to defining your leading and lagging indicators is it sets you up to establish meaningful goals successfully.

In most organizations, leaders use the SMART Goals methodology to craft **specific**, **measurable**, **achievable**, **relevant**, and **time-bound** goals. This helps ensure the goal is crystal clear and energy can be focused on goal achievement rather than discussions about what was meant by a specific goal. It is helpful to use a goal template to ensure this methodology is followed consistently. It takes the guesswork out, ensures that the "source of truth" is identified at the beginning of the measurement period, and lowers people's anxiety about goal setting.

Goal Statement Template

Increase / Decrease / Maintain X from a baseline of Y by Z (time-frame), as measured by (tool, report, survey, etc.).

Figure 2.4: Goal Statement Template

Goal Samples:

- SMART Goal: Improve employee engagement results from the 48th percentile to the 65th percentile by March 31, as measured by the 1Q Employee Engagement Survey.

- Not-So-SMART Goal: Ensure every employee is happy and contributing in their role next year.

See the difference?

S	Specific	• What are you trying to do? • What will be accomplished? • What actions will you take?	State what you will do using specific action words. The most effective goals measure precise results and are specific enough to be achieved by implementing an explicit set of actions.
M	Measurable	• How will you measure your results? • How will you assess your achievement?	Quantify the goal. Provide a way to evaluate using metrics or data targets. Example: Employee engagement results are easily measured. While it might sound more fun, "happy and contributing" results are not. Goals should be outcome-driven versus process metrics. Leading indicators are process measures that will increase the likelihood of achieving the outcome or lagging indicator.
A	Achievable	• Is the goal doable and realistic? • Can you reach your goal with the tools, skills, and resources you have? • If not, what do you need?	Goals should be realistic. Use your expertise and experience to identify a reasonably achievable goal. Don't be afraid to set stretch goals. But recognize that unattainable goals are demotivating and can backfire when a leader's internal dialogue goes something like, "Well, I can forget about making every employee happy, whatever that means! I may as well forget about achieving this goal!"
R	Relevant	• How does the goal align with broader goals? • Why is the result important?	Think about the big picture. Understand why achieving this goal contributes significantly to the organization's overall health or specific business units. In the "Not-so-SMART" example above, you could argue that employee happiness is not essential for organizational success.
T	Time-bound	• What is the time frame for accomplishing the goal?	Specify the date or timeframe. Clarity on the specific measurement end-point is critical. More disputes about how to reflect goal results come from a lack of clarity in this component of the goal statement than any other. Know where you've drawn the finish line for this measurement period.

Figure 2.5: What is a SMART goal. Reference: George Doran, Arthur Miller, and James Cunningham; 1981, "There's a SMART way to write management goals and objectives"

Goal Alignment

One of the most powerful accelerators of organizational performance is goal alignment. An organization's overall scorecard may reflect a "Growth" goal to increase patient visits from X to Y. To achieve that organizational goal, individual leaders must contribute in unique ways. Your facility manager may carry a goal to complete renovations for 18 clinic exam rooms, while the physician recruiter's goal is to employ two new family practice physicians. Your finance team must implement the new scheduling system, and your clinic manager must improve patient satisfaction. This is an example of vertical alignment.

Horizontal alignment across work groups is also critical. For example, in several organizations Huron has coached, both inpatient and emergency department leaders have goals related to throughput. The environmental services leader will have a goal to improve turnaround times following patient discharge. Goal achievement by one department significantly influences the ability of other departments to achieve their goals. When each leader's individual goals are aligned with the organization's goals or with each other, and they understand how their contribution influences overall organizational performance, the resulting synergy and momentum are undeniable.

As Pablo Picasso once said, "Our goals can only be reached through a vehicle of a plan, in which we must fervently believe, and upon which we must vigorously act. There is no other route to success." (To date, the most expensive Picasso sold went for $179.4 million. He may be on to something!)

Connecting Back to Purpose

You might ask, "Don't you think we focus too much on the numbers?" I'll give you an answer that might not be what you expect.

If you focus only on "the numbers," then yes, you are on the wrong path.

It's not the number. It is what that number means. The number is just the map to the treasure. We need it. It guides us. It helps us stay on course, but it is merely a representation of what matters.

Think of it this way. The graduation ceremony isn't what matters. That ceremony represents the hard work and dedication it took to get there, which is what is important.

A "9" or "10" rating or an "Always" is certainly awesome, but what it represents is priceless. It means a patient feels seen, heard, cared for, watched over, valued, and safe. It represents relieving pain and suffering. It represents healing and wholeness. It represents the best that human beings can be. It means for that person we were their hero, their light, their hope.

The number is outstanding, but it is a symbol of something far greater, something sacred even.

Because of the compassion we showed, the care we delivered, and, yes, the love we extended, we're making existence better for another human being who is vulnerable, hurting, and afraid. Our teams always have to be reminded and shown that these measurements represent meaningful, life-changing, beautiful things.

Like my friend Liz said in the story earlier in this chapter, things of value are measured. That measurement can guide us to excellence, and with that information, "numbers" can create massive and meaningful change. Change is not just to move a metric but to move a human being to wholeness and a healthcare team to inspiration and empowerment. If we care enough about something, we will measure it, learn from it, and become better because of both.

As anthropologist Margaret Mead told us, "Never believe that a few caring people can't change the world. For, indeed, that's all who ever have." I would venture that those who have changed the world had some way to gauge their progress, wouldn't you? After all, how do you know "change" has happened in the absence of measurement? They always say, "Numbers tell a story." In sports, in finance, in politics, and certainly in healthcare. Our numbers, those we follow and reach for in healthcare, tell quite a story. The story of healing and resilience. The story of overcoming obstacles and, yes, sometimes, even the stories of miracles. We measure what is important because, for us, each patient, each caregiver, each leader, and each provider that we encounter represents our impact on this world. A world we seek to make better in all that we do and with all that we say, and with all that we are, one carefully and lovingly measured step at a time.

Principle 2 Summary

In summary, Principle 2: Measure the Important Things, helps leaders define specific targets, measure progress against them, and align the necessary resources to achieve them. Just as measuring a patient's vitals is crucial to their care plan, measuring the important things provides the vital signs and the key to developing a treatment plan for an organization.

With a strong commitment to excellence (Principle 1) and key measurement in place (Principle 2), you can confidently move forward to practice the principles outlined in the following chapters to help drive the treatment plan and achieve desired results.

PRINCIPLE 3: BUILD A CULTURE AROUND SERVICE

Serve Others with Great Care and Concern

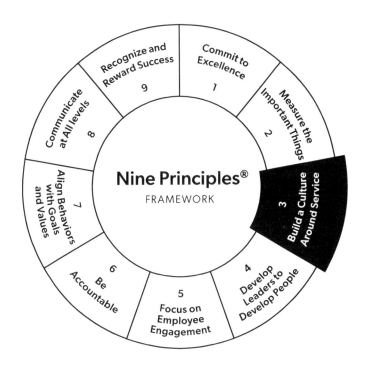

"The best way to find yourself is to lose
yourself in the service of others."

Mahatma Gandhi

Building a Culture of Service— How to Read This Chapter

We focus on building a culture around service by defining what it looks like for people, their families, and the community. Without question, creating a culture around service for co-workers and colleagues from different departments is also important. Culture is like a warm summer breeze; no matter who you are, you will feel it if you're around it.

In this chapter, you will explore concepts central to the "Culture of Excellence" you aim to nurture in your organization. It encompasses many lessons learned in years of working with caregivers, patients, providers, and physicians. There's so much to share on the concept of "service" that we have divided this principle into three sections to help you dive deeper into specific needs at your organization. As with any significant task, taking one step at a time rather than trying to do everything at once will make it easier to reach your goal.

SECTION 1:	SECTION 2:	SECTION 3:
Caring with Connections, Compassion, and Communication	Caring at the Bedside	Caring for Internal Customers

SECTION 1:

Section 1 focuses on what all employees can do to care for people. No matter your job or title, you are all in this together.

In this section, you will discover powerful strategies and tactics that impact patient/customer-centered care and productive working relationships.

These include making personal connections with compassion and specific tactics such as the 10/5 Rule, the AIDET® Communication Framework, and Service Recovery.

SECTION 2:

Section 2 focuses on tactics that drive excellence and care delivered at the bedside.

In this section, you will discover tactics that, when done with intention and heart, become a solid basis for patient care excellence, not to mention a solid foundation for efficiency and improved engagement.

This includes nurse leader rounding, patient communication boards, Bedside Shift Report℠, Hourly Rounding®, pre-visit calls, care transition calls, and individualized patient care.

SECTION 3:

Section 3 focuses on areas that take care of the people taking care of patients.

In this section, you will see how departments and roles that may not be at the physical bedside daily can play a critical and vital role in the care delivered to the people you serve.

This section will also examine rounding by support service department leaders within and across teams.

We need each other. We are truly stronger together than we can be alone. As the Bondei proverb teaches us: "Sticks in a bundle are unbreakable."

Introduction

It is easy to get lost these days. Even with GPS, if you have a poor connection or stormy weather, that guidance can yell out "exit now!' as you watch the exit in your rearview mirror. There's no doubt we in healthcare have the "wiring" to navigate our work, but sometimes that "stormy weather" may look like a pandemic, limited staffing, tough clinical cases, or sad outcomes. A "poor connection" may be feeling stressed, separated from purpose, or overwhelmed. We have those days where we constantly feel like our emotional and spiritual GPS is repeating "rerouting now!"

The quote that begins this chapter speaks a relatable truth: No matter your work in healthcare, you have served others. When we say build a culture around service, we speak to this. If we agree that we sometimes feel a bit "lost" in the traffic of work, it will ultimately be those moments of serving that let us know our signal is clear, the path is open, and we are on the right road.

We all want to feel like we work somewhere that "sees us." We all want to be part of something meaningful and worthwhile. When our organization prioritizes these things, it reconfirms that we are in the right place. When we feel part of a culture of compassion, we elevate as humans. And that elevates our self-worth and passion, care delivery, and the entire organization.

Patient Experience— Words to Get Us Started

The Agency for Healthcare Research and Quality (AHRQ) states that "patient experience encompasses the range of interactions people have with the healthcare system, including their care from health plans and doctors, nurses, and staff in hospitals, physician practices, and other healthcare facilities." Beryl Institute defines patient experience as "the sum of all interactions shaped by an organization's culture that influence perceptions across the continuum of care."

Do you see the common thread in these definitions? It is the human interactions that shape a patient's perception and experience. These interactions also aren't isolated to face-to-face. They can be in person, over the phone, through a virtual visit, or via written instructions.

So, why is there so much emphasis in our industry on the patient experience, and why the urgency to build a culture of service? The simple answer is that it's the right thing to do and what separates the good from the excellent.

Think about it. Patients make some minimal assumptions. They expect a clean facility with providers with the skills to care for them, keep them safe, and do everything possible to improve them. However, how they *EXPERIENCE* care... now that is a whole other conversation.

For example, when someone is admitted, they may not expect a Michelin-Star-rated meal, but they do expect the chicken to be cooked properly, the soup not to be too salty, the hot food to be hot, and the cold food to be cold. But, if a thoughtful server adds a hot cookie to their tray after they mention how much they love cookies, then their experience is elevated.

What if you overheard this conversation? Anyone: "Oh my goodness! I heard you got engaged! Was it romantic? How did you feel about it?" Newly engaged person: "I was satisfied."

We don't want our patients just to be satisfied. That isn't fulfilling for either the patient or for us. It isn't enough to have satisfied customers; they must be engaged.

Patient Experience and Patient Engagement

In a recent study, Gallup found that companies delivering the highest customer impact levels have *72% more fully engaged customers*. This is excellent news for the industries outside of healthcare, but we don't just want our patients to be involved—we need them to be. Because when a patient is engaged in their experience, they are actively involved in their care and collaborate with their healthcare team to maximize outcomes.

When thinking about "patient experience," many of us instantly return to "patient satisfaction." While on the surface, they seem identical, there are some significant differences between them. A diamond and a pebble are technically minerals, but the song didn't say that a pebble was anyone's best friend! "Satisfied" is a good thing, but like a pebble easy to crush and forgettable. An "experience" is like that diamond; memorable, sustainable, and inspiring to everyone.

CAHPS® and Patient Experience

CAHPS®, which stands for Consumer Assessment of Healthcare Providers and Systems, is a standardized survey that measures patients' perspectives across the healthcare continuum in the United States. It assesses various behaviors of care team, such as understandable communication, demonstrating courtesy and respect, careful listening, and the overall quality of care provided. CAHPS® was created to collect patient information about the frequency and **consistency** of how the care team demonstrates behaviors that patients feel are important.

The answers are not based on "how happy you were with…" but on "how often did that happen?" It is about being consistent in processes, services, and interactions. "Happy" can be a moment or dependent on who works that day. Like the adage says, even a broken clock is right twice a day! This principle focuses on tactics and strategies that enhance patient experience and move CAHPS® outcomes.

 Harvey—Experiences That Stay With Us Forever.

When I was a leader at a large community hospital, I received a phone call from a social worker at the large county hospital where I used to work and where my dad worked most of my life. He had recognized the last name of someone listed as "next of kin" for an accident victim as being the same as mine, and they had been unable to reach that person.

The "next of kin" contact was my brother, and the accident victim was his best friend. This former colleague called me because of the gravity of the situation. My brother's best friend, Harvey, and his wife had been in a horrible crash. Harvey's wife was going to need surgery but was expected to survive. Harvey's condition was not as hopeful.

My former trauma team co-workers asked if I could come to the hospital. "Your brother's going to need you," they said. I could not reach my brother on the phone on my way there. As I arrived, I was met by the surgeon, a few nurses, and the social worker. They had reached my brother, who was en route to the hospital.

I could sense that something had changed. They gently broke the news to me that Harvey had passed away. I went and saw this man whom I had known since I was a kid and who was like a family member. I held his hand and bowed my head, saying my goodbyes. Leaving the trauma bay, I stood just inside the waiting room door waiting for my brother, and when he arrived, he was shocked to see me there. I hugged him and broke the bad news as best I could. It was devastating and one of the most challenging things I've ever had to do as a nurse or loved one.

I was not an employee then and hadn't worked there for around five years. But this team of caregivers didn't see our beloved friend as "trauma patient #2677665." This social worker took the time to think about the big picture and what was best for those who loved Harvey. He made sure that I could be there to support my brother. As sad as the outcome was, my brother and I remember the compassion and respect of that experience and the opportunity to say goodbye to someone who meant the world to him.

There are no "satisfied" or "happy" moments in challenging stories like these, but there are experiences. Whether positive or negative, they stay with us forever. Sometimes in our healthcare journey, decreasing some of the pain is all we have to offer. But sometimes,

that can be a lot.

Section 1: Caring with Connections, Compassion, and Communication

This section will concentrate on some of the basic behaviors and foundations of the care experience—the important elements before, during, and after patient care. First, **Connections**. We will review how little effort it takes to make a personal and meaningful connection face-to-face with a patient or in the hallways of your organization. Second, **Compassion**. We will capture the power of compassionate acts to improve patient care and outcomes. And finally, **Communication**. We will discuss how to focus communication on people's needs and how to recover when things don't go as expected, because if there's one thing we can count on in healthcare, things often don't go as expected.

40-Second Personal Connection

In the books Compassionomics and Wonder Drug, authors Dr. Stephen Trzeciak and Dr. Anthony Mazzarelli provide robust evidence that personal connections aren't just for the person receiving, but also for the person giving.

The authors write, "Imagine our surprise when we uncovered a preponderance of the evidence that signaled that the association between compassion and burnout is inverse. Low compassion; high burnout.

High compassion; low burnout. This suggests that more human connection can be good for you." They note, "The counterintuitive finding here is that caregiver compassion not only can improve patient outcomes, but it can also transform caregiver experience."

If this is true, what keeps us from using these behaviors we know impact each of us and the people we serve? Many reasons—technology issues, cultural barriers, lack of training, or feeling burned out and tired. But the overwhelming number one answer is "time."

Time – Time – Time

So, let's talk about time. If you are like most people, you might feel you don't have time to spare to make these connections. Valid point. That clock is always ticking. But how much time does it take to connect with a patient or an employee? Five minutes? 10 minutes? An hour?

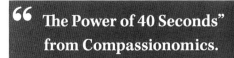
**" The Power of 40 Seconds"
from Compassionomics.**

To address the question of time, researchers from Johns Hopkins University performed a randomized controlled trial on cancer patients during a consultation with an oncologist. The primary outcome measure for this study was a well-validated measurement scale for patient anxiety. If you understand what it's like to receive a cancer diagnosis, you already know that reducing anxiety is a critically important outcome for cancer patients.

The researchers found that, compared to a standard consultation from an oncologist, patients randomized to an enhanced compassion intervention from an oncologist had significantly less anxiety at the end of the consultation. So, what was the enhanced compassion intervention? A few words were offered at the beginning and end of the consultation.

Here was the message from the oncologist at the beginning of the consultation: "I know this is a tough experience to go through, and I want you to know that I am here with you. Some things I say to you today may be difficult to understand, so I want you to feel comfortable stopping me if something I say is confusing or doesn't make sense. We are here together, and we will go through this together."

And then, at the end of the consultation, the oncologist said: "I know this is a tough time for you, and I want to emphasize again that we are in this together. I will be with you each step along the way."

So how long did it take? They timed it: just 40 seconds.

Source: Compassionomics, Chapter 8

The authors cite another study from Northwestern University where researchers used a validated methodology to measure compassion opportunities from patients and the corresponding responses by physicians in general internal medicine practice. They identified compassionate opportunity-response communication sequences that took, on average, 31.5 seconds. The authors challenge the reader that it is "time to take the time" and ask, "If a single sequence of communicating compassion takes half a minute, can healthcare providers spare that for compassion?"

Meaningful and emotional connections can be made in under a minute. No one here is diminishing how busy we all are. We are just pointing out that the distance between our patients feeling a sense of compassion and even us feeling less burnt out could be 40 seconds—or less.

Making Your Time Count

There are infinite ways to make meaningful connections in our conversations. As human beings, we probably have more in common than we don't. But those little moments of connection are the very moments that can change it all for the better.

Very few patients and families in your healthcare setting are there for a "fun" reason. Even positive events like childbirth or cancer-free determinations have their share of challenges and stress. The reality is that meaningful connections must be fostered. The less stressed patients feel, the easier the flow of care. The less stressed the team, the better team members think about what they do.

To a patient, it might sound like this:

- "Ms. Sanchez, I know you have a procedure scheduled for this afternoon. You are in the best hands with our team. We want you to feel safe and cared for today. You will be gone from this room for about two hours. But I'll be waiting for you when you return. Do you have any questions I can answer while we get you ready?"

- "Ms. Samms, my name is Melanie, and I will be your nurse and take care of you today. I saw you had some special young visitors a bit ago. Tell me about them. I have children about the same age."

To an employee, it might sound like this:

- "Carmen, I know your mom has been sick. I can only imagine how concerned you've been. I've been thinking of you since you shared this with me. How are things going? Can I do anything for you?"

- "Christina! It's so good to see you! Tell me about Luca's first day of kindergarten. He's such an amazing kid. I love all your funny stories about him."

Once, when sharing this concept with an organization and getting some healthy pushback about time, our coaching team handed one of the staff a watch. After timing several versions of the "meaningful conversations" like the examples above, they saw firsthand it didn't take but a few seconds to make these connections. That's one thing to remember as you continue this book and journey. Things take a lot longer to describe or write about than they do to practice. Nurses probably have hours of reading and discussion about starting an IV. However, when they do the first stick, it takes seconds. In "theory," it was a lot. In "practice," it was brief.

Try this connection concept "in practice" yourself. Come up with a few phrases you would potentially say and time them. Once you feel confident, role-play these interactions with your staff. Have them time you to see how long it takes. You'll be surprised. It might only take three seconds to say, "I always enjoy seeing how you make patients smile," but the impact of those words lasts much longer than the delivery.

66 Tell me your story.

Hello. My name is Dr. Dan Smith. My resident staffed a case with me for a woman with multiple complaints and a tough social situation. We determined her treatment plan, and I headed to her room to nail down some more details.

As I entered, the woman wouldn't make eye contact and seemed uncomfortable and on edge. I kept on with my assessment and questions. She interrupted me as I paraphrased what I had learned.

"Doctor, do you know about the world I live in each day?"

I was at a loss for words. I had a lot of information, but did I know much about her world? In my busyness, I might have missed something important. I humbly asked her to tell me her story.

Her gaze lifted; she looked me straight in the eye. Her body relaxed as she shared about herself and her situation. I listened with a different set of ears and eyes than I had just moments before, which helped me know how social work could assist and how to better set her up for success when she might have previously failed. It helped me achieve my goal of getting her better. And maybe, as importantly, it made me better.

When I entered her treatment room again later to review her test results with her, I was amazed at the difference in her. She smiled, and there wasn't that edge I had felt before. I gained her trust by hearing her story, acknowledging her reality, being present, open, and compassionate, and listening intentionally to connect. She thanked the team for all we had done for her.

I am so grateful for that experience. As brief as it was, the lesson will last a lifetime.

10/5 Rule

At Huron, we are often asked for something one can do or recommit to that has an almost-instant positive effect on a service-focused culture. We suggest implementing the "10/5" rule. It is a straightforward yet impactful tool.

It doesn't matter the type of measurement you use, but rather the "heart" you use. Whether it is the 8/4, 11/6, or 12/7 rule, the key is to keep it simple and do what makes sense. And remember, the 10/5 rule is for all of us—every leader, employee, and team member.

The beauty of this simple act is that when it becomes the "way we are," it contributes to the feeling of compassion and a positive impression for all who pass through your doors. When an organization has a solid service-centered culture, it is usually doing something like this. These organizations make it an actual expectation that if you do it, you receive a compliment. If you don't, you respectfully receive coaching. This is the difference!

As you approach someone:

10 FEET	5 FEET
"I see you!"	**"You matter to me!"**
Within 10 feet of an individual, acknowledge the person with some form of expression.	Within five feet of an individual, make eye contact and acknowledge the person verbally.
Make eye contact	"Hello/Hi."
Nod	"Good morning/afternoon/evening."
Smile	"Good to see you."
Wave	"How are you today?"
*You're letting them know: "I see you!"	*You're letting them know: "You matter to me!"

Figure 3.1: The 10/5 Rule

But again, there's always the "what if" crew. So, let's just put some of that to bed with a fluffy pillow and some tight hospital corners:

- "What if I'm running down the hall for a code blue?"
  You can run free. Run like the wind and focus on that.

- "What if I'm in a deep and serious conversation with a patient's family member?"
  Keep your focus there to show respect for that person. The folks walking by will be able to interpret that body language most of the time.

- "What if we are transporting an unstable person to the ICU?"
  Please focus on the patient, their monitor, and drips, and don't bump the stretcher into the wall. The folks passing by are most likely smart enough to "read the room" and wouldn't expect a greeting from you.

- "What if there's a fire, and we're evacuating?" (Yes, we've been asked this.)
  Please evacuate, grab the person when they're five feet away, and bring them with you.

In all seriousness, for the other 89.7% of the time when you're walking to a meeting, wheeling someone to x-ray, on the way to lunch, going to pick up a lab, or bringing a bed back to a room after transporting a patient, the 10/5 rule still holds. But don't feel guilty if you or your team are not doing this. None of us mean to ignore people intentionally.

Our heads are often down because we're thinking about something or processing critical information we just heard. Often, we forget that our work areas are also shared spaces with all the people that find their way to our buildings. Consider this your hall pass on that (pun intended)!

Before you write this off as "customer service fluffy stuff," consider how a simple action can make people feel. That person walking toward you might have just learned their dad has six months to live, their mom needs to go to outpatient rehab, and it's 50 miles away, or their four-year-old needs heart surgery. There is a myriad of reasons they may feel scared, alone, or anxious as they walk down your bustling, unfamiliar hallways.

A simple "good morning" might make that fellow human being feel less invisible. Sometimes, it even leads to a conversation. Sometimes, those conversations create these "mini relationships" that bring people together, heal spirits, and engage that part of our beings that reminds us of why we are here.

People will remember that nurse, physician, EVS worker, lab tech, finance, or executive who "took the time to talk to me." Those simple moments can be what your organization becomes known for as those individuals tell stories about when they were there. Those moments are closer than you think. Sometimes only five to 10 feet away.

Compassion

Leading with Compassion

> "If we have no peace, it is because we have forgotten that we belong to each other."
>
> *Mother Teresa*

One of the most impactful definitions of compassion is "the feeling that arises when you confront another's suffering and feel motivated to relieve that suffering." In any given week, we most likely spend more time with our patients, colleagues, and co-workers than we do with those at home and in our personal lives. As healthcare workers, we don't think twice about treating total strangers compassionately, just as we would for those we know and love. Compassion is in our veins.

Sympathy – Empathy – Compassion

Sympathy, empathy, and compassion are used interchangeably. While these words are related, each has its power and place and they are not synonymous.

Sympathy is when we care but don't necessarily have a personal connection. You hear a sad story and feel sorry for the person, but you don't necessarily act or make a deeper connection. It is not dissimilar to pity. One could say it is a feeling you have FOR someone.

Empathy, on the other hand, is a more vulnerable state. It is the ability to share someone else's feelings and put yourself in their shoes. It is a feeling you have WITH someone, not FOR them.

Compassion magnifies and expands empathy. It transforms that feeling into action. Compassion is when you do something to alleviate the suffering of others. It takes culture and empowers it; it heals your patients, heals you, and the world we live in.

" ANGEL-A."

Hello. My name is Margaret. My dad lived in an assisted living facility before he passed in March 2022. He had many people who cared for him during his time there—Debbie, John, and Katie. But there was one whom he adored. Her name was Angela, although my sister called her "Angel-a" because when she was on, somehow, Dad's suffering seemed to lessen, and he smiled a bit more.

I asked him one day, "Dad, why do you like Angela so much?"

He thought a moment and said, "To Angela, I'm not just a patient in AL214. Did you know she brings me a hot cup of coffee every morning, just like your mother used to do? She also helps me make my bed each morning because she knows I like my room clean in case visitors drop by. She doesn't look for what she HAS to do but what she CAN do. That's what makes her a great nurse."

A cup of warm coffee. A made bed.

It may not seem like much, but Angela's kindness made a beautiful difference to my dad each day. It wasn't what she did as much as how she made him feel.

When the pandemic hit and Dad had to quarantine for so long, my sisters and I asked if he would like us to discharge him and let him live with us for a while. He said, "No. I am going to stay put. They care for me here. When the caring stops, I'll tell you it's time to go."

I know for a fact that Angela had everything to do with his response. It was her acts of compassion that made him feel safe and secure.

So, thank you "Angel-a." Even though the world seemed to come to a stop, your care and compassion never did. We are forever grateful to you.

Communication

You will see one theme woven through all we talk about in this book—communication in all its remarkable, diverse, and unique ways. Communication can make or break a relationship, prevent undesirable outcomes, save lives, and create a compassionate environment for all. Communication can also help create efficiency and make our work life better.

One can never overstate the power of "words." It brings to mind a quote I once heard attributed to Rumi, a 13th-century Persian poet. Rumi said, "Raise your words, not your voice. It is rain that grows flowers, not thunder." Words are that powerful.

Keep this thought in mind: You will comfort and console with more words than pills, explain and educate with more words than diagnostic reports, and relieve anxiety and worry with more words than any device or technology presently existing. While no one likes to be told what to say, it is helpful to highlight ways to use our voice more effectively.

Huron commissioned a research study of 1,500 individuals to assess healthcare consumption. In the U.S., this longitudinal study, completed in September 2021, was benchmarked against Huron's 2019 and February 2021 consumer studies to understand what may have changed and remained the same as healthcare continues to evolve. The research found three common problems stem from poor communication during care interactions:

1. **Patients especially dislike feeling like just another number.** Poor communication in care interactions can come across as indifference or a lack of empathy on the part of the provider, caregiver, or staff, negatively impacting the patient's perception of care.

2. **Patients want greater transparency in their care interactions.** When patients don't understand what providers and staff are doing

for them and why, the lack of clarity can lead to a lack of motivation to stay healthy, derailing adherence to treatment plans.

3. **Poor communication is a source of burnout.** Struggling to communicate with patients and their families during care interactions is a significant source of burnout for physicians, nurses, and staff.

Key Words at Key Times

> Key words at key times are things said and done to "connect the dots" and help patients, families, and visitors better understand what we are doing. They align our words with our actions to give a consistent experience and message.

Let's face it, when anyone is in the hospital or your care, they're probably feeling distracted, scared, and maybe even in pain. So, even if we think we're communicating clearly, the message may not be heard.

That's where key words come in—they're simple and easy to understand. They help people understand their care better and feel more in control of their care.

But it's not just about making things easier for patients. Key words also help those who deliver care to align our behavior with the patient's needs. It's ultimately about building a mutually beneficial relationship with our patients.

So, what are some examples of key words?

- "I am going to close the curtain now for your privacy."

- "I am rounding on you today to ensure your safety and quality of care."

- "I want to make sure you are very satisfied with the cleanliness of your room. Have I missed anything? Is there anything I can do before I leave?"

- "Your doctor wants to see how you are doing. I need to draw some blood now, so the results will be available when she looks in on you."

In thinking about whether key words make a difference for patients, imagine if we didn't use them. What important information might be lost?

Let's take the first example. If you quietly close the curtain in front of a patient, they might start to worry and assume all sorts of things. Maybe they're bothering you, you're hiding something from them, or even think that something scary is about to go down, and you're trying to protect other people from seeing it. So, by using simple phrases like "I'm going to close the curtain now for your privacy," we can put our patients at ease and make sure they feel informed and cared for.

See? It's the little things that can make a big difference.

AIDET® Communication Framework

You are likely familiar with the Huron AIDET® Communication Framework, which has evolved to become a leading practice in our industry. We developed this communication framework from our early work with organizations around using key words at key times.

We discovered that patients had recurring needs, anxieties, and requests, and we brought together five powerful key communication elements to create this framework. Its purpose is to facilitate proactive communication that promotes positive patient and organizational outcomes.

> The AIDET® Communication Framework drives communication that enables healthcare professionals to engage in a way that demonstrates compassion, improves clinical outcomes, increases efficiency, and reduces burnout caused by miscommunication. AIDET® stands for Acknowledge, Introduction, Duration, Explanation, and Thank you.

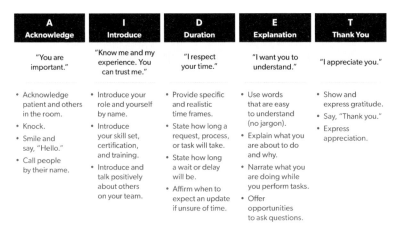

A Acknowledge	I Introduce	D Duration	E Explanation	T Thank You
"You are important."	"Know me and my experience. You can trust me."	"I respect your time."	"I want you to understand."	"I appreciate you."
• Acknowledge patient and others in the room. • Knock. • Smile and say, "Hello." • Call people by their name.	• Introduce your role and yourself by name. • Introduce your skill set, certification, and training. • Introduce and talk positively about others on your team.	• Provide specific and realistic time frames. • State how long a request, process, or task will take. • State how long a wait or delay will be. • Affirm when to expect an update if unsure of time.	• Use words that are easy to understand (no jargon). • Explain what you are about to do and why. • Narrate what you are doing while you perform tasks. • Offer opportunities to ask questions.	• Show and express gratitude. • Say, "Thank you." • Express appreciation.

Figure 3.2: AIDET® Communication Framework

How does it work?

Each element of the AIDET® Communication Framework plays a key role in communicating with the patient. Let's review each, what it communicates, and see the actions that make it come alive.

The "Why" of the AIDET® Communication Framework

I often refer to the AIDET® Communication Framework as a "fire prevention tool." We must put out many complaints or "fires" throughout our day, starting as small dry sticks. Add a little spark; before you know it, the forest is a raging fire.

AIDET®, when used well, can dampen those sticks before they burn, preventing one's day from being spent on something that could have easily been put to rest with a few words spoken at the right time about the right thing.

So why does it work?

- **It makes patients feel like individuals and decreases anxiety.** It provides an authentic interaction that will help to recognize and alleviate anxiety, fear, or pain as we address the patient's condition with compassionate care. They feel like a fellow human rather than a "disease process" or "condition."

- **It engages patients and helps them to take better care of themselves.** An anxious patient doesn't retain information and can't best collaborate on their care plan, essential for healing and maintaining health. This framework provides the "why" behind the treatment plan and makes it more likely that the patients will check their blood sugar, avoid certain foods, or exhibit other healthy behaviors to care for themselves. They feel involved and empowered, which inevitably leads to a better experience.

- **It decreases complaints:** Often, complaints come from a misalignment of expectations and delivery—they expect one thing and get another. This is where communication is critical. Also, we are seeing increasing anger directed at caregivers. Although there are complex factors contributing to that, I always say, "It is a short trip from 'anxious' to 'angry.'" If we can decrease the "anxious," perhaps we can also decrease the "angry."

- **It gives staff a greater sense of purpose and connections.** The conversations that flow from this framework pave the way for more human and authentic encounters and relationships with the patient and serve as a reminder of why we work in healthcare in the first place.

- **It creates efficiency.** For example, when you are communicating efficiently, you decrease anxiety. When people we serve are less anxious, they are easier to care for. This creates efficiency for you and for those in your care.

> 66 **CPR isn't the only acronym that saves lives!**

I was so frustrated with all the falls we were experiencing in our organization. As a director of risk management and patient safety, it was my job to fix this. As a nurse, it hurts to see people suffer needlessly. With each broken hip, dozens of our caregivers' hearts broke, too.

Around that time, I became familiar with AIDET®. Many viewed it as a communication tool to improve engagement, but I realized it could be much more. The "E" part jumped out as I analyzed the fall data. Were we "explaining" fall reduction to the PATIENTS?

We had the usual things in place for fall precautions—a pink armband with "Fall Risk" written on it and red socks/booties on our patients deemed at risk. But was there more we could be doing?

So, I did what all leaders should do, round on my patients. And I asked each one on fall precautions two simple questions: "Do you know you're on fall precautions? And if so, do you know what that means for you?"

Guess what? Most of them had no idea! I asked about the pink armband, and several couldn't even read the "fall risk" on it without their glasses or if it was underneath their identification armbands. I asked about the red socks. One hilarious elderly gentleman from New York told me he wouldn't wear them. "I'm a Yankees fan... I wouldn't be caught dead in red socks!"

Maybe we had a little problem with our "explanation" piece of the puzzle.

I held stand-up meetings with my nursing leaders and supervisors. I did 5–10-minute huddles with all shifts in all departments and asked them to ensure that for all fall-risk patients, we explained that they were on fall precautions and what we needed from them to make that successful. I even created a patient handout explaining in simple terms that the pink armband wasn't just to make them "pretty in pink" (and I made the print on the armbands a lot larger and bold) and that the red socks were for everyone, not just those from Boston.

The staff took the "explanation" piece seriously. The patients thought the handout was funny, making it memorable for them and more accessible for the team. To my absolute amazement, we dropped (pun intended) falls by an incredible 77% in the first few months. Within two quarters, as we adjusted and this became more embedded, falls with injuries went away.

On my follow-up rounds over the next few months, we were close to 100% on patients' knowledge of fall precautions and how they could help us protect them. They are part of my "fall prevention team" now!

We didn't purchase complicated fall alarm systems or bubble wrap the floor. Nor did we have to increase the time spent at the bedside or provide thorough training. We elevated our words, and we saved lives. All thanks to AIDET®. (CPR isn't the only acronym that saves lives!)

Misconceptions

As we teach and implement this powerful tool, we want to clear up some common misconceptions that can block effectiveness and buy-in with an individual or an organization:

- AIDET® is not a script. Think of AIDET® as a language everyone can understand. It should be your "voice," using key words that are right for you. If you are concerned about feeling "forced," remember we always use key words. Try going to a birthday party and NOT saying "Happy Birthday." We say "please" and "thank you" because it's the right thing to do. Is it expected? Sometimes. Is it forced? I don't think so. Personalize and flow the conversation in a way that feels natural and authentic to you. This is just a framework.

- You don't have to use the five elements in a specific sequence. Use them in an order that makes sense to the customer and the interaction. Sometimes you may even leave out a component. For example, if you know the person well or have been caring for them for the last two weeks, an introduction is probably unnecessary. Don't worry about the acronym. Focus on the efficiency and effectiveness of the communication.

- AIDET® should not be optional. If it is, you will get optional results from it. When practiced consistently, you will see consistent results. Based on Huron's many years of implementing this and measuring thousands of these interactions, we are confident you will be thrilled with the results.

- AIDET® is not only for patient interactions. The elements of this framework are essential in every interaction, including with customers and between colleagues and departments. It creates clarity and efficiency.

The beauty of AIDET® is not only its simplicity but its humanity. What we say and when we say it can make a difference. Think about when you've had a rough time or were dealing with a loss or a challenge. What most often helped you in those moments? Most likely, it was friends or loved ones talking to you. They used words to comfort. To inform. To lessen worry. To help you feel cared about and looked after.

66 My Mom.

As I write this, I think about the year I lost my mom. She wanted to live as independently as possible, so we were fortunate that an assisted living facility was within walking distance from my home. It was the best of both worlds. We could see her every day, and she had a beautiful place to live, surrounded by friends and excellent caregivers while also having the independence she insisted upon.

Mom took a turn for the worse after surgery, and I was able to be by her side around the clock. Many of you may have had this experience, and you know the grind, the emotional highs and lows, and the physical and emotional exhaustion that accompany these days.

While much of that time is foggy, I have "microbursts of memory" of moments that bring me peace. I recall a hospice nurse taking my hand and explaining the medication my mom was on and how long it would take before it started decreasing her pain. It lowered my anxiety because, above all, I didn't want Mom to suffer.

I remember the physician who sat with me and shared her background and why she chose to be a hospice physician. Her story brought me a sense of calm. This physician wanted to be here and loved what she did, which showed in the care she gave my mom.

I remember the young CNA who told me how much she loved my mom and wanted to show her gratitude for all the times my mom made her smile. When we bathed my mom, I fought back the tears as I saw how lovingly and sweetly this young woman spoke to my mom.

I remember the young man who brought my mom her meals when she could still eat a little; he always made sure to get her an extra piece of cake. And no matter who was in that room visiting her, he always acknowledged us and introduced himself, and told us how lovely and polite my mom always was to him.

Yes, the baths, meds, and cake were all part of helping my mom, but I truly held the words they spoke so close. It's how AIDET® has the impact it does. It helps remind us of the recipe for bringing compassion, humanity, and soul to our work.

With a song, it isn't so much the written notes and lyrics that can lift your heart but the singing—the power of the music brought to life. AIDET® is that song. It may not seem like much on paper, but once "sung," it is much more.

Service Recovery

The Huron healthcare consumer report quoted earlier in this principle provides some additional findings to make us stop and consider as we talk about service recovery.

The research states that consumer loyalty continues to soften. The percentage of consumers who are willing to switch providers for nearer location, trust and respect, lower cost, shorter wait time, and virtual care availability have all risen, indicating that consumers are generally more willing to change providers than in 2019.

And does word of mouth matter? Our research also shows that while reasons for switching providers vary, recommendations are still the number one way to choose healthcare. A full 55% report that they rely on the advice of family, friends, co-workers, and other healthcare providers to guide their provider decisions. Online referrals also play a role, with one-quarter of people turning to online reviews and ratings to guide their choices. This creates many opportunities for organizations to identify unmet needs and invest in ways to maximize the experience and meet their needs while receiving care.

Let's look at some additional research. The 2021 Accenture Health and Life Sciences Experience Survey of nearly 1,800 people in the U.S. reveals how the healthcare experience is changing. It reports that better experiences can improve engagement with a healthcare system. But perhaps most surprising were the findings about the patient experience.

When asked about the different factors that can be detrimental to a good healthcare encounter:

- Only 33% of respondents could say they'd never had a bad experience.

- 22% of respondents said an inefficient visit led to a poor healthcare experience.

- 19% lamented unhelpful medical advice.

- 17% cited a surprise medical bill.

- 11% of patients said staff members were rude and they did not receive emotional support.

Source: PatientEngagementHIT https://patientengagementhit.com/news/2-in-3-health-care-consumers-report-bad-patient-experience, "2 in 3 Healthcare Consumers Report Bad Patient Experience"

Most startling about these statistics is that only 33% (one in three) of patients can boast they've never had a bad patient experience with a provider, hospital, or pharmacy. That means 67% (two in three) of patients can report a bad patient experience! Also notable is that 11% claimed people were rude and they didn't receive emotional support.

Let these stats from both studies sink in as we now talk about service recovery. Holding up the proverbial mirror is not usually pleasant but is generally revealing. It would be great if all our customers and patients were 100% engaged all of the time, but it's just not very realistic to expect that.

So, what can we do in an imperfect world to level the playing field a bit?

> Service Recovery is the process of making things right after something has gone wrong.

We are very hard on ourselves in healthcare. We are usually more comfortable taking criticism than compliments. So, we take it to heart when things go wrong (and they will).

Extend some grace to yourself, especially if you or your organization are fighting that battle—reading this book and investing the time and energy to improve shows where your heart is. The information about service recovery that follows isn't about beating you down. It's about being realistic that whether a "wrong" is the fault of a team member, bad weather, or bad luck, we still need the tools to make it as right as possible.

The Service Recovery Paradox

When things go wrong, we often imagine the worst-case scenario. Can people remain loyal to your business even after a service failure? There's a fascinating thing known as the "service recovery paradox," coined in 1992 by Professors Sundar Bharadwaj and Michael McCullough. It describes a phenomenon in which someone with a bad business experience becomes dedicated and loyal.

Look at the graph below. Notice that after a service failure and a well-executed service recovery effort, the line turns upward toward greater loyalty and growth. Many people never complain. They just won't come back; it's easier to do that. But people know things don't go "perfectly." So, when we can rise to the occasion, it causes people to pause. They might not be impressed with your "mess up," but they can be impressed with your "clean up."

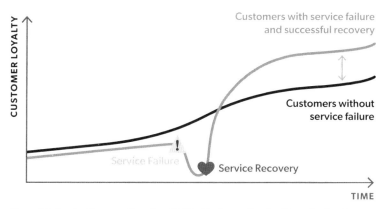

Figure 3.3: Service Recovery Paradox, 1992 by Professors Sundar Bharadwaj and Michael McCullough

What Service Recovery Should Communicate

This service recovery paradox doesn't happen by chance. In Huron's work on the front lines, we have seen that organizations with a solid service recovery program create a culture where their teams believe in it and are empowered to operationalize it. In that way, they get the best results.

Many organizations have "customer service champions" or departments, and that's outstanding. However, this is an "every person" job. Through Huron's extensive coaching experience, we have found the following components, authentically communicated, are essential:

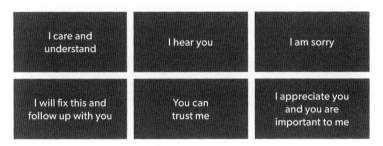

Figure 3.4 The Messages of Service Recovery

Four Steps to Service Recovery

CARE^{SM} is one tool that guides how to regain customer and patient loyalty. It is an acronym for the actions to take when service is missed that ensures you provide the critical messages of service recovery.

C: CONNECT

Introduce yourself and explain that you will listen and help resolve their concern. (Yes, AIDET® works here too!) Make eye contact and ask about the issue and how you can help make it better for them. Ask probing questions to get to the root of the problem. "Could you tell me more about...?" "Why do you think this happened?" "Can you be more specific?" "What happened next?" "Can you give me an example?" Allowing the customer or patient to vent and express their feelings is essential. This helps them feel that someone is genuinely concerned with their needs and is listening.

A: APOLOGIZE

No blame or excuses! An apology may be the most critical step in calming someone's anger. Most people want to know someone cares that they are upset and will do something about it. Offer key words like, "I'd be unhappy if that happened to me." "I'm sorry to hear that." "I'm sorry this hasn't gone the way we planned." "I'm sorry we kept you waiting today." "I regret you had to go through that experience." Whatever words you use, be authentic and heartfelt and allow that compassion to show.

R: REPAIR

This step is where the turnaround is most likely to occur. I always remember my dad telling me, "If someone apologizes for doing something but doesn't do something about what they did, then they didn't do anything!" Repairing the problem to the best of your ability may not always mean giving people exactly what they want, but sincerely improving the experience will be deeply appreciated. Remember that a small percentage of people will never be satisfied with your effort. They feel like the majority because they're the loudest and most memorable, but you'll find most people are reasonable and want things to be better.

E: EXCEED

This step is where you will likely recapture loyalty. Don't just meet expectations, exceed them. Recruiting a customer or patient costs five times more than it does to retain one; exceeding expectations is well worth the investment. Do this by addressing and resolving problems quickly while showing gratitude for the opportunity to make amends. If possible, reassure them it won't happen again. Tell them you will take steps to ensure others don't have the same experience. If you give a time frame to resolve or address the problem, be sure you can accomplish what you say in the time frame you provide, so you do not have to do MORE service recovery because you dropped the ball. That will erode confidence and put you right back where you started.

Taking the Next Step

After you complete the CARE^{SM} steps, what will you do with the information you learned? One best practice is to share these events across departments/areas/floors/practices. If something has gone wrong in your part of the world, there's a decent chance the same or similar can happen elsewhere. We are all teachers and students regarding excellence, and transparency should reign. Eleanor Roosevelt once said, "Learn from the mistakes of others. You can't live long enough to make them all yourself."

Track complaints and use this information to remove barriers and improve the customer and patient experience. This also helps with harvesting wins. We find our "informal leaders" in these events, the colleagues who stepped up, thought outside the box, and made an impact. Recognize that and heap praise upon the people who made it right.

Train employees on common complaints and the appropriate solutions. Don't expect that everyone will instinctively know how to do this. For some, this skill may come naturally and may only need a little polish. For others, this may feel foreign, and they'll need much more training. The investment of time upfront is well worth not having to spend the time and energy afterward. The great news is that once we've familiarized our teams with these standard solutions, they tend to stick. As the great musician B.B. King taught us, "The beautiful thing about learning is that nobody can take it away from you."

Give front-line employees the authority to handle complaints fully the first time. The more you can agree on what that "first voice" can do (in other words, the first person to be made aware of the issue), the more quickly that issue can be mitigated. It's perfectly okay to have the customer service team get involved, but make it so everyone understands that they, too, are on this team. The time lost waiting for someone else might make or break your success here.

Usually, people closest to "the work" know where the issues are, so they harvest ideas for process improvements from front-line employees. That's why, when rounding, it's crucial to ask your team if things need to be improved or about any safety issues or concerns they have. To paraphrase a centuries-old saying, don't wait for the mountain to come to you, go to the mountain.

Having the skill to make these wrongs right and to do so consistently across all areas and levels is a gift you give to those you serve and lead and to yourself. It takes some work and sometimes time to get it right, but most of all, it takes a different way of thinking.

Section 2: Caring at the Bedside

The previous section covered strategies for any organization, role, or department. This next section will concentrate on the various evidence-based practices delivered at the patient's bedside. It will focus specifically on six highly effective techniques:

- Nurse Leader Rounding

- Bedside Shift Report℠

- Hourly Rounding®

- Pre- and Post-visit Calls

- Patient Communication Boards

- Individualized Patient Care

You can test the power of things by their impact and timelessness. For decades, Huron has been creating, honing, and coaching these evidence-based best practices. They are proven, sustainable, and powerful. These methods have successfully and consistently improved the quality and safety of the care provided, helped ensure staff communicates with patients and family members in a way they understand, reduced anxiety for patients and their loved ones, improved efficiency, and decreased overall workload for care deliverers—all of which help the people who need healing. Isn't this the reason you got into healthcare in the first place?

Sequence and Pace

It is no surprise that healthcare people have a "STAT" mentality. As you read this, you're likely ready to hit "go" and start or renew things that you know will move service and quality. We get it and share that drive. But be careful not to do too much at one time. Start with one of these practices and get it embedded before moving on to the next. It will help with focus and balance and help sustain results over time.

> **66** **The Pillow at the End of the Bed.**

My wife and I always check on our kids before bed. It is a habit we've had since they were babies. One day at dinner, we were teasing our younger daughter about how restlessly she sleeps. The night before, we had to move her from the bottom of the bed and put her back in place.

As we all laughed, our teenage son asked, "Do you still check on me before you go to bed?" Knowing he was at that phase between "kid" and "young adult," I was afraid he might feel we were treating him like a baby, but I answered honestly that we did.

"Could you do me a favor?" he asked. We held our breath, waiting for his protest that he was too old for that. Instead, he surprised us and said, "You know how I always put my extra pillows on the chair next to my desk when I go to bed? Maybe you all might put the smaller one at the foot of my bed when you check on me, so if I wake up in the middle of the night, I'll see it and know you had been there. I don't want to sound like I am five, but it would be nice to know you were there like you were watching over me."

This was not what we expected from our mature, grown-up acting, second-degree black belt son. And he probably didn't expect his mom and dad to jump up simultaneously and hug him. But there you have it.

So that's what we do when we go to bed at night. If he's asleep, we move one of the small pillows from his chair to his bed to let him know we are "watching over him." And if he wakes up in the middle of the night, he sees that pillow and knows we have been there.

The lesson for us all is that it doesn't matter how old, strong, or independent you are. Everyone feels a little better when they know someone is watching over them.

Nurse Leader Rounding

Knowing that we are being watched over, especially when we feel afraid or vulnerable, is central to a sense of well-being and is a big part of healing. Nurse leader rounding may be the most critical action you can implement to drive patient-centered care. As a nursing leader who rounded on patients, a senior leader who has rounded, and someone who has coached rounding to hundreds of nursing leaders, I have found this practice is nothing less than life-changing.

> Nurse Leader Rounding is a structured, well-timed conversation with a patient about the care they can expect to receive while in your care and a real-time assessment of the patient's experience with their care.
>
> It is meant to build relationships, identify gaps or opportunities in the patient's perception of the quality of care we provide, harvest recognition opportunities, and gather feedback from those we serve.

Nurse leader rounding is meant to keep you on top of what is happening in your department. It allows you to celebrate good things patients share with you as wins and address concerns before they escalate. It is time invested upfront—a proactive rather than reactive approach—to avoid even more time spent dealing with issues later.

What does nurse leader rounding communicate to the patient and their loved ones? It emphasizes:

- I am the leader and take seriously my ownership of the quality of care delivered here.

- I am part of the team. We are all here for you, and I model compassion and empathy for those in my department who provide your care.

- I want to know what we are doing well so that it can be repeated, and I can let my team know they're making a difference.

- I want to know what we can do to be better. We are all about progress, improvement, and excellence.

- I want you to feel safe and know that many eyes are on you to ensure that quality and safety are top of mind for all.

- I want to fix anything broken, acknowledge your concerns, avoid any issues or worries, and ensure we provide service recovery ASAP rather than playing catch-up.

The Why of Nurse Leader Rounding

The "why" behind nurse leader rounding is directly connected to compassion. It is the "pillow at the end of the bed" for our patients, creating an atmosphere where they and their loved ones can rest assured they are being cared for. It is NOT about logging complaints or trying to catch people messing up. (If you need to round because you're that worried that people aren't doing their jobs, you have more significant issues to focus on.)

Experience has shown that even the biggest skeptics about the worth of nurse leader rounding become true believers once they live and breathe it. But don't just take our word for it. We have evidence to back it up. Evidence demonstrates that when a nurse leader rounds with a patient during their stay, the patient feels better about the care they're receiving. Nurse leader rounding not only helps improve patient perception, but it also gives you a chance to connect with them and evaluate the quality of care you're providing.

Let's review some evidence that come from effective nurse leader rounds and patient experience.

Nurse Leader Rounding and Overall Rating

One adaptation organizations make to their practice of nurse leader rounding is custom questions on their patient engagement surveys. These provide additional quantitative data that can be evaluated with feedback harvested during rounds.

For example, ask, *"Did a nurse leader round on you during your stay?"*

Results from 40 of Huron's client organizations show a clear correlation between the consistent practice of nurse leader rounding and patients' overall hospital rating after discharge. Look at the marked difference between those who were visited and those who were not.

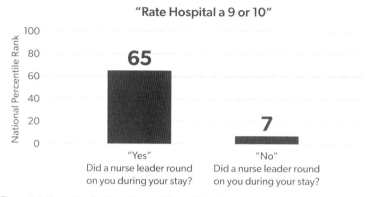

Figure 3.5: Nurse Leader Rounding and Overall Rating

Nurse Leader Rounding and Overall Nurse Communication, Responsiveness, and Likely to Recommend

Here is another graph that uses the custom question to demonstrate the difference in CAHPS® performance (measured by percentile ranking) in various domains. Note how patients who reported that a nurse leader had rounded on them during their stay rated each domain significantly higher than those who did not.

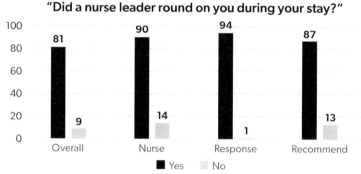

Figure 3.6: Nurse Leader Rounding and Overall Rating, Nurse Communication , Responsiveness and Likely to Recommend

Nurse Leader Rounding and CAHPS® Domains

This graph also uses the custom question to further demonstrate the effectiveness of nurse leader rounding. Note for this system, the patients who were rounded on by a nurse leader during their stay provided significantly higher CAHPS® scores across all domains.

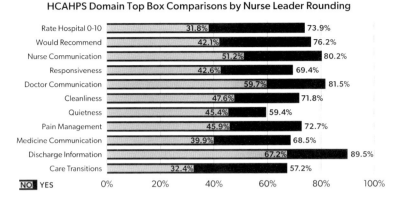

Figure 3.7: Nurse Leader Rounding and CAHPS® Domains

You can clearly see how nurse leader rounding significantly impacts patient experience outcomes. But another effect is that the efficiency it creates saves you time.

When I started nurse leader rounding, I was not what one would call an "early adopter." I thought I was already doing this anyway. I always said "hi!" to my patients and "checked in" on them. This seemed like one more task on an already overflowing list. I already worked 40+-hour weeks to deal with all the patient, staff, equipment, and supply issues. How in the world was this rounding going to make MY life better? I didn't get it.

Until I did.

After about two months of rounding, I started to notice something. I had more time. No glitch in the matrix or a bend in the universe—the difference was that I was more efficient.

Yes, I had to learn to round. I had to make the time to round. I even had someone validate my skills. That all took some time. But once I had it down, there was a dramatic shift in how I could lead. I was in front of issues, not behind them. I addressed minor concerns in minutes that previously would have ended up as complaints that took me hours to resolve.

When rounding on one patient, she told me the sink was "acting up." When the maintenance department checked, they found a significant pipe leak in the wall. The entire unit would have flooded and shut down if it hadn't been caught early. Who would have thought nurse leader rounding prevented floods?

I was rounding on another patient who said they had "weird pains" in their neck. They thought it was their pillow and didn't want to bother the nurse. My nurse, "spider-sense," told me to dig deeper. After further assessment, I helped get an EKG for them. It was a myocardial infarction. That rounding episode probably saved that patient's life and kept us all from what could've been a much more stressful situation

I always think of our ancestors who didn't have overnight delivery options or groceries shipped to their door and had to "store up" for winter. I'm sure it took a lot of time to can the fruit, salt the meat, chop the firewood, and all the ancestor things they had to do. Up front, it "took a minute," as the expression goes. But when the cold came, and the blizzards raged, I am sure they reaped the rewards of their time spent upfront.

Remember this; time spent being proactive will reduce the time you have to spend being reactive.

Maximizing the Impact of Nurse Leader Rounding

So how do you maximize the impact of nurse leader rounding?

Good question. By this point, it should be clear that nurse leader rounding is more than just "visiting" or "saying hi!" to your patients. (By the way, there's nothing wrong with doing either. Just don't call it "rounding.") There are three main elements of impactful nurse leader rounding: frequency, quality, and follow-up.

This is your recipe for optimizing these rounds and getting the best outcomes:

- **Frequency** refers to the number of daily rounds and the number of patients who recognize a nurse leader rounded on them. Ask yourself, what are the number of daily rounds and the number of patients that recognize a nurse leader rounded on them?

- **Quality** is determined by all components of the round itself –– personal connection and asking specifically about the actions of the caregivers. How well is the round conducted, and are the critical components used efficiently?

- **Follow-up** refers to what is done with the information after the round, including recognition and coaching opportunities. What do you do with the data from the round?

We are often asked about frequency, so let's discuss that now. This is where it usually takes the most effort to figure out and will often create a bit of anxiety. It's tough for busy people to do yet another thing and can often be met with some lack of excitement as one begins these rounds. This is why spending time explaining the "why" to those who will be rounding is so essential. Show the data and known outcomes before getting into the "how."

So what is the best practice frequency?

> The best practice frequency goal is for nurse leaders to round on 100% of their patients in the inpatient setting.

Here is an example of best practice frequency:

FACILITY TYPE	% OF PATIENTS	TYPICAL FREQUENCY
Inpatient	100% of patients (May delegate up to 50%)	7 days/week
Outpatient and Ambulatory Surgery Patients	10% of patients or a minimum of 40 patients/month (whichever is greater) 100% of patients who are new to episodic care (rehab, infusion, etc.)	Random sample, service recovery, and at staff request
	All patients in the waiting room when you round once an hour	Waiting room rounding once an hour, 7 days/week
Emergency Department	25% of treat-and-release patients	7 days/week
	100% of patients who have been waiting to be admitted into the hospital for more than two hours	7 days/week
Intensive Care Units	100% of patients/families	Priority on new admits and day-of transfers

As many of you read this, you might think, "This sounds great, but Is it possible to achieve a 100% rounding frequency?"

While it may seem daunting at first, trust the process. It has been proven time and time again and is worth it.

Like most things, you will get out of it what you put into it. So don't get too hung up on the numbers as you start. Once you know how and feel competent doing it, increase your frequency until you see the results you are working toward. My dad always told me, "You don't have to be good at a thing to start, but you do have to start to be good at a thing." The more you do, the better your outcomes.

The Four Cornerstones of Nurse Leader Rounding

Let's talk about how the four cornerstones will help you to build your castle of nurse leader rounding.

1. Understand the Importance of the Nurse Leader's Role

Nurse leaders are the best resource for coaching and developing staff in a way that yields these positive results.

Explain the "why" to those who will be rounding. Show the data and known outcomes before getting into the "how."

Remember, the purpose of nurse leader rounding is to ensure patients are receiving safe care ALWAYS.

Maintain a balance between delegation and personal involvement in the rounds. Nurse leaders can prioritize their presence during rounds to ensure they are available to guide and support their team.

2. Delegate Thoughtfully

It is widely accepted as a best practice for the primary nurse leader to round on their patients personally. However, let's face it. There are days when nurse leaders are unable to complete rounding alone. In such cases, delegating a portion of nurse leader rounds can provide flexibility for leaders on days off or during heavy meeting schedules.

While delegation may be an option, it is advised that no more than 50% of the rounding responsibilities be delegated to charge nurses, educators, assistant managers, CNOs, or others who have been trained and proficient in nurse leader rounding. This ensures that the primary nurse leader remains actively involved in the rounding process and maintains a strong connection with their patients.

3. Round by Nurse Assignment

The best practice is to round by nurse assignment, which can also help delegate rounds to other leaders for efficiency in rounding and the most significant impact. It is essential to determine which nurse's assigned patients the primary nurse leader will round on and which nurse's assigned patients they will delegate to other leaders. For example, the primary nurse leader rounds on two newer staff members' entire patient assignments and delegates to their charge nurse rounding on the float nurses' entire patient assignments. This allows the primary nurse leader to assess the development of the newer staff members while the charge nurse's rounds ensure float staff provide safe and high-quality care to the patients they are assigned on the unit.

4. Get the process started right

> "You can't be that kid standing at the top of the waterslide, overthinking it. You have to go down the chute."
>
> *Tina Fey*

Sometimes the hardest part of a task is "going down the chute" or taking that first leap. Here are a few suggestions to start the process and get to the frequency needed for more significant results.

- Make the mental commitment: Decide "This is what I am doing, and I intend to get the results that will transform our care and outcomes." Everything worth doing starts with this type of passionate personal statement.

- Set frequency goal and timeline: Set an initial goal for the frequency of rounds and establish a timeline for increasing frequency until you can meet the best practice frequency guidelines.

- Commit to a daily goal: Whatever the initial number of rounds you decide on, commit to meeting that goal daily.

- Increase frequency gradually: increase the number of rounds as you feel comfortable until you reach the best practice frequency.

The Essential Elements of Nurse Leader Rounds—Prepare, Round, and Follow Up!

Let's move now to what makes for a high-quality round. The secret lives in these three steps: pre-round preparation, patient conversation, and post-round follow-through.

Figure 3.8: Prepare to Round

A. PREPARE TO ROUND

Alexander Graham Bell once said, "Before anything else, preparation is the key to success." Preparing for the round is well worth the time. Ask yourself these questions before you set off to round.

- *How can I make a personal connection with this patient?*
  Remember the power of personal connections we talked about earlier in this chapter? Ensure you know something personal about each patient and any issues before entering their room.

- *Who should I round on first?*
  Sequence your rounding based on nursing assignments to see trends with specific caregivers. Also, prioritize the patients who have had a miss or need service recovery. It's always good to get that out of the way up front.

- *What do the rounding logs say from prior rounds?*
  Review the logs to familiarize yourself with what was learned before.

This is particularly important if multiple leaders make rounds. It helps you project consistency and team connectivity with the patient and will also help answer the first two questions above. Follow up on previous comments as needed.

- *What custom questions do you need to ask?*
  Add questions as appropriate to focus on initiatives you are currently working to embed. Perhaps you are trying to reduce patient falls. You might ask how regularly the patient sees a care team member to assess the rounding frequency. Or, if your focus is on improving nurse communications, you might ask the patient to tell you about their care plan to determine who is doing a good job explaining care and answering questions from the patient and family.

B. CONDUCT THE ROUND (ESSENTIAL ELEMENTS)
In no order, here are the eight essential elements of a good round. Remember, this is not a script to be followed word for word. Use words and phrases that are comfortable for you and your environment.

1. Set clear expectations.
"Hello, Mr. Mosier. I am Jackie, the nurse leader on this unit, and I like to round on patients during their stay so I can learn about their care. We're all very committed to delivering exceptional care, and this is one way we support that practice. I have a few questions, which will take about 3-5 minutes. Is now a good time?"

2. Make a personal connection.
This is job #1 of an effective round. Earlier in this chapter, we reviewed data about the importance of personal connections and evidence that it only takes as little as 40 seconds. Here are some examples:

- *Jim mentioned that you love golf. Tell me about your golf game!*

- *I heard you were born in New York. So were my parents. Where are you from?*

- *Those flowers are beautiful. Someone must think you are special; tell me about them!*

- *I see you are reading a good mystery novel. I love to read as well.*

3. Validate the safe and high-quality care delivery of the care team.
Now ask a few questions to validate whether your focus areas have the intended impact from the patient's perspective. Although it is tempting to do it all at once, limiting your focus to 1-2 areas will yield the most

actionable results. Prioritize your focus area, embed practices, then add the following new practice.

- *We must take the time to listen to your needs and priorities. Tell me about what we have shared about your pain and comfort plan.*

- *Tell me about what our team has shared about your plan for today.*

- *I see you're on fall precautions, as you recently had a fall at home. Have the staff talked to you about that, and do you know what that means? What are some of the things they've shared with you about how you can collaborate with us to prevent falls?*

- *Have you used your call light? What things have you used it for? How quickly did we respond?*

4. Manage up throughout the conversation.

Throughout the conversation, the leader has excellent opportunities to manage the care team and providers while rounding. When patients and families hear this from a leader, it carries more weight than you may realize. You can learn more about managing up in Principle 8: Communicate at all Levels.

> Managing up is positioning someone or something in a positive light.

- *"I see Dr. Harenstein is your physician. She is excellent, and we get many compliments about her care and concern. You are fortunate to have her as your physician."*

- *"I understand you are going for an MRI today. Our team in that department has had extensive training. And they take a lot of pride in getting the very best images. I think you'll love the team. They always have smiles on their faces."*

- *"You have Jose as your nurse today. He is one of our most experienced nurses. He leads our training program for newer nurses because he is so good at what he does."*

- *"Your CNA is Joshua. I heard you like to laugh. Ask him to tell you some of his jokes. He does stand-up comedy on his days off! Our patients love him."*

5. Harvest reward and recognition.

Don't forget this critical step! Determine if team members have provided outstanding care and who you can reward and recognize. Remember, this is a fantastic gift for your staff and you! It feels good as a leader to let someone know they're doing a great job. And most of us want to know the work of our hands, minds, and hearts is impactful. It is validating.

6. Perform service recovery if needed.

Sometimes the patient has not had an excellent experience. It happens. No one is perfect. So, when the organization fails to meet a patient's expectations, it is best to transition the round to service recovery. Take a deep breath. You've got this.

- *"I am so sorry you had that experience."*

- *I apologize. That is not an experience I would want anyone in our care to have had."*

- *"I am very sorry that you've been through this."*

7. Use closing statements.

No round is complete without a closing statement. When the leader says, "Is there anything I can do for you before I leave?" it tells the patient that the hospital caregivers do not want to leave if something needs to be done and lets patients know their input is important.

This builds trust with the patient and demonstrates compassionate leadership to your team. It means a lot to them to see you working alongside them. For every cup of water you pour, question you answer, or box of tissues you grab, you make a deposit in the emotional bank account of your team. It shows that you are in the arena with them and that you care. It also shows humility.

As the 1913 Nobel Prize in Literature Winner Rabindranath Tagore reminded us: "We come nearest to the great when we are great in humility." It also makes an impression on our patients. They see leaders caring about their team, which communicates the culture is all about caring.

- *"Is there anything I can do for you right now? I am happy to help."*

- *"It was so wonderful to meet you/ spend time with you/ talk with you today. Is there anything else I can do for you or you might need?"*

- *"Here is my card. Feel free to contact me if you need me. It was a pleasure seeing you again today. I am glad you're feeling a little better."*

8. Document the round.

A rounding log, either electronic or paper, enables you to house your specific rounding questions and collect real-time patient responses. Complete the rounding log while the information is top of mind. This will be a living document that helps you stay organized and ensures you follow up on questions or needs for the patient.

C. FOLLOW-THROUGH AFTER THE ROUND

It is so easy to finish rounds and quickly get right back into the tasks of the day. But nurse leaders who embed follow-up actions as part of their practice gain maximum benefit from the time they invest.

Take the time needed to assimilate what you've learned through patient interactions and close the loop by taking appropriate steps. You may need to reward and recognize those staff doing a great job, coach and develop staff with opportunities for improvement, improve processes that were identified as not working, or address environmental safety issues.

Remember that the round isn't complete until the follow-up is done. The "magic" of rounding happens only partially in bedside interactions. The actual lift to team performance comes when a nurse leader acts on the answers to these two questions:

- *"What have I just learned?"*

- *"What must I do with that information?"*

One nurse manager we worked with said it best. "Before adding these follow-up questions to my patient rounds, I think I was harvesting the wheat but never baking the bread! I was doing the initial work but not getting the maximum benefit from my time and energy. My team used to think I was spying on them or trying to catch mistakes. When I began taking compliments back after my rounds, they began to look forward to the time I could spend with their patients. It was a game changer."

 Top 10 Tips to Conduct a Successful Nurse Leader Round

1. Nurse leader rounding and rounding logs are mandatory. The log must be taken as seriously as the staffing schedule or department head meetings. Optional practices usually deliver optional results.

2. Track frequency and findings. Remember, if it isn't documented, it isn't done. Tracking helps you follow up, focus, and stay streamlined in a world where things can get busy.

3. Trust but verify. Skills labs, shadowing, and coaching are excellent ways to ensure the quality of the round. Plus, we benefit by watching others do something they are good at.

4. Take notes. Let the patients and their loved ones know that what they say is important and that you want to remember their words.

5. Consistency, Consistency, Consistency. Hardwiring this behavior comes with practice. Most new skills take time to feel right. Keep going. Practice.

6. Round by nursing assignment. This allows you to identify patterns and trends more quickly.

7. Share rounding focus and questions with staff. You want them to know this is about supporting them, not investigating them.

8. Reward and recognize. Rewarded behavior gets repeated! Act quickly to reinforce trust in the process.

9. Incorporate technology and software. Use software such as Huron Intelligence™ Rounding to track and compile reports and follow-up activities.

10. Ask open-ended questions. Responses to open-ended questions yield richer insight into your patients' experiences and allow you to connect more personally.

11. Beware of delegating your rounds. We aren't saying you cannot delegate nurse leader rounds. Nurse leaders take PTO and have emergencies like everyone else, and when they do, someone has to take on the rounding, or the results will falter. This works as long as the delegee is another leader trained and competent in all the elements of nurse leader rounding. Nurse directors, assistant directors, managers, clinical managers, and charge nurses can all be influential leader rounders.

I'm not going to lie. Nurse leader rounding isn't "easy," not at first. But it is powerful. From personal experience as a nurse leader, I know what it feels like to feel powerless—like you will never get it all done. Rounding will take some adjustment initially, but it will change how you lead for the better. It will give you back time that can be used on developing and mentoring your team and developing your vision for where you want to go. It moves you from surviving to thriving.

The poet Rumi said, "When setting out on a journey, do not seek advice from someone who never left home." Huron has been on this journey with thousands of nurse leaders, and we know the path well. We hope you'll take this journey for the good of your patients, your team, and yourself.

Patient Communication Boards

"Simplicity is the ultimate sophistication."

Leonardo da Vinci

We often think that the more complex something is, the better it must be. This belief sometimes causes us to overlook behaviors, practices, and tools that are simple yet powerful. A hammer may not be the most "complex" of tools, but it is rare not to find one in most home builders' toolboxes. A paintbrush is not the most "complex" of things, but in the hands of a master artist, it can create quite a breathtaking work of art. One of the easiest ways to get results related to "patient care" is through another simple yet impactful tool: patient communication boards.

Call them whiteboards, grease boards, etc., but nursing teams have used boards for years to communicate staff assignments, shift changes, and patient placement. Whether dry-erase or electronic, they can make workflow more manageable, keep patients safe, help manage pain, and even make people smile.

The patient communication board is an invaluable tool to help patients and their family members organize the many moving parts of their care and proactively eliminate some of that anxiety through transparency. The information on the board assists other providers in giving care, or meeting needs while in the room, and it is a subtle reminder to the patient that all care team members are knowledgeable about their care.

> The patient communication board is a physical, visual tool for communication between the patient, the patient's family, the care team, and care team members.

Patient communication boards should be updated throughout the day and used as an interactive tool during any change of shift report. Some patient communication boards include areas for housekeeping and dietary information. This enables non-clinical and clinical staff to recognize and respect what's important to the patient.

In life and at work, we may assume or guess how someone is feeling. It is like taking a mid-term test on a chapter you read at the start of the semester but haven't brushed up on in a while. Using that analogy, the patient communication board is like having an open-book test with highlighted answers. The teams that use these correctly don't have to guess what is important to the patient or try to figure out what makes them feel good. It's right there!

When designing your board and deciding what should be on it, it would be wise to involve a group of front-line team members. There are several components that Huron clients have found to be helpful. These include:

- A plan for the patient. Personal or healthcare goals for the patient for the day or stay include "to get home in time for my son's wedding" or "to walk around the floor two times without a walker."

- Date and day to help keep the patient oriented, especially if they have or are recovering from neurological issues.

- Nurse's name, shift time, and, if applicable, CNA/care technician names, shift, and phone numbers. Include other important team members like physicians, therapists, dieticians, and the nurse leader or charge nurse's name and numbers as appropriate.

- Pain scale. (Numbers with associated facial expressions are helpful with younger patients and those with language barriers). You can also include pain goals, medication, and the last dose/next dose.

- Personal information about the patient, like their favorite things or hobbies (these are great conversation starters).

- Confirmation of Hourly Rounding®. (We will talk more about this tactic in the coming pages.)

- Questions that the patient or their loved ones have for team members.

Your board may have very little or be loaded with information. The main point here is to use the boards primarily to clarify things, ease continuity of care, and bring patients and their loved ones into a space where they feel informed, empowered, and collaborate with their care team. Keep in mind that boards only provide value for patients when they are used consistently. If a more straightforward board leads to better staff compliance, opt for simplification.

Seeing through the communication board.

While rounding with nurse leaders, a Huron coach asked a patient what worked well during her hospitalization. The patient spoke highly about the value of the patient communication board, but the coach was confused because the patient was blind. He asked how the board was valuable to her.

She shared that on admission, her nurse took the time to explain that there was a board in the room and how it would be used. The nurse explained that she would document on the board how the patient needed to communicate because of her blindness.

Regularly, the team would clearly express to the patient what was on the board and ask for updates to involve the patient in the experience. Knowing that the team had her needs on the board resulted in less awkwardness and anxiety and provided a better experience for this patient even though she couldn't "see" it herself.

Tips to Make the Patient Communication Board More Effective

- Mount it where the patient can view it from the bed. (This may seem obvious, but you'd be surprised how many organizations miss this.)

- Make it large enough to read from 10-15 feet away.

- Use a black erasable marker for better legibility. (Pro tip: Inevitably, someone will accidentally use a permanent marker on the board. Believe it or not, tracing over the permanent marker writing with a dry-erase marker and then using a damp cloth to wipe it off works wonders. Trust me, this life hack will come in handy.)

- Require that all sections are complete. Patients can interpret blank sections as a failure to follow through on the commitment to share important information.

- Refer to the tool as a "care board" or "patient communication board," not a whiteboard or other generic term. (Words have power. "Care" and "communication" are valuable concepts that reinforce their importance).

- Use key words that convey compassion:

  - "The patient communication board is our commitment to sharing important information you need to know during your hospitalization. We promise to review it with you at each shift change and throughout the day as things change related to your care."

- – "I am updating your patient communication board to keep you informed."
- – "I know it's hard to be in the hospital. What's one thing our team can do that's important to you to help you through this stay? I'll document that so the rest of the team can be aware. It's one way we work together to help you feel less anxious and well cared for."

• Use the patient communication board in other key practices, like AIDET®, nurse leader rounding, Hourly Rounding®, and Bedside Shift Report℠.

 To Laugh. Priceless.

Being a patient is not easy. People sometimes feel like the "pancreatitis in room 217" or the "post-op brain tumor" rather than what they are: a human being with a voice, a soul, a personality, and a life outside and separate from their illness.

I recall Irving, an 80-year-old man who was a frequent patient in the hospital where I worked. During one admission, under the "What is important for us to know about you?" section on his care board, he had us write: To laugh! Please make sure you tell me at least one joke today!

We took this so seriously that one staff member brought a large book of jokes from home and kept it outside Irving's room. Team members would pick a joke to tell him (and cross them off as we went, because he'd tell you if you recycled a joke, trust me!) and he loved this. When he was discharged, we gave Irving that book with signatures and notes from all of us.

I stayed in touch with him until he passed away about three years later, and whenever I called him, he'd always tell me one of the jokes from the book. I cherished those brief chats with Irving. The cost of the patient communication board was $75.00. The value of making this great-grandfather laugh and feel loved... you guessed it... priceless.

Bedside Shift Report^{SM}

Shift change can be a time of high anxiety for patients. They've often developed a sense of trust and comfort with their initial caregiver. Many of us who have worked at the bedside have had a patient or their loved ones nervously say to us, as we are wrapping up a shift, "You're not leaving, are you? Who's taking your place? Are they like you? Will you be back tomorrow?"

If you've had that happen, you know that is the highest compliment. You made that patient feel safe and cared for. Now, to them, a "stranger" is about to show up who might not be as "good" as you were, and they're experiencing a form of "stranger danger" because the unknown is scary. It's a big responsibility to manage this transition well. Bedside Shift Report^{SM} (BSR) is proven to help patients feel more at ease and comfortable and improve the safety and quality of care.

> A Bedside Shift Report^{SM} is a change-of-shift report between the off-going nurse and the oncoming nurse that takes place at the bedside and includes patients in the care delivery process.

- By taking nurse reports to the bedside and involving your patients, giving them a better understanding of their condition and treatment plan, and allowing them to collaborate, you often avoid misunderstandings, reduce patient questions, and prevent errors before they occur. You move from "handoff" to a well-communicated "handover." Is that just semantics? If you believe that, pause to conjure the image that comes to mind when you say each word.

- Hand Off- "I am off! They're your problem now!"

- Handover- "I'm conveying something of value into the hands of the next person who will care as much as I do."

Even just reading those words, you can see and feel the difference.

Why is Bedside Shift Report^{SM} Important?

The "why" behind nurse reports at the bedside is patient safety. When we talk about a "patient safety team," we can sometimes be guilty of forgetting one member of that team—the patient!

"Bedside shift reports are viewed as an opportunity to reduce errors and are important to ensure communication between nurses and patients. Models of bedside reports incorporating the patient into the triad have increased patient engagement and enhanced caregiver support and education. Nurse shift reports, and handovers are 2 of the most critical processes in patient care that can support patient safety and reduce medical errors in the United States."

Source: The Journal of Nursing Administration (JONA); Volume 44, Number 10, pp 541-545; copyright © 2014 Wolters Kluwer health | Lippincott Williams & Wilkins; Bedside Shift Reports – What Does the Evidence Say?)

According to the article "Bedside Shift Report: Implications for Patient Safety and Quality of Care," research has shown that "sentinel events" are more likely to occur when patients are alone during traditional change-of-shift reports at the nurses' station. "BSR eliminates that alone time and gives the patient a feeling of inclusion with the nurses as part of the healthcare team."

For the leader committed to reducing sentinel events and smaller issues, BSR is an essential component of patient care. It also provides benefits to your staff. It helps an oncoming nurse ensure that the off-going caregiver leaves things in an ideal state, allows the oncoming staff to have a brief baseline assessment, and prioritizes the shift's first few activities more effectively. It is the ideal time for the off-going nurse to transfer some goodwill they've built with the patient and their family to the oncoming staff.

Also, during this time, the patient can ask questions and set short- and long-term goals with the nurse. BSR can help catch mistakes or errors before they occur. Most importantly, it puts the MVP of patient safety—the patient—squarely on your team, giving them some empowerment and a feeling of personhood that often gets lost in healthcare.

Handling the Skeptics
It's our job as leaders to ensure that the "why" is shared and that we show evidence that this will improve the staff's work life and benefit their patients. Without this background, skepticism is not only possible but likely. There are two main areas of concern people raise:

- Time. Through thousands of observations, Huron has seen that reports can be delivered effectively in 4-5 minutes for each patient. If you have more than six patients, you must modify the practice or extend your reporting period beyond 30 minutes. But abandoning

BSR is not the answer—the benefits of this practice are too great, and the time spent upfront will be well worth the investment.

- Sleeping patients. In one organization, nurses devised a system of reversible magnets. "Wake me for the report" was printed on one side, and "Please let me rest" was on the other. Absent such a system, use your clinical judgment when deciding whether to wake a patient. Either way, the best practice is for the oncoming and off-going nurses to enter the room to briefly assess the patient and make sure there are no pressing needs or issues.

How Bedside Shift Report℠ is Done

While the details of BSR will vary from facility to facility, the framework is the same. The current nurse gives a verbal report to the incoming nurse. They include the patient in the conversation at the start by introducing the oncoming nurse and asking the patient to listen and ask any questions or add any comments before they conclude the report. Here is an overview of the critical components of an effective BSR:

BSR ELEMENT	KEY COMPONENTS
Introductions	• Introduce and manage up the oncoming nurse. Nurses should position themselves where a patient can easily participate in the conversation.
Explain bedside handover	• Explain the process of BSR and the reasons for the practice. (If the patient has been there for several days and knows this well, consider whether this needs to be repeated.) • Consider privacy and confidentiality for your patient. Invite visitors to leave for the report's duration unless the patient requests that they remain at the bedside.
Safety	• Verbally report to oncoming nurses using a standard communication framework like SBAR, which stands for Situation, Background, Assessment, and Recommendation. • A brief physical assessment includes a pain scale, IV sites, pumps, and wounds. This is not the time for a complete head-to-toe assessment unless indicated by the patient's clinical condition. • Use the teach-back method as appropriate (asking the patient to confirm their understanding by explaining it back) to support patient involvement in the conversation. For example, discussing medications, you may ask your patient to tell you their purpose and side effects.

BSR ELEMENT	KEY COMPONENTS
Information	• Wipe the care board clean and review the importance of each section as you fill in new information. • Address discharge planning. • Review the plan of care and ensure that the patient understands and agrees with the plan.
Pain Management	• If pain is a concern, ask the patient about their current pain score and have them describe what has helped manage pain during the prior shift. Document this on their board, along with the time their next medication is available. • Review any non-pharmacological interventions you will employ to help increase comfort, e.g., ice packs, the elevation of extremities, etc.
Assess Environment	• Narrate care so patients take comfort knowing you are attending to their comfort and safety details. • Be deliberate about letting your patient know why you are repositioning their overbed table, phone, call light, etc.
Closing	• Invite final questions from the oncoming nurse and the patient. • Thank the patient. • The oncoming nurse sets expectations for their expected return time.

Figure 3.9: Effective Bedside Shift Report^SM *Sample*

Many organizations have adopted the SBAR framework as a standard communication practice. It helps nurses wholly and accurately relay information between healthcare team members, including conversations in front of the patient. The report might sound something like this:

BEDSIDE SHIFT REPORT –
Sample Discussion (Off-Going Nurse, On-Going Nurse, and Patient)

Off-Going Nurse:

- "Hello, again, Mr. Sanchez! It's Tasha, and I'm getting ready to go home to my family."

- "I want you to meet Max, who will care for you tonight. Max is amazing! We've been working side by side for more than three years, and he's a highly skilled nurse. He has an excellent reputation for helping patients understand their medications and help manage their pain. You're in good hands with Max!"

- "Max and I will spend a few minutes in what we call our 'bedside shift report.' It's a chance for the three of us to gather before I head home and talk about your care and our tasks. This way, Max knows what's important to you and has all the information he needs to take excellent care of you. We'll also chat about the plan for the night, let you know what to expect, and update your patient communication board. Sound good?"

- "This might be a good time for your visitors to step out and stretch their legs while we talk...?"

- "Max, this is Mr. Robert Sanchez. I've had the pleasure of taking care of him today after surgery. He is a 56-year-old male admitted today after abdominal surgery..."

- "Let's review Mr. Sanchez's medical history and background..."

- "Let's discuss medications. We are giving... Mr. Sanchez, can you tell Max about the new medication you started today? Tell Max why you are taking it and what comm side effect we discussed."

Patient:

This is where the patient talks about their care.

The off-going nurse shares any other clinical details, such as medication doses or frequency, that the patient might have left out. A similar conversation should occur for any part of the report for which the patient can offer input. This is a conversation between the patient and the two nurses instead of the patient being a passive listener in the report.

Oncoming Nurse:

- "Again, my name is Max. My name and phone number are updated here on your communication board. This is how you reach me today if you have an urgent need. I'll be here—or another caregiver will be—in your room about every hour during the day to manage your pain, position you comfortably, and help you up to the restroom for your safety."

- "Let's review and update the rest of the information on the board. It's important to keep you and other team members updated about everything happening with your care."

Example Discussions:

- "Let's talk about your upcoming discharge plan…"

- "Please talk with me about your pain management. What's helped you most over the past 12 hours? I want to be sure I'm keeping you as comfortable as possible."

- "Your medication is scheduled to be administered again at… In the meantime, let's talk about the other pain management therapies I'll be using, and I will write them on your board."

Off-going Nurse:

- "Mr. Sanchez, what questions can Max or I answer before we go?"

- "Is there anything else you want Max to know so he can take the best care of you tonight?"

- "I'm heading home now. Thank you for allowing me to join your care team today."

Oncoming Nurse

- "Mr. Sanchez, again, my name is Max. I'm so happy to meet and care for you tonight."

- "I'm going to take a look around before I go to be sure things are neat and that you have everything you need within easy reach—that's one of the ways we keep you safe while you're here with us."

- "Tasha will go, but I'll be back with you in about an hour to see how you are and ensure you have everything you need."

Tips to Maximize Bedside Shift Report^{SM}

1. Include the patient in the conversation to gain maximum benefit from your time spent. They feel better about their care when they are part of their care.

2. Protect patient privacy by inviting visitors to leave during the report. Exceptions can be made at the patient's request.

3. Anticipate 4-5 minutes for each patient.

4. Use a communication framework such as SBAR (Situation—Background—Assessment—Recommendation).

5. Use the report as a show-and-tell opportunity. Example: "Ms. Gonzales, as you know, we are working on healing your wound. I want to show Sarah how it's doing if you don't mind."

6. Use the "teach-back" methodology to ensure the patient fully understands the explanations given. Example: "Mrs. Gonzales, can you share with Sarah what we discussed regarding your wound, so she knows the plan for ensuring it continues healing as she provides care for you?"

7. Validate for patients that expected care has occurred. Example: "Ms. Gonzales, as you know, we've been repositioning you every hour to two hours to be sure we give that wound the best chance to heal. Sarah, she's most comfortable on her right side."

> ## 66 Bedside Shift Report℠—Save a Life.

Many years ago, as a bedside nurse, I recall how BSR saved the day (or night, as it were). A new patient was admitted to our unit, and the emergency department nurse was "too busy" for a BSR, so she only shared a phone report with the nurse caring for that patient. (BSR was still new to the organization, and the ED nurse was known to be less amenable than her peers.)

A mere 45 minutes after the patient arrived, I was the night shift nurse. We were in the middle of BSR when the off-going nurse read from the chart, "... the patient has an allergy to peanuts."

The patient sat straight up and said, "I'm not allergic to peanuts. I'm allergic to morphine!" The ED nurse confused two of her patients and documented them incorrectly. And guess what had been prescribed for pain?

The patient shared with us that morphine caused them difficulty breathing and swallowing, requiring emergency intervention. We wouldn't have caught that until too late if it weren't for the patient. We fixed that right away. Thank goodness the patient was there to add their voice. BSR can be a lifesaver. Literally.

Hourly Rounding®

We started this section by talking about nurse leader rounding. Now we want to discuss a rounding practice that relates more directly to patient care and outcomes.

> Hourly Rounding® is the practice of rounding on patients consistently and frequently to perform specific behaviors proven to improve the safety and quality of care while improving and easing caregiver efficiency and workflow.

Typically, these rounds are about every hour during the day and every two hours at night.

Making a Case for Hourly Rounding®

In a study published in September 2006 in the American Journal of Nursing (AJN), nurses who rounded hourly on telemetry, surgical, and medical-surgical patients reduced call lights by 37.8%. Imagine the positive impact on your team if over a third of their interruptions vanished overnight. That is just the beginning of the benefits we gain with this practice.

Best Practice Update: Seminal Study Findings

- Call lights decreased by 37.8%

- Falls decreased by 50%

- Hospital-acquired pressure injuries decreased by 14%

- Patient experience improved by an average of 12 mean score points

---

This study is the largest conducted to date on the impact of hourly rounds on patient experience, quality of care, and call light reduction. Since its publication, Huron has helped organizations worldwide successfully implement this practice. The original study has been replicated in countless inpatient settings with similar results.

When you realize this is more than just "checking in" every hour, you will see how it leads to the results described. Many organizations have found that an embedded system of hourly rounds correlates with additional benefits—decreases in lost charges, incidental overtime, and medication errors, for example. It has also been shown to be empowering, leading to an increase in nursing satisfaction.

What Hourly Rounding® is Not

Hourly Rounding® is NOT

- Peeking into the patient's room and ensuring that they are stable.

- Peeking in and asking the patient, "Are you doing okay?"

- Saying to the patient, "I'm here to check on you." "Checking" is what we do every time we enter the patient's room—it is pervasive. We need to use key words that identify to the patient what we are here to do when we conduct their hourly round.

I will ask to observe when I am at an organization implementing Hourly Rounding® but not achieving results. I often catch the "howdy round" or the "threshold round." It goes something like this.

> **❝ The "Why" of Hourly Rounding®**

"We've tried this already. It doesn't work." Tomara, the nurse manager, was shaking her head with her hands on her hips and a wary look in her eye.

"You tried rounding, and it didn't work? Tell me more," I probed.

This organization had tried and failed to get its culture turned around for the better. After a much-needed change in leadership, they chose Huron to help them get on track. I had been coaching them for a while. I listened respectfully, but I had my doubts.

"I know y'all have all those studies, but we have a TOTALLY different patient population here."

"Would you do me a favor and show me how you conduct rounds on a few patients, and I'll just observe?" I asked. She agreed, and we were off.

Tomara knocked on a nearby patient's door. As we entered the room, the patient smiled and looked up from the book she was reading.

"Hi, Mrs. Jacobs. How are you?"

"Hi Tomara, how are you?" the patient smiled. (They knew each other well since Tomara had been doing her nurse leader rounding and seeing good results with it.)

"Oh, I'm fine. This is Rich," Tomara pointed over her shoulder to where I was standing in the hallway. "He's my coach. He's just observing me, if that's okay?"

"Of course. What can I do for you?"

"Oh, nothing. I just wanted to see if you needed anything?"

The patient shook her head. "No, I think I'm good."

"OK, thanks, hon!" said Tomara, still standing at the door with her hand on the doorknob. "Take care, Mrs. Jacobs!"

Tomara closed the door and went to the next room, repeating the same process. Knock, hover half in/half out, say hello, ask if the patient needs anything, and then close the door. After the fourth patient, we paused in the hallway, and before I could speak, Mrs. Jacobs' call light went off.

We went back to her room, and she requested more tissues. Tomara got them for her, and then we moved away and took some time to chat.

"See what I mean? I did the rounding, and, like, five minutes later, Mrs. Jacobs was on her call bell!" said Tomara.

There's nothing wrong with "saying hi" to your patients. But what I had just witnessed was not much more than that—what I call "threshold rounding." Right intention, wrong steps.

I smiled at Tomara and said, "Let's talk."

So yeah, let's talk about Hourly Rounding®, which, when done correctly, is one of the most significant things you can implement in your organization.

The Eight Behaviors of Hourly Rounding®

One of the things you may have noticed is that we define and describe this as a practice. That means multiple components– behaviors—create a specific desired outcome. Staff and leaders are often tempted to "modify" rounds by eliminating specific steps. But in doing so, you're also possibly reducing the impact and losing some of the successful outcomes you can achieve with the complete, time-tested, proven approach. If someone makes the best chili you've ever had and they give you the recipe, if you alter it, it may no longer be the best chili you've ever had. This applies here as well.

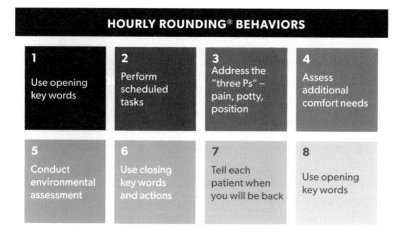

Figure 3.10: Eight Hourly Rounding* Behaviors

1. Use opening key words.
Let the patient know who you are, your role, and your expertise level. Frame the interaction as a "round" so they know what to expect each time you round.

"Good morning Mr. Ali, my name is Ava, and I will be your nurse today from 7 a.m.-7 p.m. I've been working on telemetry for 18 years, and we have an awesome team. I want you to know that we do rounds hourly here, which means, at a minimum, we will be here about every hour to assess you and ensure you have everything you need. It's how we ensure you are safe and provide excellent care. I'll assess your pain, help you with the restroom, and ensure you're comfortable."

That may sound like a lot, but I timed myself at only 21.23 seconds. The "key words" might be more or less for each patient, but the important thing is that the patient knows you'll see them at least once per hour (Increases Efficiency, Increases Patient Experience, and Reduces Anxiety).

2. Perform scheduled tasks.
Complete any scheduled tasks needed for the patient—medications, treatments, procedures, feedings, etc.—as part of the rounding process so that everything can be done in one trip (Increases Efficiency).

3. Address the "three Ps"—pain, potty, position.
The Ps represent the needs each patient typically uses a call light to address. Originally these were pain, potty (bathroom needs), and position. However, many organizations have customized their Ps to include pumps, personal possessions, etc. (Increases Quality and Efficiency).

4. Assess additional comfort needs.
Perform basic comfort measures for the patient, such as adding pillows, straightening sheets, filling water pitchers, and helping to reposition the patient. These activities lead to additional call light requests if left undone. These can also be done by non-clinical staff when in the room (Increases Efficiency and Patient Experience).

5. Conduct environmental assessment.
Do an environmental assessment of the room, including ensuring the call light, bedside table, phone and charger, tissues, and garbage can are all within reach. Empty the garbage if needed, and make sure the bathroom is clean and neat. Any staff, clinical or non-clinical, can do this step (Increases Efficiency and Quality / Safety).

6. Use closing key words and actions.
Use key words like, *"Is there anything else I can do for you? I have time."* Or *"I think I got everything taken care of. Do you need anything else before I go?"*

This phrase was initially a call light reduction strategy because it is designed to elicit requests from the patient while you are still there. Like with AIDET®, make it your own if the basic concept is straightforward (Increased Efficiency and Patient Experience).

7. Tell each patient when you will be back.
Before leaving the room, use key words and actions that tell the patient when you will return. *"Mrs. Johnson, I will return to round on you again in about an hour."* When you tell patients when you will return, they cluster their requests in the context of your rounds rather than relying on the call light. Seeing that you come back every hour helps them relax and not be anxious about being alone. A less anxious patient is easier to care for (Increased Efficiency and Patient Experience, Reduced Anxiety).

8. Document the process in a rounding log.
Before leaving the room, the nursing staff needs to document the round. This accountability measure helps the nurse manager ensure the rounds are complete (Increased Quality / Accountability, Efficiency, and Patient Experience).

Distraction is the leading cause of accidents on the road or the unit. You're distracted when taking a medication order over the phone, and a call bell goes off. You're distracted while doing patient/family teaching and a call bell goes off. You're distracted when reading through orders and your call bell goes off. Distractions can cause busy staff to miss a decimal point or write something wrong. Hourly Rounding® impacts that directly.

When I launched Hourly Rounding® in my hospital years before I coached it, nurses were less than enthusiastic until they started seeing its benefits. When a nurse is asked to do something because it will "improve patient engagement," they also need to understand how it will improve other things like safety and how it will improve their workflow. That's not selfish. It's smart. Most nurses think holistically. So how do you show an intelligent, thoughtful nurse the beauty and effectiveness of this practice?

 Your Mailbox and Hourly Rounding®

How do you get your mail? Do you walk to the mailbox, grab your electric bill and bring it inside and then go back out, grab a catalog and bring it inside, then go out and get your Amazon package and bring it inside? Probably not. Instead, you go to the mailbox and bring everything in at once. Because you're there, and it makes sense.

Yet how do many nurses and other caregivers sometimes practice? Your IV pump goes off, and you run into the room and reset it. Then the call light goes off, and you run to get the patient some water. Then you realize 20 minutes later that it's time to hang the antibiotic. You are back and forth, getting the mail one envelope at a time.

The point of Hourly Rounding® is that while you're at the "mailbox" (in the room), Get. It. All. Done. And then, take a second to ask the patient if they can think of anything else they might need before you return in an hour.

With everything signed, sealed, and delivered, your day might feel more in control.

Pre-Visit Planning and Calls

Between family responsibilities, work schedules, errands, chores, hobbies, etc., we are all busy and can use a helpful reminder. Pre-visit calls are one of those practices that are so simple you might underestimate the impact. How often do patients miss or arrive late for a scheduled appointment? How often do patients show up having eaten when the test requires fasting? Most importantly, how often is much-needed care postponed, causing more suffering and stress for a patient due to miscommunication or misunderstanding?

> Pre-visit planning and calls are contacts made before an individual arrives at a specific location for a scheduled appointment or visit. It aims to establish initial contact and gather relevant information to ensure a seamless experience.

A pre-visit call can reduce these issues, which improves access by creating more capacity for patient care. It can significantly improve patient collaboration, safety, and the patient's perception of care. It can also improve staff engagement, as they can feel better about the care they deliver and have a better "partner" in the patient. Finally, it can help increase revenue and decrease wasted time and resources.

A note on automated pre-visit calls or text reminders: They are a great way to use technology to make life easier for everyone involved. At a minimum, they are a reminder and helpful in decreasing "no-shows." Some can provide arrival time, parking information, fasting instructions, or the option to confirm, cancel, or reschedule. The downside is that the technology only allows for a one-sided conversation. Many organizations Huron has worked with note the importance of connecting with patients to build a trusting relationship and allow the patient to ask questions that might clear up confusion or decrease their anxiety.

The elements of a pre-call can vary depending on your area of practice, but here are some standard components and implementation ideas:

- Confirm the appointment date and time and set expectations for arrival and departure timeframes. Having the patient restate this or encouraging them to write it down is often helpful.

- Introduce yourself and the team to decrease patient anxiety.

- Discuss any restrictions for diet or activity and whether the patient needs to arrange transportation for their safety.

- Explain safety protocols, confirm allergies, and discuss possible side effects of medications.

- Include practical information like address, directions, parking, and visitor/waiting protocols.

- Use open-ended questions to see if the patient has any questions, e.g., "What questions do you have?" or "What can I explain better?" Not "Do you have any questions?"

- Make the call as friendly as possible. Treat the patient as you'd want someone you love treated.

- Create a "script guide" if that helps but make it authentically your own. Be transparent that you will go through a list of points to ensure they have all the information they need to feel safe and get the best care possible. Most people will appreciate the mix of "mandatory information" and human connection.

- Mix it up. Pre-calls can be made by direct caregivers, medical techs, people on light duty, retired nurses, etc.

Huron loves coaching pre-visit calls. They are like a double espresso shot for results. In one organization, patient no-shows decreased by 70% and late arrivals by 50-60%. In addition, patient experience improved by 25-30%. For those of you who care about the bottom line, the financial impact of these phone calls was estimated at a staggering $750,000 a year!

Care Transition Calls

> Care transition calls are phone calls placed by care team members to patients within 24–72 hours of their discharge to confirm that a patient understands their follow-up care. They are meant to help to reduce the risk of preventable readmissions, ensure high-quality clinical care, and aid in effective recovery.

It doesn't take long to make a phone call to a patient discharged from your area. But much like a pre-visit call, the benefits of those few minutes can be significant. These calls may offer an opportunity to reconnect with a patient you cared for and see the progress on their journey to improved health. Still, they also reduce costs, generate revenue for your organization, and above all that, they can save a life.

Why are these calls important?

All healthcare workers know the importance of a patient accurately executing their discharge instructions. Unfortunately, research tells us this doesn't happen often. One study found that 81% of patients requiring assistance with basic functional needs failed to receive a home care referral, and 65% said no one at the hospital talked to them about managing their care at home. Additionally, other researchers have found that in the U.S.:

- 19.6% of Medicare patients are readmitted within 30 days (approximately 2 million).

- 90% of these readmissions are deemed unplanned.

- Only 50% of those readmitted had seen their physician before readmission.

- These readmissions are estimated at $17.4 billion for one year.

A resounding body of evidence demonstrates that calls placed by care team members to patients within 48-72 hours of discharge can positively impact patient health. The reason for this is simple. Discharge occurs at a time that is often very busy. Patients have a lot of information coming their way and are often not in the right frame of mind to receive and process it effectively. As a result, patients may overlook follow-up appointments, fail to fill prescriptions, or miss signs of declining health.

There are several other benefits to care transition calls, including:

- Improved clinical efficacy (patients get better outcomes because you affirm the essential things).

- Validation of patient's understanding of discharge instructions (avoid miscommunication and assumptions).

- Clarification of medication instructions (vital for people who are on new medications or require a specific regimen).

- Reduced patient anxiety.

- Reduced complaints and claims (in a practical sense, saves time on service recovery and conserves resources).

- Improved patient perception of care (patient feels genuinely cared about, not just a number and a diagnosis).

- Opportunity to harvest staff recognition (remember to ask about it!).

How to make care transition calls

These calls, typically three to five minutes, allow care team members to hear firsthand the status of recently discharged patients and confirm they have the information and resources required to recover effectively. To get the most out of these calls:

- **Gather Your Tools.** You will need your call list, information source, and any potential auxiliary/referral numbers. You will also need access to your call documentation system. Finally, you will need your call script.

- **Get Organized.** Review patients to be called (this includes the previous day's discharges and those patients discharged 2-3 days before who have not received calls). Prioritize your calls using your clinical judgment.

- **Get Ready.** Review the length of stay, diagnosis, and discharge instruction information for your first patient. This review generally takes 1-2 minutes.

- **Place the Call.** Know your script. Have your introduction, list of questions, and closing ready. Be prepared with a message script in case the patient doesn't answer.

Here is a sample call script (this is just a guide; be sure to adapt it to reflect your organization's highest priorities):

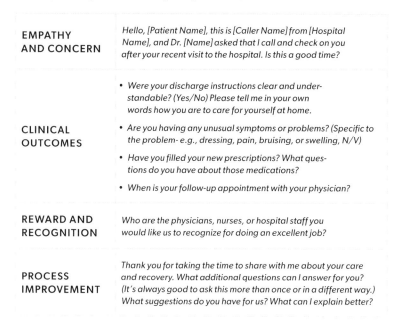

EMPATHY AND CONCERN	Hello, [Patient Name], this is [Caller Name] from [Hospital Name], and Dr. [Name] asked that I call and check on you after your recent visit to the hospital. Is this a good time?
CLINICAL OUTCOMES	• Were your discharge instructions clear and understandable? (Yes/No) Please tell me in your own words how you are to care for yourself at home. • Are you having any unusual symptoms or problems? (Specific to the problem- e.g., dressing, pain, bruising, or swelling, N/V) • Have you filled your new prescriptions? What questions do you have about those medications? • When is your follow-up appointment with your physician?
REWARD AND RECOGNITION	Who are the physicians, nurses, or hospital staff you would like us to recognize for doing an excellent job?
PROCESS IMPROVEMENT	Thank you for taking the time to share with me about your care and recovery. What additional questions can I answer for you? (It's always good to ask this more than once or in a different way.) What suggestions do you have for us? What can I explain better?

Figure 3.11: Care Transition Call Example and Key Words

On occasion, your patient will have needs that extend this time. Remember that your goal is to ensure they have the knowledge and skill to continue their care at home. It is worth the time to prevent an emergency room visit or readmission.

Also, remember to document the call, as this could be helpful to your care team if the patient calls back with any questions. Most of all, share the stories. These will both teach and inspire. Healthcare workers are hungry for positive feedback and affirmation and should know how they are making a difference.

Individualized Patient Care

Individualized patient care (IPC) is a simple yet profoundly impactful tactic demonstrating respect for your patient. In standard practice, patients exhibit less anxiety, higher trust in their care team members, and greater engagement in their recovery.

> Individualized patient care refers to gathering information from patients about their preferences, using a standard methodology to share this information across the care team, and considering these preferences as care is delivered.

Information gathered through IPC can be personal, like, "I can't wait to get well enough to go fishing again. It's my favorite hobby." Or something related to their illness and healing, like, "I want to get strong enough to walk again." There are several ways to share this information with the staff who will encounter the patient, including their chart (although this excludes non-clinical staff), their patient communication board, or, in a clinical setting, cards they complete at check-in that are provided to caregivers before they enter the examination room.

Figure 3.12: Sample Preference Card

66 Who's Your Caddy?

Recently admitted and with few visitors, Dewayne was one of those patients who kept to himself. He was a retired aeronautical engineer who spent most of his days quietly reading a book or watching TV. Although polite and always ready with a smile, his time in the hospital seemed to be draining him.

Shavon, one of his physical therapists, noticed the "What's Important to Me" section on his communication board was blank. She said, "Dewayne, it looks like we forgot to ask you what's important to you. We use this to get to know you better and ensure we care for you the best we can. So, what is important to you? Could be personal goals or hobbies, or healthcare goals, whatever you like."

Dewayne looked up from his book, thought for a second, and smiled when he answered, "Golf."

Two days later, Shavon showed up for her scheduled appointment with Dewayne holding a miniature putting green, several golf balls, and a few putters. As Dewayne looked up and saw what was in her hands, his polite smile changed to one that would light up a room. Shavon explained how she wasn't a golfer but borrowed the equipment from her uncle to see if Dewayne would be interested in incorporating it into his PT. Before Shavon could continue, he was out of bed explaining grips, swings, and golf.

Shavon incorporated some of the PT that would be helpful to Dewayne into some "golf moves." One of the nurses, Kelly, had been a golfer in college and came by to share stories and "talk golf" with Dewayne. He was a different patient after that. His progress sped up, and his engagement was through the roof. Now, he told jokes, asked questions, and laughed easily.

On the day of his discharge, Shavon and Kelly presented Dewayne with a t-shirt they found online. It said: Who's Your Caddy?

"I will never take this t-shirt off!" laughed Dewayne. He high-fived his two favorite caregivers, thanked them profusely, and asked Shavon to thank her uncle for trusting a stranger with his clubs.

Dewayne was able to go home a full three days ahead of plan. He was undoubtedly made whole, better, and stronger by the surgery and medical care he received, but maybe more so by having that one word written on his board, being met where he was, and seen as a human being, unique and special.

Section 3: Caring for Internal Customers

"Service to others is the rent you pay
for your room here on earth."

Muhammad Ali

No discussion about building a culture around service is complete without addressing service to one another within and across teams. Like puzzle pieces on the healthcare board, the picture is incomplete without that connection. The workplace becomes far more productive and purposeful when we foster a sense of belonging for each other. Unfortunately, it is easy to forget to do that in the intensity of an average day working in healthcare.

Internal Customer—Survey and Rounding

More than merely getting along, interdepartmental collaboration requires two or more parties to work together to reach a common goal. My mom always used to say to me, "One raindrop won't make the flowers grow, but a cloud-full sure will!" In this case, collaboration helps provide an exceptional experience to patients and their families.

Often, the primary culprit in interdepartmental strife is a historical lack of understanding and siloed thinking. Two key tactics to foster positive interdepartmental relationships are the support services of surveying and rounding on internal customers.

Surveying Internal Customers

The internal teams that provide the necessary support to direct care team members are known by many names. Essential Services, Ancillary Services, and Support Services, to name a few. Just as patients and families evaluate the care team with a standard tool such as the patient experience survey, these departments are evaluated using an internally developed support services survey (this tool is also often called the interdepartmental survey).

It can complement the rounding process by identifying areas of strength and opportunity. It also helps departments serve each other better and find common ground and opportunities to share rewards and recognition.

This survey is designed to take less than five minutes for leaders to complete. It uses the same scale found in the CAHPS survey and asks respondents to rate each support department in four key areas:

- Communication: My team communicates with you effectively.

- Attitude: My team treats you with courtesy and respect.

- Responsiveness: My team meets your needs with an appropriate sense of urgency.

- Accuracy: My team provides consistent and reliable services with appropriate follow-up.

You might include additional open-ended questions:

- What service is most important to your team? What are your expectations related to this?

- What service does our team provide that is exemplary? Which individual team member do you consider to be exceptional?

Rounding on Internal Customers

Interdepartmental rounding occurs when an ancillary department leader proactively and purposefully connects with departments they serve on a regular frequency with the intention to:

- Demonstrate commitment to delivering quality and service excellence.

- Build and maintain relationships/teamwork.

- Harvest reward and recognition.

- Identify processes that are either successful or require improvement.

Rounding in any form—employees, patients, or areas served—is critical to maintaining clear lines of communication, identifying barriers to improvement, and proactively solving problems.

Interdepartmental rounding is critical because support services play a vital role in patient care. Rounding removes the "us and them" and fosters an "us and us" way of thinking. And it is one of many ways to empower strong professional relationships and teamwork.

Knowing your internal customer preferences

Don't try to guess what your internal customers consider their top priorities. Better to ask and listen to what they need. To help this critical discussion, many organizations have successfully started interdepartmental rounding with an "Internal Customer Preference Card." With just three questions, it uncovers your customer "what" early and sets the process off to a great start.

The timing for rounding will vary and is based on support survey results. Priority may be given to areas with which the department regularly collaborates or where volume/risk is high. Many leaders dedicate one hour a week to round on four or five other directors in high-volume/high-risk departments and one other on a rotational basis. You can expect each round to last about 10 minutes.

Department: _____ Date: _____

Customer Names: _____

What three things can we do to ensure that we meet your expectations in providing excellent/very good service to you and your department?

1.

2.

3.

What is one item you would like to have improved?

What three things do you need from me and my team to be successful?

1.

2.

3.

Date of next rounding: _____

Date to update preferences card: _____

Figure 3.13: Customer Preference Card

ROUNDING WITH INTERNAL CUSTOMERS

Each round should include the following elements:

☑ Use the AIDET® Communication Framework—Acknowledge, Introduce, Duration, Explanation, and Thank You.

☑ Establish rounding expectations.

☑ Review accomplishments.

☑ Review wins.

☑ Harvest recognition.

☑ Identify opportunities for improvement.

☑ Discuss support services survey or critical customer expectations.

☑ Offer to help.

☑ Schedule the next rounding.

☑ Show appreciation.

Figure 3.14: Rounding with Internal Customers – Key Elements of an Effective Round

The value of interdepartmental rounds is only fully realized when leaders complete needed follow-through. That may mean working to resolve an issue, delivering recognition to an individual or a team, and managing the department that provides positive feedback. What gets rewarded gets repeated.

Take ownership and work with your internal customers to set realistic expectations. Be transparent if you need to discuss options to resolve a complex issue, and remember to communicate progress or resolution so your efforts are visible. Working together to develop solutions ensures departments will be more supportive of each other in the long run.

Principle 3 Summary

We have come a long way since the first pages of this chapter. We've reviewed Caring with Connections, Compassion, and Communication; Caring at the Bedside; and Caring for Internal Customers.

To paraphrase the Greek philosopher Heraclitus, no one steps in the same river twice, for it is not the same river, and they are not the same person. In the best possible way, I hope that you are not the same person as when you first stepped into this river.

As you reflect on that, what spoke to you in this chapter? What made you laugh out loud or tear up? What did you highlight, bend a page to bookmark, or electronically flag? What made you think so much that you shared it with someone else? What story reminded you of someone you took care of or worked with?

Exploring how to build a culture around service is an extension of who healthcare workers naturally are. This is one part of the journey that the experts at Huron, the people in your organization, and you and I share. To grow. To improve. To inspire. To look at tomorrow and think, "I am going to be a little better tomorrow than I was today."

If this chapter is like that philosopher's river, the person you are now might read this all again and see it in an entirely new way. That's the fun of it all. It will change as you change. Keep doing that. That is the optimism, hope, renewal, and empowerment we want for you.

PRINCIPLE 4: DEVELOP LEADERS TO DEVELOP PEOPLE

Coach people to be their best at work.

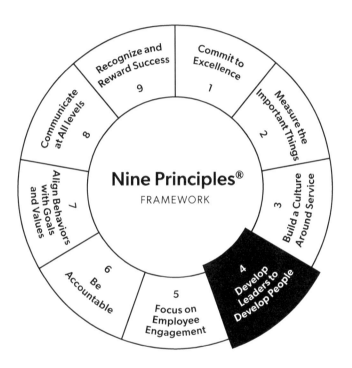

"Before you are a leader, success is all about growing yourself. When you become a leader, success is all about growing others."

Jack Welsh

Principle 4: Develop Leaders to Develop People, focuses on coaching people to be their BEST at work. It is a crucial principle for anyone reading this book because developing high-performing leaders is your organization's pathway to achieving and sustaining outstanding performance.

While every principle of the Nine Principles® Framework sets the stage and turns the flywheel, whatever gains we achieve cannot be sustained without making leader development a key priority. So, what makes Principle 4 so important?

People in healthcare choose this profession because they have passion and want to be part of a place where they feel they have a purpose, do worthwhile work, and can make a difference. They want to know they are part of something meaningful, and they should be recognized and appreciated for that.

With so many headwinds against us, it can be daunting to be a leader. The development of people is now more critical than ever. It can—and should—take shape in different ways. These include in-person leadership development institutes, virtual leadership development, coaching and mentoring, and integration into leadership meeting agendas.

In fact, building opportunities to learn and practice new skills and behaviors across all of these settings addresses the diverse needs of adult learners. It also increases the "stickiness" of how well they apply their learning. As you leverage different approaches to build competence, the goals must remain the same: to ensure that a focus on leadership development is top of mind to create excellence and inspiration.

Great People Need Great Leaders

Great leaders are self-aware and invest in both their improvement and in the teams they lead. People are an organization's greatest asset. Jim Collins, author of Good to Great, says it well: "Great vision without great people is irrelevant."

Yes, healthcare comprises buildings, devices, equipment, and technology, but all of that is expected. The unexpected is what stops people in their tracks when they experience it. That is what we strive for.

If you think about a time you were blown away by a business you interacted with or a place where you were a patient, it probably wasn't the "things" that impressed you. No one gives a restaurant five stars because the table was set well, or the wallpaper matched the tile. No, it was usually because the food and service were incredible. No one walks out of a healthcare institution after being a patient and thinks, "Wow! Those wheelchairs were so quiet. It was like riding on a cloud!" or "The alarm on that IV pump was beautiful. I want to make that my ringtone!"

Guaranteed, what makes an impression is the people, the energy, and the vibe. That is not an accident. Never. It is passionately desired, fervently pursued, precisely measured, and embedded into the very fabric of the culture.

"Satisfactory" can happen accidentally. Even "good" can be accidental. "Excellent" cannot be. This is true in any line of work.

66 Lawnmowers, Birthdays, and Crowns.

I know this lawn-care person named Charley. He charges around 10-15% more than most lawn-care people in my area, yet you see him everywhere. He beats his competition. In one subdivision of 80 homes, his crew does about 70 lawns there!

So, what gives Charley the edge? On the surface, you might be confused. He has trucks and trailers; the other lawn crews do as well. Like the other folks, he uses lawnmowers, leaf blowers, rakes, and hedge trimmers. He has two or three-person crews, same for the others.

But when you look more closely, it becomes apparent. Charley knows all the birthday dates of the crew. He also knows their kids' birthdays. Oh, and when it is their birthday, he has a little gift for them. If they work on their birthday, they have fun with it. That birthday-celebrating crew member wears a crown the whole day. There's cake, too.

The customers love this as much as the crews. When was the last time you saw royalty mowing a lawn? Not only that, but Charley has team leaders (similar to charge nurses or shift leads) who check in with the crew and make sure they have what they need.

Charley's company has grown so much that he now has managers in charge of several crews. And guess what? The team leaders are almost always the ones who get promoted to those manager jobs. So, there are growth opportunities for team members.

He does this through an internal leadership development plan he created, where his team leaders take a leadership seminar at a local community college that he pays for. He also developed a **"Leadership Apprentice Work Network"** (L.A.W.N.) where team leaders with leadership potential and interest shadow managers and learn the components of what it takes to lead. The managers give Charley real-time feedback on who is a "stand-out," then, Charley invests time and effort in ensuring a "Mower Mentor" program where the team leaders are trained for manager roles. He is building his kingdom from within!

It is noticeable as you drive by and wave. Charley's teams seem to smile more. They take the initiative because this company empowers the managers, team leads, and crew members to make decisions that will improve their work life and the service they provide.

Bottom line. These folks WANT to work for Charley, while other lawn companies have turnover rates that would even make us healthcare leaders wince.

None of this can be claimed as "luck" or "accident." Charley didn't win the "lawn person hire lottery." Charley creates a positive and engaging work culture. He leads by example. He develops and nurtures leaders, giving them a place to work and grow. His team does fantastic work and he has great employees.

Whether someone is mowing a lawn, sterilizing an OR, prepping a patient for surgery, transporting someone to radiology, or setting up home care for a discharged patient, they want a leader that cares. Be a "Charley" to your team today.

Worth the Investment

Record numbers of employees are leaving their jobs searching for better leaders, work-life balance, and pay and benefits. Another reason why employees are quitting jobs is due to a lack of professional development opportunities. In a fall 2021 report by Monster, 45% of surveyed employees said they would be more likely to stay at their current jobs if offered more development. (Crowns and birthday cakes weren't mentioned, but I bet they might sway a few people if they were options!)

And here is more data. Huron surveyed 718 healthcare leaders and workers, including clinicians, nurses, staff and leaders, about what they value in their workplaces and their satisfaction with those factors. This unique approach to measuring healthcare worker sentiment provides new data and insights into where leaders are united and divided in the workplace.

Key differences emerged between leaders' beliefs about what is essential to staff and what employees value. This variation signals and opportunity for organizations to change how and where they invest. One of these factors was **professional growth opportunities**.

Gallup also has discovered that one of the most crucial factors in creating a high-performance workplace is instilling a high-development culture that values individuals' growth. Gallup states, "Organizations that have made a strategic investment in employee development report 11% greater profitability and are twice as likely to retain their employees."

And have no delusions. It is an investment. But just like the old story goes, when a senior leader was asked by a senior leader at another organization how she could "afford" to invest so much in developing her team, she wisely replied, "How could I afford not to?"

It's like buying expensive technology for your energetic and distracted 13-year-old. Wouldn't it be wise to invest a few extra dollars for a protective case that can be dropped at least two stories without cracking? You might even spring for the insurance while you're at it. (Some of you just got that pang of distant regret, didn't you? It's okay. We've all been there.)

Managing Performance— highmiddlelow®

We have established that to be successful leaders, we need employees to be at their best. But before we dive into the ways to develop yourself, leaders, and staff, we want to start by talking about the performance curve.

Why talk about this first? Because let's be honest, many people struggle with performance management, yet this is one of the most critical skills for leaders to possess. It strengthens the ability of ourselves, as well as our teams, to grow and change.

The Performance Curve—The Three Levels of Performance
In life and at work, performance can be categorized into three areas: (1) high performers, (2) middle/solid performers, and (3) low/sub-par performers. Typically, an organization will have about 8% low/sub-par performers, 58% middle/solid performers, and 34% high performers.

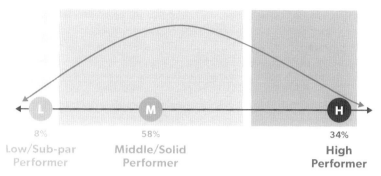

8%
Low/Sub-par
Performer

58%
Middle/Solid
Performer

34%
**High
Performer**

Figure 4.1: The Performance Curve

We can all sit around the campfire and debate the "definitions" of High, Solid/Middle, and Low/Sub-par performers all night until the fire is reduced to embers. But unless unlimited s'mores are being served, why do that? Let's land on what we have found most, if not all, teams agree are at least some working definitions for the three groups.

The High Performer

Let's begin with high performers. These people want to achieve so badly that when they see a new tool or technique, they quickly move to implement it. It's like they "vibrate" at a higher frequency. They are like powerful neon lights that are on day and night and shine brightly!

High performers are people with whom we place our utmost confidence. You can "exhale" when they are at work. They are your rock stars. They exude, "I love being here!" They also aren't just "delivery vehicles" for problems. Rather than boxing up problems and dumping them at your door, they proactively contribute to solving them!

They are creative thinkers, individualists, heartfelt, committed, and as authentic as they come. Roughly 34% of most work team members fall into this category.

The Middle/Solid Performer

The middle/solid performers look to high performers to see "what right looks like. "While they need some guidance, they are dependable. Their light is like a dimmer switch. It can be mid-level, but with a little "lift," it can move to "bright." They might waver because high or low/sub-par performers can significantly influence their actions.

Although they help identify problems, middle/solid performers may not be confident enough to present a solution (and risk rejection). They may need that "influence" that comes from their high-performing peers to step into that role of "problem-solver" over "problem-deliverer."

This is why mentoring is so vital. My dad always told me I should always show up with "two hands full" when bringing an issue or problem to the table. One hand should contain the problem, fully described, with a combination of clarity and brevity, and the other hand should hold at least one suggestion or solution as to how to fix or handle it. He prepared me by reminding me not to expect all of my solutions to become implemented immediately but to take comfort in the fact that just by "being that person," I would be viewed differently.

That is excellent advice for those who are or work with middle/solid performers. We want our middle/solid performers to always feel "more than enough." A middle/solid performer is progressing in the right direction. They want to be successful for all the right reasons. We can get them to shine.

And consider this: even if they stay "solid," that's pretty darn good. As I used to say as a coach, "Even If I can make 'solid' 'more solid,' it's been a good day!" They need to know they are vital players with valuable ideas. We want to build them up, empower them, and retain them. They represent about 58% of your workforce.

The Low/Sub-par Performer

Low/Sub-par performers do not meet performance expectations. Often, they have bad attitudes; they point out problems without offering solutions. They show up with one hand full. They may manage down leadership as well as their co-workers. They are permanent "victims." Their "light" is like a loose bulb that flickers on and off (sometimes more "off" than "on").

They are sometimes masters of we/they and are the first to blame others. It is rare to hear a low/sub-par performer say, "It's my fault"—they skipped that line when the "accountability gene" was handed out! They also may be passive-aggressive, thinking they will outlast the leader (and some of them have!).

But interestingly, many low/sub-par performers actually may have good attitudes. I know that may seem counterintuitive. However, that's why we are thoughtful going down this road. Maybe something inside of them has been squashed or wounded or, like the Grinch's heart, "shrunken," but with a bit of "love," it can be regained. Sometimes they lack the skill set to do the job, even when given additional support and resources.

These coworkers can be the most challenging for us in many ways. And yet we have to find it within ourselves as leaders to address these lower performers, even when it's uncomfortable. But an inspired leader will not hesitate to take on challenges not only because they have to, but because they know it is the right thing to do.

Redemption is a beautiful thing, but also not guaranteed. However, trying to help someone get back up when they have fallen is worth the effort. We owe it to ourselves and the team. No matter how tough it is to lead lower-performing team members, imagine how tough it must be to work alongside them, having to clean up all they do and speak. When we work on them, we also work on behalf of the whole team.

Also, self-awareness is always a great trait in a leader. So, the first step is holding the mirror up to ourselves. How are we doing with the "communicate at all levels" part? Do low/ sub-par performers know they're not meeting expectations? Have we communicated what "high performance" or what "right" looks like? It is unfair to expect people to read our minds and think, "Well, they should just KNOW what to do." Their life path and professional journey may have been very different than yours.

We need to start from a perspective that perhaps people not "meeting expectations" could be unaware of those expectations. Unless you are 100% sure this has been directly communicated and documented, it's safe to assume they may not know.

Skill and Will

Often a low/sub-par performer has one of two underlying issues. The first is about "will," and the second is about "skill." Issues of "will" can be more challenging to manage. These people have the skill to do the job but don't have the right energy, attitude, or motivation ("will").

Issues of "skill" are slightly easier to address. This is when someone has the right attitude and is friendly, positive, and helpful ("will"), but doesn't have the necessary skills to do the job correctly. If you're working with someone with their heart in the right place, getting their mind there is usually just a matter of time and patience.

Let's look at what occurs if leaders fail to assume this responsibility.

The Intolerable Gap

As you work to fulfill your mission statement and strive for the highest quality possible, you'll probably aim to move up to a top-tier or top-decile performance. What an incredible goal.

As you move toward this goal, the gap between low/sub-par performers and everyone else becomes obvious. At first, it's uncomfortable. Soon, it's intolerable.

It's like if everyone has been slowly walking around a track, and 92% of the team has been secretly training for a track meet. Then one day, they take off, leaving that 8% limping around the track. The difference will become undeniable.

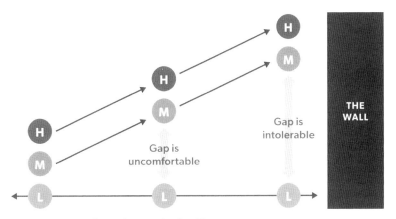

Figure 4.2: HML – The gap becomes intolerable.

About this time, the high performers are getting a little frustrated because they now know what type of performance is expected. They see people not delivering it, and those people are still employed. How can this be? They're running full speed ahead and want to win this race. They are sprinting and leading the middle/solid performers like, "C'mon, we can do this!"

The middle/solid performers are in the same boat. Most of them are also starting to run, but something else is happening to them. They're starting to be targeted by the 8%.

Many low/sub-par performers, especially those with attitude issues, don't want the organization to change. They've survived so far, but with new goals, new standards of behavior, and more consistency, they will have to make drastic changes.

And so, these low/sub-par performers try to sabotage the effort. They know they can't get to the higher performers who have already launched down the track. So, figuratively speaking, they are trying to trip the middle/solid performers, "flat-tire" their sneakers, and heckle them in the hopes they'll give up running ahead and instead sulk along slowly with the lower performers.

As Ralph Waldo Emerson said, "People wish to be settled..." and that applies to low/ sub-par as well as middle/solid and high performers. But the high and middle/solid performers also get the second part of Emerson's quote: "... that only as far as they are unsettled is there any hope for them."

The 92% of high and middle/solid performers feel hope as they race down that track. They are in it to win it! But the low/sub-par performers are fighting against change. So the organization now has an issue; the race will be lost if it isn't addressed.

The Performance Wall

Things are moving, and the gap suddenly becomes intolerable, and POW! you hit a wall. Your results decline, and your new initiatives are more likely to fail as work slides backward (See Figure 4.3).

The race could be lost if you don't address it.

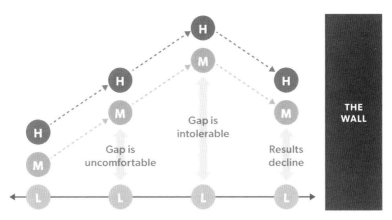

Figure 4.3: The Effect of Low/Sub-par Performers on Organizational Performance

Once an organization hits the wall, leaders look for new approaches to the same old problems, thinking the efforts must have been misguided. They move to the next great initiative they've read or heard about, only to be disappointed down the road.

Why do leaders hit that wall?

- High performers are getting tired. They are frustrated leaders are not holding low/sub-par performers accountable. They may still seem like high performers, but they slow down and pace themselves. If they decide not to exit, they will fulfill their innate desire to learn and grow by placing their energies elsewhere.

- Middle/Solid performers simply slow down. They are watching what the high performers do. When they see their behavior shift, they also shift their behaviors.

- The low/sub-par performers continue as usual, knowing they will outlast this "initiative" like they've done most of their professional lives.

Up and Over the Wall

Many organizations might struggle to get over the wall. When things get tough, there might be a tendency to slow down and back off instead of powering through. When you hit a wall, don't stop. There is a way to get up and over that wall.

By the way, it's not about a new buzzword or program, although those might help for a while. The real solution is to address performance issues—to recruit and retain high performers, retain and develop middle/solid performers, and move low/sub-par performers up or out.

Remember the graph that showed sudden backward movement? The good news is that when you address performance issues quickly, you might not have that backward slide at all. High-performing leaders build momentum through performance conversations to push the organization up and over the wall (See Figure 4.4).

Plus, the sooner you address it, the less painful it is to your organization because your high and middle/solid performers aren't as exhausted. Make it so that gap doesn't get so uncomfortable that it's unlivable.

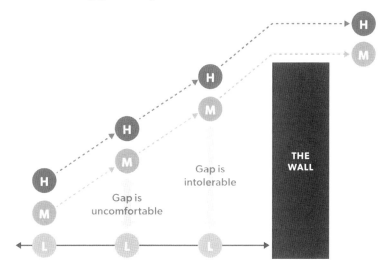

Figure 4.4: Getting Over the Wall

Moving the Performance Curve

Developing leaders to support high and middle/solid performers and address low/sub-par performers is essential to achieving organizational excellence. Specifically, it brings:

- System-wide high-performing results.

- The right leaders in the right place.

- A clear understanding of the keys to success by everyone in the organization.

- Disciplined people and processes.

- Proactive leadership.

If you want your high-performing leaders to build momentum to push the organization up and over the wall, provide them with essential leadership skills that move excellence across the board. Developing leaders to develop people positively shifts the results, tightening the performance curve and moving it to the right. Individual performance improves across the board, and performance levels have less variance (See Figure 4.5).

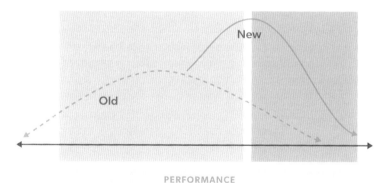

PERFORMANCE

Figure 4.5: Moving the Performance Curve Right and Tight

The best organizations develop their leaders to develop people to close the spread of performance levels. Excellent organizational leaders do important work by helping their organizations get over the wall and accelerate results.

Having highmiddlelow® Performer Conversations

As you're reading this book, I am sure that you want to move beyond "concept" and into knowing—knowing how to work with, lead, and create positive change with your team. You also want to know how to communicate across all performance levels to ensure excellence.

Our basic methodology, or template, for these conversations follows. But, before we get into it, one more thing: You have to have these conversations. You do. I could write and re-write all the backdrop to this. Still, it comes down to the fact that if you put off these conversations, you will be stuck staring at that "wall." It will become increasingly overwhelming, especially regarding addressing your lower performers.

What I've learned is that when you put off dealing with something, you surrender your power/influence over that thing, and then that "something" takes on its power, and its influence grows as there are no obstacles in its path. We can't risk that as leaders. We can't allow the negative impact of an unyielding and intentional lower performer to go unaddressed, untouched, or unchecked.

I always say you can have difficult conversations now, when it can create change, or later, when it can create chaos. Words are like water to a fire; pouring them out earlier rather than later can save the whole forest.

Transparency is your friend. When starting a formal performance conversation process, explaining the "why" to your team will serve many purposes. Let them know what's coming. The simpler, the better. You can say something like, "I want to be the best leader I can be, and part of that is communicating as clearly as possible with you all. You deserve honest and consistent feedback, so I will meet with everyone individually to give you meaningful and specific feedback on how you're doing."

Remember, these conversations are going to sound and feel a little different. They also might be new to you. Something new can be a little intimidating, even uncomfortable, so while that may be true, we can optimize this for you and your team to get the most from it.

If you've never lifted weights before, I won't give you the most strenuous workout of all time, pushing you to lift at the edges of your strength and abilities right out of the gate. Not only would you most likely injure yourself and hate me, but you probably would also never come back to the gym! It would be wiser to start you at a point where you can feel a sense of where you are strong, and give you a warm-up and a plan that would increase your confidence so that, as we progress, you can take on a more challenging workout.

So, take a swig of your protein shake, put on your sweatpants, and get those muscles pumped Here's how to hold each type of performer conversation (sweatpants and protein shakes are optional).

The High Performer Conversation

At Huron, we've found it is most optimal to meet with the high performers first. This is because they will light you up inside and get you pumped. After all, they are your enthusiastic superstars and are probably more excited to talk to you than you are to talk to them. They've been WAITING for this moment.

These folks have sometimes been left alone because we leaders know how good they are, so we spend much of our time trying to "teach up" our middle/solid or "build up" our lower performers. You can even say we've inadvertently neglected our higher performers—not because we don't care about them but because we thought, "They got this. They don't need me."

But they do.

They WANT to be part of something bigger. If we can feed their spirit, fire them up even more, and inspire them to co-lead those notable changes we want to put into place, we've created an almost unstoppable force.

Remember, there are two types of leaders: formal and informal. Managers, directors, vice presidents, etc., are formal, and that's essential. But these high performers—even though they might not hold a "title"—are your informal leaders. They are the ones most people look up to. They wield tremendous influence in day-to-day operations and functions, maybe even more than you, so tapping into that reservoir can quench the thirst for inspired excellence for your entire undertaking.

We suggest leaders follow the process outlined in Figure 4.6 when talking with high performers.

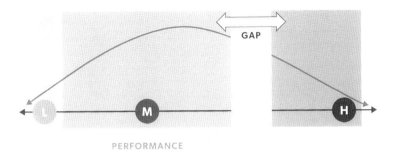

PERFORMANCE

HIGH PERFORMER CONVERSATION

Goal: Reward, Recognize, and Retain Individual

Gratitude	Thank them for their effort and work.
Value	Outline specifically why they are so crucial to the organization and why you value them.
Organization Direction/Plan	Explain where the organization is going and what is done to meet those goals.
Input	Ask them for input.

- "We want to retain you. Is there anything that we should be doing better?
- "What do I need to do for you?"
- What do you need more of to continue to feel excited, inspired, and challenged?"

Figure 4.6: Moving the High-Performer Conversation

Gratitude: Start the conversation positively and thank them sincerely for their work and effort.

Share Their Value: Tell them how incredibly essential they are to the team in concrete terms. Tell them you value their work ethic, values, and influence. Be specific. It's not enough to say, "You are a valuable team member." That's just "OK." High performers are the way they are because they like details. So, tell them something that sounds like this: "You bring so much value to this team in so many ways. A few that come to mind are how you always share timely articles in our huddles about new advances in our work, take the lead in precepting newer employees, and pour yourself fully into their development, and your compassion for our patients is awesome. I want to read you this letter from a former patient mentioning their positive interactions with you." This is a great way to start. This will get their attention. They need to hear this, and here's a bonus: You will feel amazing.

Yes, my fellow leader, this is for YOU too! We spend so much time being "corrective" as leaders that it can be draining. This fills your bucket to have this uplifting, positive conversation. It reminds you that you have some pretty incredible people on your team, and you will feel both honored and grateful during these conversations.

Share the organization's direction and plan. Be specific and transparent about where the organization or department is going and what is being done to make these exciting new changes—including these performance conversations.

Ask them for input. You want them to know they aren't just facilitators, but are contributors and drivers of the inspired excellence you want to create. "I want to ensure that you continue to love working here. I want this to be your professional 'forever home,' and I want to make sure that we do what it takes to retain you, so is there anything we should be doing better? What do we need to do for you? What do you need more of to continue to feel excited, inspired, and challenged?"

Interestingly, most high performers ask for more opportunities, responsibilities, and growth, not less. I've been in many of these conversations from the perspective of a leader, coach, and even an employee, and I can say sometimes they get beautifully emotional. Authentic recognition touches high performers, and they are sometimes even taken aback by it as they are often so humble and natural at what they do they don't think anyone even notices.

If you have 30 employees, and 30-40% are high performers, you've now had 10-13 extraordinary meetings.

You're building that "muscle" the right way.

The Middle/Solid Performer Conversation

Now it's time to take that newfound leadership muscle into conversations with middle/solid performers. Follow the support-coach-support conversation framework (See Figure 4.7).

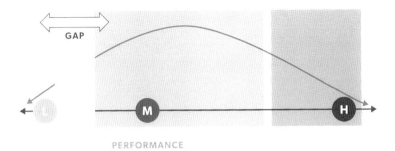

PERFORMANCE

MIDDLE / SOLID PERFORMER CONVERSATION

Goal: Reassure and Re-recruit Individual

S	Support	Describe good qualities—calm their anxiety.
S	Coach	Cover development opportunity
S	Support	Reaffirm good qualities

Figure 4.7: Moving the Middle / Solid Performer Conversation

S – SUPPORT:
Describe good qualities—calm their anxiety.

Start these conversations by explaining to the middle/solid performer that you're meeting with everybody one-on-one. Then tell them something like, "We want you to stay" or "We want to keep you." Whatever words you use, the clear message demonstrates that this is a positive conversation. We might even bluntly say, "When we finish talking, and you walk out of this office, I want you to feel better than when you came in." The idea is to alleviate any anxiety the middle/solid performer may have and to set the tone that this is a "positive" conversation.

After you say you want them to stay, tell them why. Spell out precisely what they add to the team: "I appreciate how dependable you are, and I never have to worry about you clocking in late or missing meetings. I also hear excellent feedback from some supervisors about your willingness to step in when we are short, and that is really a gift to us all, so thank you!"

C – COACH:

Cover development opportunity.

Next, talk about their developmental needs. We know that it's vital for people to feel that the organization and leadership value their advancement. So say, "We want to develop and invest in you and your career and growth."

Suppose there's one thing you want that person to do better. In that case, discuss it precisely. "I know you've shared with a few people that you don't fully understand the new automated charting system and that you've had to stay late to make some corrections, so I want to get you with Mauritia, who is one of our 'super users' and have her work with you on that. How does that sound?" If there are multiple things to review, still keep it to one. It's best not to overwhelm them; the goal is for them to walk out of the conversation feeling positive.

S – SUPPORT:

Reaffirm good qualities.

Finally, close with what's right. Talk about what they do well, and they leave feeling better than when they came in, as we promised! They know you want them to stay. They know what they do well. They know you're committed to their development. And now, the middle/solid performer might even be more excited than the high performer.

An excellent pro tip is to see if they'd like to be mentored by one of your high performers. Like the example above with "Mauritia," perhaps you know they both get along well. So, in addition to the specific help Mauritia can give them with the charting system, maybe you can facilitate a more meaningful connection between the two. Perhaps weekly 30 minute "meet-ups" or partner them up on a project. Many organizations have created formal mentoring programs with the built-in goal to have the high performers work with others to help them grow. This might be a great opportunity, even if it is done informally.

The Low/Sub-par Performer Conversation

Dealing with low/sub-par performers is a hot topic. But take my word on this. You want to do the other two—high and middle-performer—conversations first. Don't "pull a muscle" just because you wanted to show off in the gym!

You've already gotten fired up by your high performers, encouraged by your solid, and you are now ready for the next step. For many, this is the conversation that creates the most dread. But there is good news here. This is going to be a smaller percentage of people.

The other good news is that having a proven template and process makes the low/sub-par performer conversation much less complicated than just "winging it" would be. Honestly, "winging it" might be fun when you're trying a new recipe or choosing what to watch on Netflix, but with those options, if they don't go well, you can order pizza or change the channel. This isn't that.

So now you're sitting across from the low/sub-par performer and ready to have this conversation. It's just the two of you. You tell the low/sub-par performer that this is a serious conversation. Then I'd coach you to follow a strategy we call DESK (See Figure 4.8).

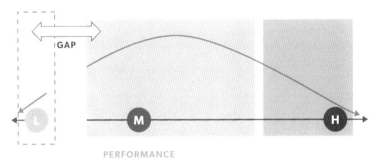

LOW/SUB-PAR PERFORMER CONVERSATION

Goal: Redirect, Record, Resolve, or Remove Individual

D	Describe	Describe what has been observed.
E	Evaluate	Evaluate how you feel.
S	Show	Show what needs to be done.
K	Know	Know the consequences of the continued same performance.

Follow-up

Figure 4.8: Moving the Low/Sub-par Performer Up or Along Conversation

D – DESCRIBE: Begin by describing the issue. Spell out exactly where the person is not meeting expectations.

- *"As you know, Mark, you are required to clock in no later than 0700 for your shift, and for the last several shifts, you have clocked in as late as 0725, and the earliest was 0716. I've talked about this with you three times before. Here are the dates and times of those conversations, and here's a printout from the attendance system to show you this pattern."*

E – EVALUATE: Next, evaluate how that makes you and the team feel. Perhaps they're being difficult about scheduling, or when someone asks for help, the low/sub-par performer is always "too busy." Maybe you've received consistent complaints or feedback about them. This is the chance to connect their behavior to a more significant issue, like the behavior standard "commitment to co-workers."

- *"Mark, when you do this, you are not only affecting patient care, as there have been delays getting patients to tests because the off-going shift has to wait to give you a report, but this is unfair and inconsiderate to your co-workers who have been working for 12 hours and need to clock out to get to evening classes, pick up kids from babysitters, and just get home to rest. I am sure you don't like waiting to clock out after a full day, either."*

- You might also say, *"As you'll recall, you signed the performance standards, including the 'commitment to coworkers' part. Your tardiness is affecting the team."*

Around this time, you will likely be interrupted. Ask the person to please wait to comment and let you finish, and when you're done, they can talk. Maintain control of the conversation.

It may go something like this:

- Mark: *"Oh, so now we all have to be perfect? You know how traffic is. I can't control how slow people drive. Plus, all this construction on 1-95 slows traffic."*

- You: *"Mark, I will ask you to hold your comments until I am done speaking. It's important right now that you understand how serious this is and that you listen. Please respect this conversation."*

Chances are that the low/sub-par performer will try to point fingers or shift the attention to someone else. You may need to remind them you are there to talk about them and no one else.

- Mark: *"I hope you're also talking to Selva about this. She's always running late."*

- You: *"I'd again ask you to listen now and not interrupt me. We are having a one-on-one conversation. I am not discussing anyone else's issues with you. This is about you, Mark."*

S – SHOW: Now, show the low/sub-par performer what needs to be done. Say, in essence, "Here's what I'm looking for," "Here's 'what right looks like,'" "Here are the expectations."

- You: "Mark, I want to be clear about what I expect moving forward. Starting tomorrow, when you come to work and every shift after that, you should clock in no later than 0700. Here's the policy you signed when you started working here and every year since, where you indicated that you would adhere to this."

K – KNOW: Let the low/sub-par performer know the consequences. Spell out the current consequences of the low/sub-par performer's behavior and the consequences they will face if it continues.

"Move 'em up or move 'em out" is a phrase that sounds bold coming from the person on the stage saying it, but they do not have to live it. I understand this. Please know that I do.

Making the tough decisions now may prevent you from making even more challenging decisions later. There is a Native American proverb that says, "All of the flowers of all the tomorrows are in the seeds of today."

Tips for Successful Conversations

Before bringing in the low/sub-par performer and having the one-on-one discussion, you'll want to do a few things to prepare:

- Let your leader know you'll be having these conversations. If low-performer conversations are taking place in your department, it shouldn't surprise them. Be completely clear, open, and straightforward with your direct leader or supervisor. Tell them what's been happening with the lower performers you'll be meeting with. Share it all—the good, the bad, the ugly: "Here are the things I've documented, as I was supposed to do. Here are the things I haven't done. Here's where I am. Here's what I am going to say. Here's what I hope to accomplish."

  Remember, just like you don't like surprises, neither does your leader. You want them in the loop and to have their support. Hopefully, the person you report to is also somewhat of a mentor or trusted advisor to you, so they may even have some advice to give.

- Collaborate with Human Resources as appropriate. Collaborate with HR and share everything you have with them so that you can create a game plan as a team. Ask your HR partner direct questions like: Do I have to start with a verbal warning? Can I go straight to the written warning? Can I go to the final written warning, or do we have enough documentation to make the person leave the organization if things don't go well?

This is all good to know for each person you'll be talking to.

- Bring someone along if needed. Some low/sub-par performers may have been down this road before. They may have had these conversations with a previous leader, and, since nothing has changed, they may believe this is all a bluff. Also, some of these folks have mastered manipulating the system and might try to make this hard for you. Better to be safe than sorry.

You might not want to go this alone if you have an extreme case. "Can I get a witness?" Yes, you can. You may need an ally and someone with you when you have some low-performer conversations. It could be someone from Human Resources or another manager. This is a decision to make with your supervisor and your HR leader. Get their guidance and confirmation of your plan.

I have done this. I was concerned about one particular conversation, so I had an HR representative and security nearby. It got that bad, and they escalated to threatening words. In all my years as a leader, that level of caution was only needed once, and to be honest, in all of my years coaching hundreds of leaders, I've seen this level of escalation maybe twice, so this is the exception. Yet I would be remiss if I didn't put this on the table as an option.

- Anticipate and role-play the conversation. The low/sub-par performer might interrupt or even go on the offensive, so be prepared. Find your most Oscar-worthy colleague and ask them to role-play with you so you can prepare for resistance. Let them go after you, accuse you, and throw out all sorts of distractions and emotional tirades. Why? Because just like pilots practice in a flight simulator for real-life events so that they can be more prepared if things go wrong, so should you.

This might sound extreme, but we all know some people are a bit extreme. Some of your low/sub-par performers have survived as long as they have in their roles by some degree of extreme, in fact, so better to be prepared by practicing these conversations.

- Prepare yourself. It is also okay to do some personal preparation. You may very well be a bit worried about this conversation, especially if this is new to you. If you need to, do some deep breathing, prayer, or mindfulness exercises before this conversation. Whatever it takes to get you in a calm and focused state.

  I think it would be irresponsible to act as if everyone should just be "tough" and "suck it up" and "get 'er done!" This can be draining. Be prepared physically and mentally when heading toward a difficult encounter. Many leaders are legitimately anxious about doing this. I know I was when I first did this. So, take care of "you" first!

Last Thoughts: Let's Do This.

Experience has shown that approximately a third of these low-performing employees will self-select from the department or organization. Some of the "Marks" of the world figure they can go somewhere else where they can play "clock-in roulette" and land on any number. They'll leave once they know they can no longer do what they've been doing. Another third will adjust their behavior. Ultimately this is great. Maybe Mark shares with you that he's caring for a sick parent and needs another family member to help. Your support of him may mean a lot.

Like I said before, this "low/sub-par" issue may be how "Mark is" or maybe "How Mark is at the moment." Perhaps it is just a "season or a reason," and maybe this conversation is a wake-up call for him. I will repeat it. Redemption is a beautiful thing.

However, some people don't want to be redeemed. They want to do what they do and expect the world to adjust. That is a reality. So, for the remaining third, you will probably have to ask them to leave. Remember, if you have 30 employees, we're talking about only two or three people (which can still be tough).

But you know what's tougher? Keeping Mark, who is aggravating everyone else, delaying care, and flaunting the fact that the rules don't apply to him. Or, if he won't budge, letting him go, and working tight for a few schedules until you can bring in either temporary help or someone who will be a team player.

Just remember: "What you tolerate, you encourage."

Empowering and inspiring your high performers, helping your middle/ solid performers to move into their best, and engaging your lower performers in a way that gives them a chance to rise or opt-out is a journey that, once undertaken, earns you the strength one gets when overcoming great obstacles.

You become stronger as a leader when you defeat the challenges you once thought you never could. After you've done this, you will feel like the world's weight is off your shoulders.

It feels glorious.

> ## "The greater the obstacle, the more glory in overcoming it."
>
> *Moliere*

 ## It's just apple cobbler."

As a manager, I dreaded the low-performer conversations. I initially expected them to blow up on me. But as I did them a few times (and luckily, they were few), I learned something. My role as a leader was not just to manage a budget and formulate a weekly schedule. I was there to guide people toward a shared vision while empowering them to reach their full potential and help them achieve extraordinary results. By having that as my "North Star," I was more mission-focused than tactic-focused.

But Judy made that feel like "Mission Impossible." She pushed back on everything I did, complained about every change I made, and had no fear of gossiping about me to others. It all got back to me.

But, bigger than her undermining me, she was creating a lot of drama and discussing other co-workers, creating friction among the team. She was like the TMZ of the department! I had to deal with it.

While there were many examples, a concrete one was her openly discussing someone in the break room, which was overheard by three others at an adjacent table. They came to me, as they were put off by what she said about this co-worker.

I scheduled a meeting with Judy. She confirmed it. Then she ghosted me.

I scheduled another one. She confirmed it, and she canceled at the last minute.

I called her at home, left her a voicemail, and told her that either she show up at the next meeting or not bother showing up on the following schedule. (There had been some other performance issues, so she had already had a formal "disciplinary meeting" with HR and me.)

Strangely, she showed up.

I went right to it. I did the DESK steps, and I was blunt. I told her that her gossip was causing harm, upsetting her co-workers, creating a hostile work environment, and was against our values.

Her jaw dropped.

To my utter surprise, Judy didn't fight back. She didn't argue or deny. I was expecting this to look like one of those weigh-ins at an MMA match where there's smack-talking and mayhem. No mayhem.

Instead, she put her head down and started to tear up a bit. The cynical side of me was expecting this to be a distraction, and maybe she was going to start throwing out some blame, but the only blame she threw out was on herself.

"I have always been like this, and I hate it." Judy stared at her hands, looked up after a minute, and said, "I want people to like me. I was always that kid who had no friends, but when I shared scoop with others, I guess, in a weird way, people started talking to me."

I complimented her for her insight and told her I was impressed at her level of self-awareness. Most people lack that.

She thanked me.

I asked her if she ever thought about talking with someone and that we had an excellent Employee Assistance Program that worked with our psychology department.

She immediately said, "Yes, I need that." So, we set that up on the spot. We talked some more, and ended with a plan. She would seek counseling, refrain from gossiping, and find other ways to connect to her co-workers.

A few weeks went by, and Judy seemed a bit different. Several staff members shared that they'd received handwritten notes from her apologizing for the hurtful things she had said, and explaining that part of her "recovery" was to ask forgiveness. This took them all aback in a good way, and they all reached out to her in their own ways.

I got a card, too. It truly touched my heart.

One day, Judy brought in a large dish and a cooler. On her day off! She had homemade apple cobbler and chocolate and vanilla ice cream.

She told everyone gathered in the break room, "I've shared some 'scoop' with you all before, and I am sorry. I wanted to share something else I'm pretty good at scooping. It's just apple cobbler, but it's what I make best. Thank you all for giving me a second chance."

Judy shut down her "gossip column" and became one of the most liked people on the team. Second chances are good. So was Judy's apple cobbler. I took my "scoop" with chocolate ice cream.

Redemption can be sweet.

Three Critical Pathways of People Development—Yourself, Leaders, and Staff

The rest of this chapter will talk about people's development. We've broken this into three critical paths:

- Section 1: Developing Yourself

- Section 2: Developing Leaders

- Section 3: Developing Staff

Section 1: Developing Yourself

> "If you are not willing to learn, no one can help you. If you are determined to learn, no one can stop you."
>
> *Zig Ziglar, American Author and Speaker*

The best practice for any leader is to ask oneself, "What am I doing to develop myself?" If you've never said, "it's all about me!" now would be the time.

Own Your Individual Development

Are you being proactive in your own development? Are you aware of your strengths and opportunities to grow? Inscribed in the forecourt of the Temple of Apollo at Delphi is the maxim: "Know thyself." Leaders should know and appreciate their strengths and weaknesses, recognize their biases, and understand their impact on others they lead. Leaders should also understand there are high expectations for what they say and do.

It's about self-awareness. Great leaders aim to know themselves fully and understand their leadership strengths and weaknesses. That inscription on the ancient Greek temple has often been understood to mean, at a deeper level, "know thy measure."

 Connecting to Personal Strength.

As a pediatric ICU nurse, I know one of my "strengths" was connecting with kids who had experienced abuse and trauma. You see, I also had some challenging and significant abuse and trauma in my childhood.

As tough as those cases were, heartbreaking even, I never felt more engaged and fulfilled than when I could help those amazing kids. Those were my moments of truly feeling that Flywheel spin. It was where I was supposed to be and enabled me to take the pain I had endured and turn it into helping lessen another child's pain. I never felt like I was "fulfilling my life's JOB" in those moments but rather my "life's WORK."

Tapping into that strength brought me eye to eye with the truest meaning of purpose. I felt like I was part of something much bigger than myself.

It connected me to my calling.

You can use several assessment tools to gain insight into your unique profile:

- **The Hogan Assessment** describes how individuals and teams manage stress, approach work tasks, interests that drive careers, and behaviors that may emerge that can derail careers.

- **Management by Strengths (MBS) and True Colors** are assessment tools designed to understand your communication or temperament better. Armed with this knowledge, leaders and employees can work more effectively with others. The overall goal of MBS is to help build strong working relationships by learning to communicate using more temperament sensitivity.

- **The Emotional Quotient inventory 2.0** is a measurement tool designed to assess a person's emotional intelligence. Emotional intelligence is the ability to understand and manage one's own emotions, as well as recognize and empathize with the emotions of others.

Whatever assessment tool you use, the above or another, know your strengths. We all lead in our unique way.

Best Practice—Share Strengths to Build Stronger Teams

Don't be afraid to share your strengths and the strengths of others on the team.

You, as the leader, go first. Let your team know your uniqueness and your strengths. Be transparent in your areas of growth and abilities. Also, consider having your entire team assess their strengths and share them with others on the team.

One leader plotted everyone's strengths on a grid to show the diversity and breadth of the team's ability to represent all learning and leading styles. It creates a common language, and you and your team will benefit from knowing each other better and understanding how to work together to complement your strengths.

It's not much different than when you are organizing a potluck at work. If you know Tony makes the best mac and cheese and Juan makes the best Bundt cake, by all means, make that happen. If Jessie tries to stage a coup on Tony and signs up for the mac and cheese and it is known far and wide that mac and cheese is NOT her strength... deal with that! No one likes a disappointing potluck. We take our food seriously in healthcare!

Prepare Yourself for the Changing External Environment

How ready are you as a leader to adapt to the changing external environment? Are you taking the initiative to prepare yourself for what lies ahead?

Remember, what is going on with you "internally" will most certainly affect what goes on in your external world. To think otherwise is a delusion.

Healthcare is no stranger to change. We've watched the change in payment systems, the transition from inpatient to outpatient procedures, the rise of managed care, various process improvement and re-engineering initiatives, nurse shortages, and vertical integration, to name a few. And since 2020, the pandemic has changed and impacted healthcare organizations in deep, broad, and radical ways.

Excellent leaders understand that the external environment will not slow down, and change is not temporary.

Question to Ask Yourself	Possible Actions
Are you doing your part to anticipate and proactively deal with external environment changes?	Invest in reading and keep up to date on industry trends and research. Seek ways to learn and keep yourself prepared and ready.
Are you able to move very quickly to address issues after the fact?	Find someone good at moving quickly and adjusting to changes. Reach out to them for a mentoring session.
How well do you cascade information about the external environment from the senior team through the entire organization?	Use the information cascade to help others learn and understand the "why" behind decisions. As you communicate, be sure to be transparent about challenges and opportunities. Encourage them to be a part of the solution. Also, be careful not to "manage down" senior leaders or create a "we/they" culture.
Do you know the goals that need to be achieved?	Take the initiative to know how your role/department can help to achieve the larger organizational goals. If you don't know, seek to understand. For example, say the organizational goal is to "increase employee engagement by 10%." In that case, you might commit to round on all your employees every month or develop a focus group to increase understanding.

Strive to be a leader who can adapt to best practices and get great results. Be hungry for best practices. Research, read, and ask peers about their excellent results. What you are a student of, you eventually become a master of. When people do this, they become "heroes" inside an organization.

Mentoring

> "A good leader can say, 'Look what I've accomplished.' A great leader can say, 'Look whom I've helped become accomplished!' Be great."
>
> *Rich Bluni, RN, Huron Senior Director, Author, and Speaker*

Individual development doesn't mean you have to go it alone; sometimes, you need someone else to guide you. Mentors can play a vital role in our ability to develop ourselves. A mentor is someone you feel "safe" with. When you're on a journey up a mountain with a guide, your life is often in their hands. The success of your climb isn't only in your ability to manage and use the tools of the climb but also in the trust between you and the guide.

Your mentors are like guides. They know the mountain, the surrounding terrain, where the mountain lions are, and when it's best to camp and get warmed over a friendly fire. They can differentiate between a peak experience and going off a cliff.

There are a variety of names used for mentorship. But the process, no matter the title, is meant to develop another person.

> Mentoring is a professional relationship in which an experienced person (the mentor) assists another (the mentee) in developing specific skills and knowledge to enhance the less-experienced person's professional and personal growth.

Note that mentoring is more than an orientation program. Orientation is more about skill-setting and organizational training. It is super important; a good preceptor is a gift to a newer employee or leader. However, mentoring is more about connecting on a deeper level and can involve a more tenured person who is forming relationships with the intention to:

- Bridge the gap between the educational process of learning and the real-world experience.

- Enhance opportunities for each team member to achieve professional and personal development results.

- Develop and foster healthier working relationships.

- Create a "safe place" where individuals can ask questions without fear of judgment.

- Plan leadership succession.

- Address concerns, negative experiences, and/or anxieties before they become actual obstacles.

- Achieve better organizational outcomes in various ways, one of which is by creating leaders who have learned firsthand the value of creating leaders.

- Retain employees because they feel supported, heard, and valued by someone they respect and who has invested in them. That puts a lot into the "emotional bank account" for many, creating a level of loyalty you don't see in more "mercenary" settings.

Other ways to amplify individual development:

1. Research and seek information on leadership podcasts, books, virtual learning, and seminars focusing on an area of leadership development you could benefit from. Consume these voraciously. Listening to books and podcasts during "non-productive time," like sitting in traffic or waiting for an appointment, can give you that much-needed bump toward personal growth.

2. Discuss formal educational opportunities with your organizational development or education department that may enable you to continue your education and advance to a higher degree. Many organizations have tuition reimbursement and similar benefits.

3. Research professional certifications and other similar opportunities that not only have built-in opportunities for career advancement and educational training but often also provide you with the chance to network with others within your field, get exposure to diverse ideas and concepts, and meet new mentors and colleagues who could inspire you.

4. Look around you. There is someone in your immediate vicinity who is an insatiable learner and is always professionally expanding. Reach out to them. Learn from them and do what they do. Don't reinvent the wheel. Someone around you is already achieving what you hope to.

A leader who is learning is a leader who is growing. As John F. Kennedy once said, "Leadership and learning are indispensable to each other."

These are just a few ways to begin the self-development journey. The list is long. What inspires you to learn? Just know it all starts here!

Section 2: Developing Leaders

> "The single biggest way to impact an organization is to focus on leadership development. There is almost no limit to the potential of an organization that recruits good people, raises them up as leaders, and continually develops them."
>
> *John Maxwell*

Creating and continuously developing a thriving organization starts with practical and inspiring leadership. In the article "The Future of Leadership Development," Harvard Business Review said, "The need for leadership development has never been more urgent. Companies of all sorts realize that to survive in today's volatile, uncertain, complex, and ambiguous environment, they need leadership skills and organizational capabilities different from those that helped them succeed in the past."

The evidence is clear that leadership matters. Now let's challenge ourselves with this question:

How many people in leadership roles in your organization have received professional leadership development for that role?

Be honest. You might not be exactly sure about that answer. You wouldn't be surprised to learn that many aren't. We've found that this is one of the first areas we begin to focus on for many of the organizations Huron coaches because it is so foundational.

Many leaders have risen through the ranks and picked up skills based on their career experiences—"on-the-job training," if you will. Although professional training in an area of expertise, e.g., technology, medicine, nursing, or healthcare administration is common, formal leadership training in the essential aspects of their role is rarer.

This is one of those opportunities where you can truly build up the robustness and fortitude of your leadership team if you take it seriously and go all in. You would be hard-pressed to find an organization that laments: "We should've never developed all these leaders! They're just too productive and motivated now! We miss the old days when everyone just whined and wrung their hands and hoped for the best instead of doing all this proactive stuff!"

It is worth the effort. As T.S. Eliot once pointed out, "Only those who risk going too far can find out how far one can go."

Transitioning to Leadership—Buddy to Boss

 The Buddy to Boss Transition— Are you ready for this?

Mark works in nutritional services at the hospital. He just celebrated his fifth anniversary and is well-liked by his co-workers, and the patients and families also mention such positive things about his work.

He is known to exceed goals and embraces the many changes that the department has gone through. He even recently led a process improvement team where the department improved the consistency of food temperature when served. He is also a preceptor and coach for new employees.

After five years of this level of performance, the company asks Mark to apply and interview for the shift leader position. He does so and is selected from the pool of applicants to fill the role.

Mark is announced as the new shift manager at the staff meeting with his former peers. He says a few words and offers some comments and ideas. He expresses excitement about the new role and discusses the next steps.

After the meeting, several colleagues gather around Mark to congratulate him. In addition to saying they are glad he has been promoted, they express sentiments such as: "You'll have our backs!" "You can make some of the 'dumb stuff' go away." And "It'll be good to have an 'in' at the top!"

As they walk away, Mark wonders how he's going to be able to be their leader and still be their friend.

Mark's story may well represent something you have observed, or perhaps it has happened to you.

This type of professional transition requires changing roles and responsibilities and personal relationships with your staff. It is essential to establish guidelines and expectations for success. The transition from "buddy" to "boss" requires some thought.

Buddy to Boss—Tips for Success

Tip #1: Lead with your followers in mind

A leader is only a leader if they have people who will follow them because they feel secure that the leader is competent, trustworthy, and has their best interests at heart.

Gallup studied which leadership skills are the most important to a follower. What do you think they found? Maybe "good technical skills," "problem solver," motivational," or "highly committed?" While these traits are undoubtedly crucial for leaders, what they found that followers crave the most was trust, compassion, stability, and hope. Trust, compassion, stability, and hope don't come from a title. They are earned.

Tip #2: Be friendly, not a friend

This next tip is hard for many who transition into a leadership role. If you are accustomed to spending a lot of time outside work with your buddies, consider how to separate yourself to establish boundaries. The new role is expected to come with behaviors bound to shift your relationships.

For example, in your new role you will have to hold people accountable for their performance. Whereas before, when a peer came in late, you perhaps just shook your head and minded your business. Now, it is your business. You might even need to decline social engagements outside of work to prevent perceptions of favoritism. Where you might have vented with co-workers in the past, you will not be able to discuss certain topics and will now need to redirect unproductive venting quickly. Also, be mindful of your social media presence. As a leader, you represent the organization.

Buddies who shift to boss do well when establishing boundaries early in the transition. You might need to call out the change in the relationship by addressing this early and directly: "My role has changed now, which means our friendship might look a bit different as I figure out my new role. I want to be the best I can be for you and the department, so I ask for your support and understanding."

All of this will undoubtedly feel uncomfortable at first. That is expected. As we've said earlier, growth often comes with discomfort. A muscle doesn't grow if it's not made a little sore through bearing weight. A mind doesn't learn if it isn't pushed by a demanding professor to memorize and study more. Even in the most challenging times, while certainly uncomfortable, we can often find our most fantastic teachers. Experiencing discomfort is called "life," and learning from discomfort is called "wisdom."

Tip #3: Treat employees like a team, not a family
Think for a moment. How might we treat family differently than a work team member? People often say, "Work is just like family!" And while family is beautiful, have you considered that perhaps professionally, that isn't always a good mindset? Teams and families are pretty different social constructs.

- Leaders challenge comfort zones to inspire growth; family provides comfort and space.

- Leaders help employees improve or move on; family can be "forever"— no matter how poor the behavior is.

- Leaders provide honest, respectful feedback to improve the team; families might protect feelings and accept unproductive or harmful behaviors. We've all seen that parent interviewed on the news about their "darling" child who's been arrested for the 50th time for the same crime that was witnessed by 25 people, including 10 nuns and 15 Eagle Scouts, and was caught on video by three different news crews. And what does that parent say? "Not my kid! They're a pillar of society! They'd never do such a thing!" As the saying goes, "Denial isn't just a river in Egypt!" But families can certainly sail down that waterway when they want to.

- Leaders develop team morale around the bigger picture (mission/vision); family focuses on and often protects itself.

- Leaders build diverse teams with different ideas; family usually includes similar people with similar experiences.

- Leaders take time to recognize and appreciate commitment; families can take each other for granted.

Tip #4: Expect to be tested
A leader must be a figure of authority on occasion, which makes it tough on close friendships. People won't like it. This can be especially difficult for those of us who put a high value on relationships in the workplace and maybe lean toward being more sensitive or empathic.

Expect to be tested. If you aren't being tested as a leader at some point, you're probably doing something wrong. Also, remember that most things in life will be tested—your patience, your temper, your abilities, your strength, your character, your relationships, and your leadership.

Don't fear the testing. As best you can, embrace it with your all. How you come out of those tests in life and work defines who you are.

Use these opportunities to respond in a way that builds trust and confidence in those looking to you for leadership. General and former secretary of state Colin Powell once reminded us, "Trying to get everyone to like you is a sign of mediocrity. You'll avoid the tough decisions, and you'll avoid confronting the people who need to be confronted."

Tip #5: Stay humble

> "Humility is not thinking less of yourself. It's thinking of yourself less."
>
> *C.S. Lewis*

While it is vital to establish your credibility among former peers quickly, beware of what might look like a "power trip." Lead by positive example to demonstrate your character. Be authentic. We've all been around or heard about that senior leader who only picks up trash in the parking lot when they know someone is looking so their "saint-like" behavior can be marveled at. But when they're all alone with no audience to heap praise, entire trash bags could blow past them like tumbleweeds, and they wouldn't so much as lift a pinkie.

These people are not picking up gum wrappers to make the campus look better. They are doing it to make themselves look better. And in healthcare, we can smell "fake" a mile away (as a matter of fact, we are familiar with quite a few odors in healthcare!). But the authentic leader or team member picks up the trash they see across the campus when there's no one around to tell them how special they are. They do it because it is who they are and what the culture they've helped build and support has embedded into their being.

Demonstrate that culture of caring and authenticity through empathy and compassion; they go a long way. Work to see things through the eyes of someone in each role. Consider job shadowing—you may see even familiar things in a new light as you look through your new leadership lens with a humble spirit, a calm mind, and an open heart.

Tip #6: Find a mentor or trusted advisor
Leadership can sometimes feel very lonely, and leading former peers is challenging. You may feel uncertain and need some advice. Mentors will be there to listen and answer your questions. Choose someone with

more experience to provide advice and guidance. Ask someone to listen and challenge you to think differently. You may find having a standing call or coffee date helpful. Make sure your mentor's phone number is saved to "favorites." It's a life hack a few of us can tell makes a difference!

Leadership Development

The studies are clear. Most employees leave their jobs because of their relationship with their supervisor. Enter stage left, Stacy...

 The grass might be greener.

Stacy is incredible at her role. She knows her department inside and out, has an excellent attitude, and is respected and loved by her co-workers. She is somewhat of a legend in her area.

When Stacy put in her transfer to work in another area, people outside the department were shocked. But inside the department, while contemplating losing Stacy was distressing and upsetting, no one was in shock. Her co-workers were all cheering and applauding her decision.

So, what's the backstory? The leader of Stacy's area is Diane. Diane has been in her leadership position for some time and knows her job well. However, she isn't the type of leader to take the time to build relationships with her team. Diane would rather keep things professional and her emotions close. She may round with her employees, but downplays it and typically says something like, "You know, administration wants me to ask these questions. I know you have real work to do, so give me a quick answer, and I will check this off my list."

Stacy has always been a rock star, but other than feedback from her peers and people outside the department, she rarely hears it from Diane. Even after receiving a thoughtful thank you note from a patient and her family, Diane just left it on Stacy's desk with no comment or congratulations. Stacy even asked Diane about it. Diane replied, "I saw it, but don't you think our paycheck and benefits are our rewards? That patient was an easy one anyway."

That very day, Stacy started taking steps to transfer to another department in her organization. Craig leads this department. She didn't know him personally but felt like she did from how people talked about him around the organization. They seemed to enjoy working for him.

Craig always sends out thank you notes and makes recognition fun by holding "recognition huddles" to highlight those who have gone over and above. Rumor has it that a surprise or treat will appear at your desk on your work anniversary to honor your day. Stacy also knows at least three people who moved up to be managers in other departments while working for Craig.

Wow. All that sounded pretty good right now to her. Stacy loved her co-workers and her current role, but she realized she needed more.

Stacy interviewed and accepted a job. She took a lateral position but was thrilled when she received the offer. Honestly, Stacy couldn't wait to work for Craig.

Fast-forward to her last day in her old area. Stacy said her goodbyes to her team. As she was leaving her shift, she knocked on Diane's door. Diane looked up from her desk as Stacy walked into her office. Stacy said, "I wanted to say goodbye and wish you the best." Looking back at her work, Diane said, "Good luck to you. Just remember, the grass isn't always greener on the other side."

Stacy just smiled as she walked away, clutching the note in her pocket that she had found on her desk a few minutes earlier. The note was a welcome card from Craig signed by all her new co-workers letting her know how excited they were to have her on their team.

As Stacy continued down the hallway to leave, she stood at the door of her new department. She paused momentarily before entering, smiling at the note in her hand and realizing the grass looked mighty green from this side.

Sometimes the best thing we can offer an employee is a great leader. Stacy didn't leave because she hated her job or her co-workers. It wasn't because of benefits or money, as this was a lateral move for her in the same organization. For Stacy, it was because of her leader.

Stacy wanted to grow professionally and saw how Craig had done that for others on his team. Stacy wasn't selfish. She just wanted more for herself.

As far as Diane goes, judging her in this scenario seems straightforward. But before we judge too quickly, ask what training and development she, as a leader, has been offered. Perhaps Diane doesn't fully understand why employee rounding is essential to retention. Maybe education in communicating better as a leader would be helpful, as well as understanding the retention goals of the organization to help keep people like Stacy from leaving to begin with.

It is tempting to ease up on leadership training when busy, short-staffed, or even when things are going well. However, the more Huron works with leaders across the country, the more we see a great need for ongoing and consistent leadership training.

Like anyone else, leaders learn in different ways and need practice to build new behaviors. To build competency across your leadership teams you also need a holistic plan that balances organizational needs with personal development goals. This includes not only matching your leaders' learning styles with multiple settings, but leveraging the most efficient and effective ways to build competency and skills. We have found, for example, that there is something powerful in bringing all leaders together to learn.

Leadership Development Institutes (LDI)

Leadership Development Institutes (LDIs) are for people like Diane at your organization. Over the years, LDIs have proven time after time to make a positive impact and bring consistency to your organization. These sessions cultivate and keep top-notch leaders and create a clear pathway to develop leaders to develop people.

> A Leadership Development Institute (LDI) is a regularly scheduled session where a leadership team comes together for intensive training on skills that need improvement to meet organizational goals.

We call them LDIs, but organizations often customize them to their culture. Some call them "Leadership Training" or "Quarterly Learning Sessions." The name is not what is essential. They must occur consistently, focusing on leadership skills across the entire team.

LDIs—Lessons Learned

At Huron, we have been an advocate of leadership sessions for years. However, as we continue our work, we have learned some essential lessons to help maximize this opportunity.

Consider frequency and timing.

Meaningful skill-building, inspiration, and leadership development cannot happen with a one-time training event. When motivational business speaker Zig Ziglar was told, "That motivational stuff is great, but it doesn't last!" He responded, "Neither does bathing, that's why you should do it regularly!"

Who could argue with that? The same can be said of any development. LDIs need to be a regular thing. Many organizations hold three to six dedicated sessions annually. The period between sessions allow leaders to practice and be coached as they integrate new skills into their daily practice.

Hold sessions off-site.

We also see great success with holding these sessions off-site. It allows leaders to escape the noise and the tasks of their area. It's too easy to get that text or call requiring you to duck out "just for a minute," and then before you know it, the whole day has gone by.

Being together for a day will enable you to strengthen relationships—the entire organization benefits. When introducing this idea, the first response is often, "Our leaders can't be away from the building for two days. The place will implode." And then we remind senior leaders that they are experts at it. They practice every week on Saturdays and Sundays with very infrequent implosions!

Consider virtual components.

Another adaptation we have seen work successfully is conducting LDIs virtually. Being together in person undoubtedly yields significant benefits in team building and creating strong personal relationships. However, virtual sessions with thoughtful attention to skill-building activity and discussion will create an immersive and interactive session. Incorporating connections to "why" through personal stories and videos and including individual and team recognition also create a positive learning environment across the screen.

We also find a hybrid approach can work successfully, where some team members attend in person while others participate virtually. You will know what works best for your organization, and a little trial and error is expected as you adapt and find the best solution.

See one, do one, and teach one.

Don't mistake management training for leadership development. Development sessions allow leaders to see what "right" looks like, practice and receive feedback, and ultimately, teach and communicate it to those employees they lead. LDIs are the perfect forum to make this happen for the learner.

Consider experiential components to increase interaction and learning. Role-plays, table interactions, and group discussions are excellent ways to make the training come to life.

Make the content meaningful.

The content has to be meaningful and purposeful. An LDI aims to develop leaders' skills to achieve organizational goals, build relationships, provide reward and recognition, and, yes, even have fun. The content aims to improve individual leadership performance and organizational consistency.

These LDIs are all about looking at the organization's goals and scorecard, identifying performance gaps, and teaching leaders the skills needed to close those gaps. It can be challenging for the leadership team to conceptualize how a generic leadership topic might apply to their day-to-day responsibilities. So, you must choose to learn objectives that are specific and aligned with a goal held by each leader.

Once an organization sets up a Leadership Development Institute, leaders who may have been initially skeptical see the enormous benefit of taking time to improve their leadership skills. Often we hear, "These LDIs aren't like those boring mandatory training meetings. I can use this learning."

To maximize your use of LDIs, our advice is four-fold:

1. Senior leaders determine the learning objectives.

They evaluate organizational performance, identify gaps, and prioritize areas of focus. The CEO must articulate the vision and expected outcomes for the LDI and review and approve the objectives, curriculum, and "Leaders Accountability Grid" (expected follow-up actions) with the senior leaders.

Senior leaders can also utilize competency assessments, where they ask other leaders to identify where they feel they need development/support, and the learning agenda can reflect those desired needs. The CEO should provide an update on results by Pillar at the beginning of each session. Our experience has shown that the senior team's commitment to this process and active, intentional presence during these learning events is essential and non-negotiable.

2. Briefly introduce concepts and theory.

Once you've established the framework, move quickly to the application. Use scenario-based learning to build in practice. It will accelerate the application of new skills and knowledge. Learning concepts is essential, but learning to apply those concepts in the real world is where performance improvement lives.

3. Make learning engagement and fun.

Pull some creative team members into the process and let them shine! We've seen some engaging ideas like building structures with blocks, skits, themes, costume contests, and trivia competitions. Some LDIs have even occurred at obstacle course parks—talk about a unique venue! If you want to add a zipline to the mix, go for it! The key is to prioritize fun, variety, and positive energy. When people are relaxed and happy, they're more receptive to learning. So, create an enjoyable and engaging environment to encourage your team to participate in the LDI experience fully.

4. Tailor the training to the needs/problems your organization currently faces.

Ensure sessions are immediately relevant and can be put into practice by your leaders, and topics can focus on specific time-sensitive performance gaps. If you're struggling to hit a revenue goal, leadership development should focus on the skills to close that gap. You may also consider the need for mastery of fundamental leadership skills like the ability to hold an effective annual review. When done well, these reviews improve performance and create loyalty.

When you think about leadership training in this way, you see that it's an opportunity to address the critical operational and leadership issues that drive success for your organization.

Best Practice—Don't forget the physicians.

No doubt, leadership skills are worth investing in. But this is true not only for leaders but for physician leaders as well.

This may require a financial commitment from the organization. In many organizations, productivity is a variable that impacts the compensation of employed physician leaders, so asking a physician leader to attend an LDI may negatively impact their compensation or revenue. To mitigate this challenge, consider conducting an LDI after regular hours of operation, such as evenings or weekends.

There is tremendous value in having physicians and administrative leaders attend the same session. One practice Huron worked with was struggling with patient access. The leadership sessions brought physicians and organizational leadership together to focus on building and developing their skills to drive better access.

We helped them ask and answer relevant questions like: Should we address the hours we're open? Should we address schedule availability? Have we standardized our scheduling templates to support more open access? Are there ways to better leverage the advanced practice providers to accommodate last-minute requests? Do we need to simplify our appointment times (i.e., instead of saying we see new patients only in specific time slots, could we find a way to accommodate new patients in any slot during the day)?

The outcome of this time together helped them solve many of these concerns and built meaningful connections with the broader organization. Several physicians received positive rewards and recognition, which they later shared was a pleasant surprise and deeply meaningful.

Planning a Leadership Development Institute

The goals under the Five Pillars guide the framework for establishing objectives and curriculum for each LDI session. Let me give you an example.

Say your organization has a significant focus under the People Pillar to reduce employee turnover. Identifying the specific leadership behaviors and actions needed is critical to achieving success. You may choose to focus on skills to:

- Round on staff

- Manage up

- Peer interview

- Hardwire thank you notes

- Conduct high, solid/middle, and low-performer conversations

- Use exit interviews to identify trends for improvement

- Roll out employee survey results and develop action plans

- Answer tough questions from staff

- Effectively manage productivity and staffing

- Rapid cycle improvement methods to gain efficiency

- Utilize financial reporting more effectively

- Manage productivity based on volume and patterns

- Utilize high-reliability tools to improve safety

There are many tactics to use to retain staff. But by narrowing the focus and providing training in some of the skills and behaviors listed above, leaders will advance their ability to achieve organizational goals.

Notice I said "some." The team and their coach must focus intently on one or two things to work on. If not, the LDI will feel like drinking water from a fire hose in a tornado! The pace is essential.

Too often, organizations want to do it all at once. That's like wanting to get stronger, so you go to the gym for the first time and rack up 700 lbs. on the squat rack because who has time for incremental stuff? Hopefully, you will have an excellent orthopedic surgeon on speed dial if you do that. Strength training doesn't work that way, and neither does leadership training.

Put a few "plates on the bar" with each LDI. Then, after you've got one skill hardwired, you move to the next. Each time, add a few more "plates on the bar," and before you know it, you and your team are carrying some real weight.

Teamwork Makes The Dream Work!

The leader of the LDI is typically the leader responsible for the overall coordination of the LDI. The duties of the LDI team leader can include facilitating agenda-setting with the CEO and senior leaders, leading team meetings, managing budgets, and working with individual LDI team leaders. This coordinating LDI team leader is a vital role, as they are the person who is also responsible for reporting results and giving updates to senior leadership. We often refer to this person as a "champion" of the LDI, and that word fits well.

We suggest creating a team to plan and execute the event effectively. The LDI team should be a mix of creative, energetic people who can execute. Multidisciplinary is best. People should want to be on this team. Indeed, as things move forward, new folks should cycle on and off the team to add variety and diversity into the LDI and give colleagues a chance to focus on being a participant as well.

And, maybe of most importance: reward and recognize this team before, during, and after the LDIs, because this can be hard work! When leaders see this, they'll also want to be on board, as it is an excellent way for leaders to show some skills and get accolades. We've seen LDI team members move up in organizations because, for some of them, it was the first time they could be in the spotlight and lean into showing their strengths. It's beautiful to see that.

Senior leaders demonstrate their commitment to the organization's goals by actively participating in all sessions, modeling the behaviors they want the organization to adopt, and holding their leaders accountable for attendance. They will also model behaviors taught in the sessions. This means phones on silent, laptops closed unless used for taking notes, and sitting in the front. While these behaviors may seem "obvious," they are basics that, if the senior team fails to model, can weaken the impact of the LDI.

The LDI team generally consists of middle managers and, as mentioned before, these events should be viewed as an opportunity for learning and professional development for them as well. The table that follows shows the functions and teams we have seen as necessary and helpful to delivering a successful LDI.

FUNCTION	RESPONSIBILITIES
Curriculum	Team Objective: Set curriculum to fulfill the learning objectives set forth by senior leadership. This team prepares training materials or secures speakers for specific topics. Don't be afraid to engage with outside experts or speakers if they're subject matter experts that can bring some "sizzle" to the LDI. The key is to make it relevant to today's challenges. So instead of reviewing an imaginary organizational case study, use your organization's current data in any case study you present.
Communication	Team Objective: Communicate and inform leaders, employees, and physicians about the LDI • For participants, send invitations, share an agenda and learning objectives in advance, and provide a Leaders Accountability Grid that calls out the expected follow-up actions of each attendee. • For the rest of the organization, be sure to communicate the purpose of the LDI, so others understand what leaders will be learning and why. This provides transparency but also a level of accountability.
Social	Team Objective: Set the theme for each session, develop skits or role-playing activities, provide decorations, and create other fun activities for leaders. A celebratory atmosphere fosters relationship-building and a more cohesive team. For instance, one healthcare facility carried the theme of Fantasy Football—"Creating the Dream Team"—through the entire day. Leaders wore their favorite team's jersey, tailgate food was served for lunch, and friendly team rivalries sparked "smack talk" amongst senior leaders as the rest of the organization cheered for their favorites. These activities break down barriers and instill fun and camaraderie in the learning event.

FUNCTION	RESPONSIBILITIES
Logistics	Team Objective: Plan and efficiently execute all logistical aspects of the event. Activities include securing facilities for the training sessions, coordinating food and beverages, securing audio/visual equipment and materials needed for scenario-based exercises and other learning activities, and room setup.
Accountability	Team Objective: Identify critical learnings at training sessions and create a list of specific assignments or behaviors that will be expected in follow-up to the learning event. This follow-up document, called the "Leadership Accountability Grid," includes what each participant should complete in the 90 days following a learning event. Here's an excerpt: *"All leaders will conduct rounding on direct reports and share their Stoplight Report with their direct supervisor at each supervisory meeting."* As your organization matures in conducting LDIs, the grid may no longer be required. Leaders instead learn to incorporate expectations into their work plans.

A Leadership Development Institute provides the essential tools and training to help lift leaders to the next level. It also creates consistency, confidence, and builds relationships between team members. These events allow the entire team to understand the organization's vision. To quote the great George Washington Carver, "Where there is no vision, there is no hope."

LDIs can be the catalyst to achieve both of those goals.

Section 3: Developing Staff

> "Someone is sitting in the shade today because someone else planted a tree long ago."
>
> *Les Brown*

We play many different roles as leaders. We have discussed in Section 1 the importance of developing ourselves to be ready for our leadership responsibilities. In Section 2, we focused on our role in developing leaders. In section 3, we will focus on our role in developing people and the staff we work with daily. The quote above teaches us that what we plant today will determine the future. As leaders, one of our goals is to develop our teams to ensure our organization's future is made in the shade!

The more skilled we are at coaching conversations and looking at them as "doable" instead of "difficult," the better prepared we are in real-time to do precisely what Principle 4 is about—Developing Leaders to Develop People. This section will focus on our role as a cheerleader and a coach. We will examine effective coaching methods, including coaching in the moment, impact messages, and specific skill-building coaching sessions.

Cheerleading and Coaching—
Two Leadership Roles

Leaders will undoubtedly serve as both cheerleaders and coaches. They go hand in hand, and the effective leader adapts the mix and timing of these behaviors to optimize team performance. Let's start by defining each.

Cheerleading focuses on making employees FEEL better.	**Coaching** focuses on helping employees PERFORM better.
• Improves morale • Lifts spirits • Provides encouragement • Motivates • Inspires • Engages our hearts	• Deepens knowledge • Increases skill • Advances critical thinking • Improves performance • Prepare for promotion/succession planning

Let's say you are at the gym with a trainer. Let's look at what a cheerleader and coach might sound like.

The cheerleader says, "Let's go! You're making progress! You can do this!" That gets our adrenaline pumping and motivates us to push and do better.

The coach says, "Back straight. Chest out. Keep your shoulders back. Focus." That sets us up to do what we need to do in the most effective way possible.

See the difference? Each is necessary to move behaviors. However, cheerleading and coaching together are a powerful duo. Let's explore each one further.

Cheerleading—Inspiring and Reinforcing Behaviors

Everyone needs encouragement, and leaders who enjoy cheerleading shine in this role. Your ability to encourage and praise good work lets employees see you care and increases their overall engagement because they feel valued. It is key to developing your people. (We will talk a lot about this in Principle 9).

It doesn't always have to be a grandiose thing, either. Never underestimate the power of a small gesture to show appreciation.

66 Superhero Stickers.

Working as a senior leader in risk management and patient safety was a bit of a pivot for me. As someone who lives for relationships and interaction, I had to adjust to how people interacted and worked with me in this role.

Think about it. Does anyone want to see the risk manager suddenly appear in their unit? (No offense to my fellow risk managers!) When you see the risk manager get off the elevator on your floor, do you get excited and think, "Oh, awesome! I'm about to hear some GREAT news!"?

Even my good friends I worked with in the past reacted similarly. I visited one of them one day just to say "hi," and when she saw me, she said, "Oh no. Not you. Not today!"

She and I laughed about this, but it made me think. I realized to do my job more effectively, perhaps I needed to balance my "let's discuss this sentinel event" visits with something a bit more "celebratory." A challenge for sure.

As I reviewed some quality data later that day, I noticed that one of my nursing floors had a significant decrease in falls that quarter. Wow. This was good. Although I usually shared this information more formally, I decided this was a great time to try something new.

I looked at my backpack, and something shiny caught my eye. It was one of the superhero stickers that I had placed in my backpack for my son to reward him when he did something awesome. (Yes, for potty training, but nobody needed to know that.)

I had an idea. It may have been a little silly, but it could help bring some celebration into this work. I was already looked at like the Grim Reaper when I walked up, so there was nowhere to go but up. Also, I know many of us are kids at heart, so why not try my crazy idea? What did I have to lose except for a few stickers?

This is what I did. I went up to the floor that had the decrease in falls, and looked for the first person I could see. It was Gerri, the nursing director, and I could see the color drain from her face as soon as we locked eyes and she waited for the negative news.

Instead, without missing a beat, I stuck a Wonder Woman sticker on her lab coat and congratulated her on successfully implementing our new fall prevention protocol. I shared the great news and asked if I could round with her on the staff. We did, and ensured everyone working that day got a sticker. Some even got a little competitive and wanted to choose their sticker. I stayed later that day and did the same for the night shift.

Guess what? Not one single person was "professionally offended" by these silly stickers. Instead, it made everyone smile. Some even moved them to their badge holders to make them more visible.

A few days later, Kim, a nursing leader from another floor, appeared at my office doorway. She smiled and said, "OK, Bluni. Where are the stickers?"

"What?" I was perplexed.

"Gerri and her staff are showing off their superhero stickers like they're the best around with falls. I just looked at today's data, and we also had a significant drop in falls. So, tell me what's good, and where are our stickers?"

She wasn't kidding. She was serious. She wanted those stickers!

But my son had been very "proficient" with potty training the last few days, so I was out. I asked, "Can you give me a few minutes?"

I kid you not. She set a timer on her watch. "Yeah. I'll see you in 45 minutes."

With the time ticking, I grabbed my stuff and went to the store to buy out all the superhero stickers. I also bought some bite-size candy. When I returned to the hospital, I went up to Kim's floor. Stickers and candy for everyone! I was like Oprah from back in the day: "You get a sticker! And YOU get a sticker!"

What surprised me was that these adult people with master's and medical degrees were excited about stickers. It got to the point where I had several other leaders seek me out to ask what they needed to do to get stickers. After a while, I just carried stickers around with me. If I saw a transporter, a security guard, an OR tech, an RT, or a phlebotomist—anyone—do anything that I thought was worthy of praise or celebration, they got a sticker. People got full-on competitive about who had the most stickers.

STICKERS!

Now, am I suggesting you go out and buy out the sticker store? No. But I suggest you find a way to recognize and have some fun. These silly stickers taught me not to underestimate even the smallest gestures. People are hungry for light-heartedness, celebration, and an uplift.

My team loved this. It made them smile. It created some fun competitiveness and allowed me to bring some good news. So, when I had to bring another type of news, it balanced out a bit. You know what else? My bucket filled a little too.

A lot of people in healthcare do amazing things that go unrecognized. Take a minute and recognize some superheroes today.

It's essential to check in with people. Listen to what they are saying, watch their body language. Be aware. As a wise leader we once coached said, *"I know the floor tiles of this organization well because I'm always keeping my ear to the ground!"*

Stay vigilant about the morale of your team. Exhaustion, stress, heavy workloads, and self-doubt can overwhelm even your highest-performing employees. If employees are stretching their comfort zones and could benefit from your pep talk, cheer away! It's not minimizing what they're dealing with, but common sense also has to be applied.

We're not suggesting that "cheer" will fix significant issues. If you encounter serious issues, those require serious actions, so it's important to mention that here. But for the day-to-day, the moments where you see people are just maybe at ¾ of a tank, being a source of hope and positive energy tells your team you believe in them.

It is also contagious. Employees who see and hear your encouraging attitude will mimic your behaviors and become more resilient. My sticker story was evidence of that. Once it caught on, it spread like wildfire, and it also helped me bring more attention and awareness to a significant safety issue, in addition to fewer people running to hide when I walked up! Win! Win!

Ensure your cheerleading comes from an authentic place, because employees can tell when you are faking it. It doesn't always have to be gifts, candy, or stickers. Sometimes simple words can do the trick. Be specific about the results you are cheering about, or it could feel patron-izing and do more harm than good. It might sound like this:

- *"This week has been exhausting, but you stepped up to get through it. I've seen you share responsibilities and comfort each other. I'm so proud of this team!"*

- *"I know you can do this. I've seen you master new processes in the past. Take a deep breath and try again. You've got this!"*

- *"We have the best team ever! You all have exceeded our goal, so everyone, give the person next to you a high five because you made this happen together. Thanks for all your hard work!"*

Cheerleaders encourage employees and celebrate successes but do not provide important information about how to perform better. When improvements are needed, it is time for the coach in you to shine.

Coaching—Taking Behaviors to the Next Level

What if leaders were only cheerleaders? While cheering is fun, creates enthusiasm, and engages people, how much would cheering affect outcomes without coaching?

Think about it this way. Let's say your favorite college football team is playing. You are in the crowd, can hear the cheering, and feel the excitement. The game is tight and ends victoriously on a last-second change in strategy by the coach and the team, resulting in a Hail Mary in the end-zone. The cheering is explosive, and the excitement in the stadium is palpable.

However, even with all of the excitement and cheering, when the reporter says to the key player, "Wow, you killed it tonight. What made the difference?" will the response be all about the encouragement from the fans and the cheerleaders, or might it be about a pivot—a strategic coaching play that won that game? Both?

Leaders are coaches, and they facilitate improvement when they provide specific, timely feedback. That input is accepted positively when the leader develops a relationship with the employee. Because the leader knows the employee, they can customize the feedback for that person to support the best opportunity for improvement.

So, when is the right time to coach? When improvement or change is needed. This is episodic coaching—initiated whenever a need arises. It is a way for you to align employee behaviors and skill sets with the level of performance required to achieve results. But that doesn't always mean telling them what to do. While we've certainly seen increased use of robots in healthcare, we are not trying to create them from our team members.

The most effective coaching guides employees in the right direction while promoting independent thinking and collaboration. Sometimes this is "in the moment," and sometimes, this is more methodical and observed. Coaching is necessary, and being prepared to do so is crucial.

Beware of being a "Data Disher," however. This is the leader who shares the data without coaching or explanation. It's not enough to share the data. We need, as coaches, to connect the dots from the data to what we need to do differently to improve the data.

Coaching and Difficult Conversations

If you needed to have a coaching conversation with someone today, what words might describe how you felt before that conversation? At Huron we ask this to a lot of leaders, and we often hear words like "hard," "tricky," "awkward," or "uncomfortable," to name a few. Many label it as a "difficult conversation."

A simple answer to why people dread difficult conversations is built into the term itself: they're difficult! If they were called "fun conversations" or "delightful conversations," we could skip over this. So, what are we so worried about?

We worry about saying the wrong thing, being misunderstood, making things worse, or upsetting someone. There might be a history with that person—perhaps a friend, church member, neighbor, or colleague. There might even be a skill gap, and we need more professional skills to have the conversation well.

One study shows that a lack of skill in coaching and development "relates strongly with medical errors, patient safety, quality of care, staff commitment, discretionary effort, employee satisfaction, and turnover." (Maxfield, Grenny, McMillan, Patterson & Switzler, 2005). It also showed that the areas where crucial conversations seem the most difficult include broken rules, micromanagement, mistakes, lack of support, incompetence, poor teamwork, and disrespect.

These conversations may not be fun, but they are essential to your growth and the coaching and development of others. From the "difficult" or "tough" comes the "better." And that makes it worth it to both the individual and the patient or customer they will serve down the line.

There are three models for coaching conversations that should be in every leader's toolkit:

- Coaching Conversation #1: The Stub Your Toe—Coaching in the Moment Conversation

- Coaching Conversation #2: Support – Coach – Support

- Coaching Conversation #3: The Impact Message

There is also the "DESK Model" (Describe, Explain, Show, and Know) conversation for low performance, which we discussed earlier. Let's review each of these coaching conversations in turn.

COACHING CONVERSATION #1
The Stub Your Toe Conversation—Coaching in the Moment

The first and least formal conversation is the "Stub Your Toe Conversation." We discussed this earlier regarding peer-to-peer conversations. This is a slight variation, with some overlap. Anyone can stub a toe from time to time, and in real life, stubbing your toe is often followed by screaming, hopping about, and maybe some choice language that's not recommended here. Even our best performers or we ourselves will sometimes "stub a toe," quite unintentionally. And, as you've most likely guessed, that's where this conversational model gets its name.

> The "Stub Your Toe" or Coaching in the Moment Conversation is used when you see or hear behavior inconsistent with organizational policies, standards of behavior, or values.
>
> This is an informal conversation during which you bring your observation/experience of troublesome behavior to the awareness of your colleague.

Your solid and high-performing employees come to work daily committed to bringing their best. Still, it's not uncommon for anyone to behave out of character when stress or workload overwhelms them. They may use language or demonstrate actions that don't uphold organizational policies, standards of behavior, or values. It does not happen often, and we call these first- or second-time errors in professional judgment "stub your toe" moments.

Although infrequent, the tough conversation still needs to happen, and these dedicated and caring employees would agree. The "Stub Your Toe Conversation" is a suitable tough conversation model for this situation.

In short, it gives you a structure to remind others that their behavior was perceived as inappropriate or unprofessional so that they will (hopefully!) not repeat it

Prepare for the Conversation.
While "Stub Your Toe" conversations are best done soon after you observe an undesirable behavior, you will still want to take a few moments to prepare. It is probably best not to speak before you think about what you have just experienced and what you want to communicate. Ask yourself: What is the desired outcome? What's the intent of the conversation? Do I need to wait and let any emotions pass? When you are ready for the conversation, find a place where you and the other person can talk privately.

Have the Conversation.
There are three critical parts of the conversation.

Figure 4.9: The Stub-Your-Toe/Coaching in the Moment Conversation

Pretty straightforward, right? Let's dig a little deeper.

• **Let them know they are valued.**

 Begin the conversation by expressing appreciation for the other person. Appreciation keeps the interaction positive from the start. "I value you," "I appreciate you," and "You are important to me" help to communicate this and put them at ease.

• **Review what you saw/heard that was inconsistent with standards, values, or policies.**

 The key to these conversations is seeing and hearing the behavior that needs coaching—with your own eyes and ears. If a third party initiates, you may enter the dreaded "triangle conversation" where Person C tries to resolve something that should have been resolved by Person A and B. These can quickly diminish into finger-pointing interactions, which is not the intent of coaching. "I saw," "I heard," and "I observed" are appropriate words to use and will help ease the tension or need to defend themselves against others.

 Be sure to pause when you make this statement. It allows the other person to process. They might even express frustration, deny, rationalize, or become emotional. That's okay. Because even if you disagree with the individual, listen respectfully and allow them to reflect on what you've said.

People sometimes express appreciation for bringing the behavior to their attention, even if hearing it might be uncomfortable. Honor that and ensure that you show respect for their openness.

However, if they deny or justify the behavior, be patient and kindly suggest that while they may be correct, they should take some time to reflect on why their actions or words seemed unprofessional to you or others.

If needed, reassure them you are not telling the person they are "bad," you are merely relating an observation. Human nature is such that we may believe personal criticism means we are "bad." Thinking back to childhood, recall how many times a kid just being a kid messed up and the adults around you said things like, "What a 'bad' child!" That stuff is hard to shake from even our grown-up minds. Simply being aware of that will make you instantly more compassionate.

- **Express your appreciation for them.**

  Finally, end the conversation by once again sharing the value of the person's contribution to the organization. Words like "I care about you," "You have my trust," and "I value you," are all statements used to reassure and help keep the conversation positive and productive.

And it is not just for leaders.

As a reminder, any employee at any level can have a "Stub Your Toe Conversation" with another team member. The conversation framework also doesn't change if the employee doesn't report to you; technically, you don't need to know them! The beauty of this conversation model is that it isn't limiting—there is no hierarchy. After all, pretty much all of us have toes!

We encourage you to share the Stub Your Toe/Coaching in the Moment steps with your entire staff. As a leader, you must make it acceptable for anyone to have "Stub Your Toe Conversations" with others.

Think of "Stub Your Toe Conversations" as preventative medicine. Once this communication framework is used daily, your team will recognize and address words and actions that do not align with organizational policies, values, and standards. And they will be able to "diagnose" and "treat" the most problematic behaviors before they infect the quality of care, employee engagement, and patient satisfaction.

COACHING CONVERSATION #2
Support-Coach-Support—Observing and Moving Skill and Behaviors

We previously discussed Support-Coach-Support as a method for communicating with your middle/solid performers, but it also does double duty here. When trying to build our employees' skills, training is not enough. As leaders, we must continue to assess if our employees continue to improve. When they need guidance and support to move their skill and behavior, the Support-Coach-Support (SCS) conversation style is what we recommend for coaching.

> Support-Coach-Support is a coaching conversation designed to (1) support the individual by describing their good qualities, (2) coach on one development opportunity, and (3) support by reflecting your confidence and providing needed help and assistance as needed to make the improvement discussed.

The goal of this discussion is twofold. You want first to support an employee's professional growth while allowing them to feel valued and appreciated. The best test to evaluate the success of your SCS conversation is to ask yourself these questions:

- "When they left my office, did this employee feel better than when they walked in?" In other words, did this conversation create a feeling of being valued, invested in, and appreciated?

- "Do they know the expectations and have everything they need to move forward and meet them?"

If yes, you have hit the bull's eye!

Step 1: Support

It is natural to want to jump in and tell someone how to improve. This is the coaching part of being a leader—you're ready to coach! But pause a moment and remember that the goal of this step is to ensure the employee feels valued. Coaching will be much better received and processed when you begin by recognizing the employee's skills, talents, and contributions.

This is a critical moment. Do not make the mistake of rushing to coach too quickly. Allow your employee to bask in the feeling of being recognized! Support might sound like this:

"Thank you for letting me observe you in real-time today. I took some good notes for you. You did an excellent job working with that patient and their family. You provided good eye contact and were very personable in your tone of voice, and I loved how you took that extra step to escort them to the room and provide a blanket.

"You have a very natural way of communicating and talking to people to make them feel comfortable. Well done. Before I give you my other feedback, what do you believe you did well?"

Step 2: Coach

Now it's time for coaching. This is where you determine the specific behavior or skill you will target for improvement. At Huron, we have learned that there is power in ONE. What we mean by that is that you identify ONE specific skill that needs to be improved. (This is based on the 3:1 Compliment to Criticism Ratio, meaning three compliments to one criticism makes for a positive experience. There is more on that in Principle 9!)

If a safety issue is involved, that will always be the number one priority. So, if someone doesn't wash their hands, document correctly, or violate a safety protocol, always start with that. Also, tell them why that is so important to the patient and ensure they are clear on the one thing they will work on. Have them repeat it back.

Coaching might sound like this:

"One thing I would like you to pay special attention to is introducing yourself to the patient and family in the room. Be sure to manage yourself up with the time you have worked here and your qualifications. I know you mentioned talking about yourself feels uncomfortable. It can be hard to do as it sometimes can feel like we are bragging, but it isn't. This puts the patient at ease and reduces anxiety. Was there anything that you felt you could've done better or differently?"

Step 3: Support

As you finalize this coaching moment, close with supportive language. This often reflects your confidence that the employee will make the improvements discussed. You may find it appropriate to indicate new opportunities available after they achieve the initial goal. This is also a perfect time to see what support your employee needs from you as their leader.

Note that this isn't a "sandwich" of coaching, meaning you support, you coach, and then repeat the support you previously shared. This second phase of support is not to rehash what was right. It should find ways to reestablish the expectations. It is an opportunity to allow the staff to COMMIT and not fear this word.

Support might sound like this:

"How can I make this more comfortable for you? Why don't you write out your introduction, and you and I will practice together and role-play? I can also round with you later this week. Does this sound good? Thank you and keep up the good work."

The SCS model is an excellent way to coach behaviors and move along. Several behaviors might need to be improved, but taking one at a time provides a manageable way to proceed toward excellence.

 ## Eva—Support. Coach. Support.

Eva is a medical assistant in your physician practice. Her role is to escort the patients into the room, take the vitals, and ensure the patient is ready to be seen by the physician. Your area focuses on communicating with the patient about any delays and how long they might expect to wait. The physician is on time today, so the wait time will be less than five minutes.

You shadowed Eva in her interaction with Mr. Savit and found a quiet place in the hallway after your observation to provide her feedback using the Support-Coach-Support model.

This is the flow of the conversation. You ask first how she thought the interaction went to allow her to self-review and reflect. You then begin to provide feedback as follows:

SUPPORT	COACH	SUPPORT
• *Wow. You did a lot of things very well.* • *What do you think you did well?*	• *I know you recently completed the communication training. Thank you for letting me observe you in real life. We use this communication framework to reduce anxiety, and I appreciate your commitment to using this with our patients.*	• *If you add that part, it will help reduce the patient's anxiety.* • *I appreciate you being the first to volunteer today in the huddle to let me shadow you. I will be back on Thursday; would you mind if I shadowed you again then?*

SUPPORT	COACH	SUPPORT
• Your caring behaviors were excellent. You concentrated on the patient with your eye contact and your undivided attention. Your caring and compassion came through in your body language. • The way you set up your time with the patient was good, too. • You also acknowledged everyone in the room, including the family—a great way to connect.	• I want you to take the opportunity to keep the patient updated about wait times. The duration part of AIDET® is so important to patients. • If the doctor is on time, you can tell them that as you manage them up, and if the doctor is running late, you can estimate how long and when you will check back. • Is there anything you think you could've improved upon?	• Is there anything you need from me before then? I will put a copy of this feedback in your mailbox in the department. It's essential to me that you get a chance to look it over, just in case you have any additional questions. • Thanks very much and keep up the great work.

Figure 4.10: Support-Coach-Support Example

Maximizing the Support-Coach-Support Conversation Framework

Developing your skills to coach, mentor, and develop your employees is lifelong learning! As leaders, we continue refining our talent with every coaching conversation. Sometimes the conversation will go exactly as you expected, but there will be times that the conversation will get off track.

The goal is to ensure that your employees feel supported and empowered and understand how important it is to continue to improve. Here are some tips to help you when providing more formal coaching to your staff:

Tip #1: Set up the coaching for success.
Get the employee ready. Assure them you want to help them be the very best. Coaching and observation are not "gotcha" situations. Also, share expectations and checklists before formally observing skills. Make sure they know what is expected.

Tip #2: Make coaching timely and realistic.
Coaching can occur after you observe employees using a tactic or process during a planned practice session or in a more formal skills lab setting. It is essential to provide timely feedback. Employees need to know what they do well to build on those strengths. There is no doubt that developing skills is a process. There will be setbacks along the way. Let them know you are available to provide support and that your coaching is intended to help.

It's also okay to ask the employee what obstacles they perceive. What are the "hills" (broken processes, lack of equipment, challenging situations) that can slow their progress? Knowing these hills can help you as a leader and make the journey less chaotic and more tranquil. Remember, these conversations are best held in person, not over email or phone.

Tip #3: Solicit input—ask what went well.
Ask employees what they thought went well before sharing your specific examples. Starting positively builds confidence and decreases potential defensiveness when you reach the coaching phase. You're reinforcing what they have already seen as positive within themselves, which sets you both up for a more meaningful conversation. Ensure your positive comments are genuine, specific, and reflect actual performance. If you're just giving empty compliments, it won't help the employee or the organization achieve real results.

Tip #4: Solicit input—Ask what might be done better.
Ask employees what they think could have improved—even if you already know—and choose one on which to focus. When you position your coaching in this way, you create a sense of ownership in employees for the next steps because they had input in the discussion.

Remember, no one argues with their own opinions, so this streamlines the coaching process as the employee is helping you to coach them on something they have already pointed out as needing improvement. Listen to your employee's perspective and then help them see things from the patient/customer perspective.

Tip #5: Agree on the ONE THING and agree to concrete next steps.
Remember to give the employee only one thing to improve so they can focus on it—one thing at a time. Even if there are several gaps in performance, prioritize ONE focus area to improve at a time. Ensure the one you choose is one that will significantly impact their overall performance.

Think of coaching as not only being an "instructor" (even though there are components of that), but also an "empowerer" (yes, that is a made-up word, but you get it). When people are "instructed," they can only go as far as that moment in learning can take them. When people are empowered, they have an internal drive, light up, and want to take that learning further than the moment. Only start giving advice and direction when the employee asks for help. They may need your experience and expertise to provide specific examples of "what right looks like."

Tip #6: Gain their agreement.
Confirm their commitment to practice the next steps you discussed and follow up with them to assess progress within two weeks of your coaching session. Do not assume employees will practice just because you had the discussion. An agreement is most likely to be fulfilled when there is a verbal commitment to act and a plan to validate improvement.

Tip #7: Be clear about what type of coaching is needed.
Coaching next-level performance is most successful with solid and high-performing employees. Employees who are consistently underperforming may require more direct coaching for improvements to occur (more on that shortly).

Ensure feedback is specific, e.g., "You made good eye contact and greeted the person in the hallway." Be real. This is the time for that. Don't generalize and say, "Great job!" if it wasn't so great. You're not doing them or yourself any favors.

Ultimately, coaching is about recognizing progress and providing guidance. It is about growing skills and unlocking their potential. Be careful not to accidentally create optionality. During coaching, phrases like "Maybe think about" and "Consider trying" can cloud the message and stall progress.

Tip #8: Follow up.
Not everyone loves to be coached. While most high and middle/solid performers appreciate the coaching and are eager to develop themselves, learning that you have an opportunity for growth and development can still be uncomfortable. One of the best ways to continue engaging your team is to follow up after a coaching conversation.

When your employee demonstrates improvement after coaching, immediately recognize and reinforce the coaching by thanking them. Sometimes, it's too early to see improvement. Still, it may be beneficial 24-48 hours later to thank the employee for their time and ensure they don't have any additional needs or questions after your coaching.

COACHING CONVERSATION #3
The Impact Message—The Next Step
The next "difficult conversation" model we'll review is the "Impact Message." The Impact Message is often a logical next step if a "Stub Your Toe Conversation" does not result in the desired outcome.

> The "Impact Message" is a coaching conversation that allows you to focus not only on the behavior but also ensure that the other person understands the impact of their actions or inactions.

Beth Keane, a dear colleague of ours who passed away in 2013, was a great person and a beautiful soul as well as a humble, funny, and wise leader. She was an amazing communicator. She could deliver a tough conversation with such agility and expertise that when you received it, you'd thank her! Beth developed and taught the "Impact Message" technique. It works across all levels of the team.

Impact messages are powerful because they allow you to focus on the "why." When people understand why they're asked to do (or not do) something, they're far more likely to relate and act. Impact messages can be a powerful tool to help you shift employee behaviors and have a ripple effect beyond the initial receiver.

66 Don't Wait for the "Easy."

My dear friend Tonia, an outstanding leader, shared that she sometimes found it hard after she was promoted through the ranks to a leader in the lab where she had worked for years. Perhaps you'll relate to this. Here's her story in her own words:

Soon after being promoted to supervisor, I quickly realized this might not be as easy as I thought. One of my former peers, Sarah, was tardy for the second time in a week. Being new to leadership, I was a bit torn about how to address this.

Sarah's lateness continued and became a pattern. Now, what was I going to do? Technically I could write a warning, but that seemed unfair since we never talked about it before. But I couldn't just let it slide, either.

Then I remembered something from a leadership development session I attended. They said to tell people when you change your behavior, so they're not caught off guard. That advice stuck with me, and I knew exactly what to do.

First, I sat down with Sarah and apologized that I had not been diligent in holding our team accountable. I told her I was committing to being a better leader and needed a meaningful conversation with her.

I told her I had noticed her frequent tardiness. I explained how this impacted the team. Specifically, it determined how quickly we could get slides to the pathologist to make a diagnosis. Imagine how that disrupted our team and the patients we were there to serve.

She was receptive to my feedback, and it especially resonated with her how this could affect our patients. "I wouldn't want my family to have their diagnosis delayed. I get it," she said.

I specifically asked her if there was anything I could do to help her. She said "no" and promised to avoid being late again. I ensured she knew that I would hold her to it, and the next time, we would document it as informal counseling.

That was hard, but it needed to be said. Oddly, I felt a great sense of relief as the conversation ended. I was proud I had moved past my discomfort, and I was encouraged by how Sarah seemed to take the feedback, especially resonating with the "why."

I've had many more tough conversations since that first one with Sarah. These conversations created a lot of anxiety for me, and sometimes they are hard. But through developing my skills, role-playing, and practicing, I'm better at it now. With each successful conversation, I become more confident and practical for my team.

I love the words of Duke basketball coach Kara Lawson who says, "So make yourself a person who handles 'hard' well. Not someone who's waiting for the 'easy.'"

For me, this quote captures the journey of leadership. I am certainly not the perfect leader, but I'm learning not to wait around for the "easy."

There are four critical steps in the "Impact Message" model:

Figure 4.11: The Impact Message

Like the "Stub Your Toe Conversation," the "Impact Message" is straightforward. It's a flexible fill-in-the-blank formula that can be applied to many difficult conversations. Typically, you'll state the first three steps together. After that, pause and allow the other person to reflect and respond.

A bit of advice. Don't hurry past the last step of getting a commitment. After you've listened to and discussed any questions or concerns, you'll end the conversation by getting a commitment. A nod, "mmm-hmmm," "I guess," or a similarly non-committal response doesn't count. It helps to get explicit confirmation that your message was heard, understood, and will be acted on. That's why every interaction ends with a question to which the other person must respond.

What differentiates the "Impact Message" approach from "Stub Your Toe Conversations" is step two, "The result is...." This step allows you to focus on the behavior and ensure that the other person understands the impact of their actions or inactions.

Here are a few situations in which an "Impact Message" might be more effective than a "Stub Your Toe" conversation:

- The behavior you're addressing is not a first-time offense.

- The other person is a middle/solid (but not a high) performer who needs external motivation and encouragement to change their behavior.

- The other person is new to the team or organization and might need help understanding the impact of their behavior.

Here is what an "Impact Message" might look and sound like:

SCENARIO 1:	SCENARIO 2:	SCENARIO 3:
A team member consistently interrupts you in meetings, team huddles, or one-on-one conversations.	A staff member is consistently late to committee meetings.	A team member's actions prevent a goal from being reached.
1. "Shana, when you interrupt me while I'm talking..."	1. "Daron, when you are consistently late to meetings..."	1. "Suzy, when you open a supply pack in the OR and then don't use it..."
2. "(The result is) I don't feel as if I've been able to explain myself adequately."	2. "(The result is) I feel you don't value my time or the time of others on the team."	2. "(The result is) I don't know if you realize the supply pack has to be discarded because it has been contaminated."

Here is what an "Impact Message" might look and sound like:

SCENARIO 1:
A team member consistently interrupts you in meetings, team huddles, or one-on-one conversations.

3. "I need you to let me finish before you respond."

4. "Do you agree that you can do that?"

SCENARIO 2:
A staff member is consistently late to committee meetings.

3. I need you to be on time or tell the team you can't participate. If you are late, I will no longer make others wait and recap what you've missed in the meeting."

4. "Do you agree that you will try your best to be on time for future meetings and let us know if you expect to be late?"

SCENARIO 3:
A team member's actions prevent a goal from being reached.

3. "Because we all share responsibility for controlling expenses, we need to consider the need for specific supplies and whether they will likely be used before you open a supply pack. It may not seem like a significant expense, but multiplied by every OR, every day, there's a lot of waste. Do you understand how your actions can impact the overall financial success of the surgery center?"

4. "Do you agree that you will be more conscientious about using supplies in the future? If you have questions, please come to me so we can discuss these implications. Okay?"

Wait, but what about change?

> "Change is the only constant in life."

Heraclitus

Throughout this book, you'll notice some golden threads and themes that underpin each principle. Two important ones to note are **communication** and **change**.

While we'll dive deep into communication in Principle 8: Communicate at all Levels, it's the perfect time to discuss "change" as we wrap up Principle 4. After all, preparing leaders and staff to navigate change is crucial to setting your team up for long-term success and growth.

As the ancient Greek philosopher notes in the quote above, change is the only constant. No truer words. We all must agree that change is an inevitable and constant force in our personal and professional lives. It is the seed from which progress grows. And rest assured, while it is as essential to leadership as oxygen is to the lungs, it can be a struggle.

One of my favorite quotes is from Frederick Douglass, who said, "If there is no struggle, there is no progress."

Yes, change can be a "struggle," but change can also be inspiring. In the fast-paced world of healthcare, leaders who resist change also risk becoming stagnant or irrelevant. On the other hand, leaders who are compassionate, flexible, and, most of all, adaptable can seize new opportunities and guide their teams through periods of uncertainty.

Have we had some "uncertainty" in healthcare? We all know that answer. Will we have "uncertainty" in the future? We all know that answer as well.

Making change part of the way we work

We've all seen "change initiatives" that are rolled out only to "roll over." To be an influential leader, it is imperative to truly understand the dynamics of change and make it a part of how you work daily. Here are a few tips and suggestions:

Understand Change is Constant. Change can feel like your best friend, and change can sometimes be as fun as an IRS audit. But embrace it. We must. The sooner we can grasp change as "the norm" and a part of our daily lives, the better our ability as leaders to plan, communicate, and manage change. "New" might be better, but if introduced poorly, it will not always *feel* better, and how people feel about change is consequential to its success.

Embrace the Nature of Change. Change is not a linear process. An astute leader will grasp change's psychological and emotional aspects, recognizing that individuals may react differently with feelings like resistance, fear, and uncertainty. That is the very nature of change.

Connect to Why. Leaders must be able to articulate the vision and rationale behind the proposed change by providing a compelling "why." It is wise to involve the team in the change process, soliciting their input, addressing concerns, and fostering a sense of ownership. It would be unwise at best, and downright dangerous at worst, to assume a common understanding when implementing change. If this is not done well, what happens may look something like this:

W.H.A.S.U.P.

Let's pretend an organization decided to make the change to no longer use pencils. They even devised the acronym W.H.A.S.U.P. (We hate all sharp/unsharp pencils) and scheduled a rollout day.

People sign up for in-service sessions in conference room B. The rollout takes place. People are given their W.H.A.S.U.P. t-shirts, and leaders and staff go through the organization gathering up all the pencils. They are done and done.

For a few weeks, there are no pencils to be found. W.H.A.S.U.P. is deemed a success. The leaders pat themselves on the back, and life goes on.

But then what happens? Several weeks after rollout, there is a rumor that a pencil was seen on the third floor. Memos are written, and emails are sent. The wayward pencil is found and removed. But more pencil sightings occur in the lab, OT, and at the front desk. How could this be?

Senior leadership raises their hands to the sky, gnashing their teeth in confusion. "We had an acronym! We had t-shirts! We sent memos and had sign-in sheets! What went wrong?"

There was no awareness of the "why," no understanding, and therefore no buy-in. There was certainly no plan for learning, performing, and sustaining the change.

The organization hurried to the finish and forgot to tell the team about new research showing that the organization's pencil-related injuries had been exceptionally high and that the wood used in pencils contained a chemical that caused people's eyelashes to fall out. They didn't inform people that reducing the presence of pencils would prevent severe harm and decrease eyelash shedding. They never shared the supporting data to show that this whole "W.H.A.S.U.P." implementation wasn't random and was instead about employee safety and well-being.

What if they had started with the "why" behind the sudden pencil ban and explained the risks versus rewards up front? They might have avoided the backsliding and erased all of the poor compliance! (Erased, get it?)

What is the moral of the story? Change cannot be announced. Not even the coolest acronym is a substitute for the power of leading people through the change journey.

Understand and Know Where Your Team Members are on Their Personal Change Journey. The change topic is broader and more complex than I can address here. At Huron, we have an entire process built around leading change. Figure 4.12 does an excellent job of trying to distill some of this for you.

Expect Resistance. You will encounter resistance because it's a natural human reaction. Getting out there and talking to people is one way to get ahead of resistance. Use listening sessions to identify and discuss pockets of resistance. Listening sessions might include rounding conversations, focus groups, town hall meetings, third-party interviews, and online surveys, to name just a few.

Be Self-Aware. As you focus on leading change, assessing your own stage in the process is equally important.

On reflection, you may find that you are not as "bought into" change as you think. Leaders can only take others as far as they have gone. To lead effectively, you must own your personal progress.

This may involve looking in the mirror, and you may not love what you see in a given moment, but that's okay. This is when you may even need to reach out to mentors and peers. The thing about change, for the most part, is that it doesn't have to be a solitary process. As a matter of fact, for the types of change we are discussing here, it shouldn't be.

Don't struggle when sometimes all you need to do is ask for help. Something is built into humans (especially in healthcare) that we are wired to help. You'd be surprised how many people will step up when needed.

Sometimes asking for help puts a new set of eyes or perspective on an issue and helps you see things refreshed. In times of change, there is no room for ego. There is no shame in needing help as a leader, but it would be a shame if you needed it and didn't seek it.

THE PERSONAL CHANGE JOURNEY

Change is a personal thing, no doubt about it. It's only when people realize that change isn't happening TO them, but FOR them, that they can truly embrace it. When someone is aware of how they're affected by the change, understand it, and buy into it, that's when they're ready to learn new ways of doing things.

At Huron, we understand that people go through different phases of change. So, what are the key phases of the personal change journey that leaders need to know about in order to guide their teams to success?

CURRENT STATE—GETTING READY TO LEARN

First, you can't just tell people what's happening and send them on the way to training. Instead, lead people through the three important first steps of the change journey.

1. **Awareness:** When a person is mindful of what is happening, why it is happening, and the risk of not changing. You can't simply announce a change without context, because only when there is awareness can people move forward effectively.

2. **Understanding:** When a person sees how the change will affect them, positively and negatively. Transparency is critical to this step.

3. **Buy-In and Personal Choice:** When a person genuinely accepts that the change is needed. They make the conscious choice to support and participate in the change.

TRANSITION STATE—PREPARING TO WORK IN NEW WAYS

Once one moves through awareness, understanding, and buy-in, "transition" can begin. This state represents moving from old ways of working to the new.

4. **Learning:** When a person learns what is needed of them, the new skills they will need, and the behaviors they will need to align to make the change happen.

5. **Performing:** When a person puts into practice what they've learned, they start to get good at it. New habits form and productivity returns.

FUTURE STATE—SUSTAINING CHANGE

This state is when a person is working in new ways with new habits and behaviors. But remember: new habits are fragile and can be easily disrupted without proper care and attention.

6. **Sustaining:** When a person acts, thinks, and behaves in new ways consistently and accepts the change as a new normal. Praise, consistency, and seeing benefits of the change help sustain the habit.

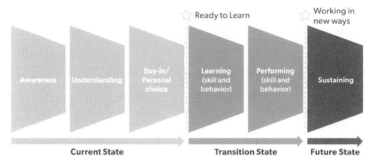

Figure 4.12 The Personal Change Journey Model

Principle 4 Summary

Principle 4: Develop Leaders to Develop People, is about coaching others to be their best at work. As leaders we must not only manage performance and lead boldly through the change journey. We also have an extraordinary responsibility to develop and grow not only ourselves, but other leaders and staff to achieve those goals.

Let's face it. We are in healthcare for significant reasons—a purpose or higher calling. Leaders who pursue a higher calling recognize that developing others is integral to their journey.

A "calling." That's powerful. According to Merriam-Webster, being "called" or having a "calling" is defined as a strong inner impulse toward a particular course of action, especially when accompanied by the conviction of divine influence.

Sit with that for a moment. Most leaders find that leadership is a calling for them. Something comes from deep inside their "spirit," where they are driven by what Merriam-Webster describes as "divine influence." Each of us may define "divine" in our ways through our belief system, cultural lens, or life experience, but for the sake of simplicity, let's agree that it means something that is beyond us, greater than us, proceeding from or all encompassed by pure, unencumbered... good.

This "pure good" creates a conviction within us, which means a firm persuasion or belief to take action. What a beautiful and perhaps unique way of looking at leadership. Some powerful state of "good" gives us a solid drive to act. If you are called to lead (as it is almost assured that you are—why else would you be reading books like this?) it comes from a bottomless reservoir of meaning. Being called to lead means tapping into, bringing down, becoming one with, and aligning with "the divine." Good for you! Literally.

Never doubt the power of this work, this journey, and your impact. Our work is rarely easy, but it is always inspiring.

PRINCIPLE 5: FOCUS ON EMPLOYEE ENGAGEMENT

Attend to Aspirations and Desires in the Workplace

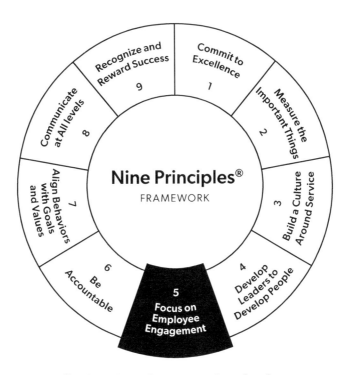

"Life asks of every individual a contribution, and it is up to that individual to discover what it should be."

Viktor E. Frankl

Setting the Stage

If a healthcare organization wants to be successful, a strong and engaged workforce is critical—both now and in the future. But with so many talent challenges in the healthcare market today, it's more important than ever to figure out what matters most to your employees. Once you know that, you can build a culture that supports them and implement talent initiatives that help both your organization and its people.

That's what Principle 5: Focus on Employee Engagement, is all about. This chapter will show you how to create a workplace culture that promotes employee engagement, productivity, and loyalty.

We'll cover everything from ensuring psychological safety to conducting employee engagement surveys. We'll also give you five retention strategies that will help you engage new employees from the start and keep your best employees around. These include onboarding new hires, conducting 30- and 90-day interviews, leader rounding with employees and physicians, retention and stay interview conversations, and senior leader rounding.

Just the Facts...

Huron recently surveyed 718 healthcare professionals, including clinicians, nurses, staff, and leaders, to gauge what they value in their workplace and the satisfaction levels related to them (Huron Healthcare Talent Research Top Opportunities for Leaders; 2023). This survey measured healthcare worker sentiment and provided compelling data and insights into where leaders are united and divided in the workplace.

Misalignment Between Leaders and Employees

According to this study, there is a significant disconnect between what healthcare workers value in their workplace and what their leaders believe to be important.

In fact, leaders only correctly identified four of the top six opportunities to improve staff's job experience. Leadership and employees recognized an opportunity to improve workload, health insurance and coverage, diversity equity and inclusion investments, and salary. Among leaders' blind spots—improvement areas identified by staff but not management—were paid time off and the ability to access and use data, technology, and analytics.

This variation signals and opportunity for organizations to make meaningful changes to how and where they invest in employee retention and engagement (See Figure 5.1).

BLIND SPOTS	ON TRACK	MISSING THE MARK
Improvement identified by staff, not perceived by management	Improvement areas identified by staff, and perceived by management	Improvement areas identified by management, not perceived by staff

• Paid time off (PTO)	• Competitive salary	• Role alignment
• Digital, technology, and analytics	• Workload	• Feeling valued
	• Health insurance and coverage	
	• Diversity, equity, and inclusion	

Figure 5.1: Huron Healthcare Talent Research Top Opportunities for Leaders; 2023

Burnout on the rise

We know widespread burnout among healthcare workers and leaders plays a significant role in employee engagement, retention, and overall perception of one's workplace.

81%
of respondents report feeling **burned out more than a few times a month** over the past six months. (This is a 17% increase in just one year.)

37%
of burned-out respondents are **considering leaving their current position** in the next 12 months.

TOP FACTORS CONTRIBUTING TO BURNOUT

- Lack of work-life balance
- Long hours
- Emotional exhaustion or stress
- Unmanageable workload
- Unreasonable time pressures

Figure 5.2: Huron Healthcare Talent Research Top Opportunities for Leaders; 2023

So, in this same survey, we also took the opportunity to do a pulse check on burnout. Not surprisingly, 81% of respondents reported feeling burned out more than a few times a month over the past six months, and 37% are considering leaving their positions in the next year.

The top five factors driving stress include lack of work-life balance, long hours, emotional exhaustion or stress, unmanageable workload, and unreasonable time pressures (see Figure 5.2).

Engagement, retention, and burnout are no doubt challenging overall. No one can dispute that. But It is up to us as leaders to work smarter, not harder. To target and focus attention on specific strategies that drive employee engagement and experience, strengthen culture, bolster retention and recruitment, and alleviate additional factors of burnout.

So, let's begin this journey to creating a workplace where your employees will attract, engage, and keep the best talent around.

66 What's the Best Thing That's Happened to You Today?"

This question surprised me as I was fumbling through my wallet in the grocery store line. The young man at the register had a big smile and was making eye contact like someone comfortable with who and what they are in this world. I was unprepared for actual human interaction and had to take my air pods out to respond.

"What was the best thing that happened to me today?" I repeated, feeling like a pageant contestant who repeats the question to buy some time to respond. "Well, my wife's doctor called her this morning with results from her annual cancer screening labs that she's been doing since she had cancer several years ago, and they were negative! Six years in a row. So, yeah, that was good!"

The young man high-fived me. "That's the best one I've heard today. Congratulations to you and your wife! My name is David. It's nice to meet you!"

"Nice to meet you, David," I smiled. "I'm Rich. If you don't mind, what made you ask me that?"

David responded, "My grandpa George used to run a general store and always asked his customers that question. I remember as a little kid, seeing how it made people happier. Also, I like addition. I feel like so much is subtracted from our day, especially at work, with people complaining, frowning, or dealing with problems, that we need more addition. So, I like to try to add to the day."

Can I say I was impressed? I was. Can I say that I was tearing up a little at register five? I was.

I was also surprised to find out David was only 17. He was excited about going to college soon, split between becoming a teacher or a physician's assistant. I said how lucky either profession would be to have him and how proud his grandfather would be of him.

David continued, "I sometimes wonder if my grandfather did this as much for himself as for others. All I know is when I get people like you who talk with me, it makes my work better".

At this point, another customer rolled up. David said, "Good to meet you, Rich, and congrats on your wife!" He then turned to a woman with a few items who looked distracted and stressed. I paused while grabbing my bag and held my breath as I heard David ask, "So what's the best thing that's happened to you today?"

She looked up and paused, and then her whole demeanor changed. While I couldn't hear her answer, I saw them laugh aloud at whatever she said.

I made my way to the store manager and told him I wanted to compliment one of his employees. He said, "This is going to be about David, isn't it?" I nodded. "He's the best hire I've ever made and is so engaged with his co-workers and customers. Everyone loves that kid. He's going to go far in life!"

I bet David is the "best thing that happens" to a lot of people regularly, wherever he is. Now that's engagement at its best.

Even without a formal definition of an engaged employee like David, we all know them when they take care of us, when we lead them, or even better, when they work alongside us. Simply put, employee engagement refers to the strength of employees' intellectual, mental, and emotional bond with their work, colleagues, teams, and organization.

We've covered patient experience already in Principle 3 and are not too far away from that when discussing employee engagement. David had a great example in his grandfather, who was, in effect, a leadership mentor to him. He saw how his grandfather loved his work and connected with his customers and the light that came through from that. He passed that light on to me, and I'm passing it on to you.

Maybe when we are engaged, we are a "light" to brighten things, to show the way, and perhaps we, in turn, feel "lighter." The heaviness of what we do and see may be a little more manageable when we are engaged. As leaders, how can we be that "light" of engagement? Once we know what needs to be done, how do we get the amazing people we lead to join us and shine their lights?

Employee Satisfaction vs. Employee Engagement

When the first edition of Hardwiring Excellence was released in 2003, we called this principle "Focus on Employee Satisfaction." Today, we realize the significant difference between satisfaction and engagement. You'll remember that Principle 3 discussed the differences between patient experience and patient satisfaction. The same applies here when we talk about employees.

> Satisfaction measures what you get from a relationship with an individual or an organization. Engagement measures the reverse—what you give back to that relationship.

It is driven by a sense of ownership, control, input, clear communication, and feedback rather than compensation or perks. Engagement is so much more than satisfaction. It's about being emotionally invested in and focused on creating value for the organization and patient daily.

Even on the most challenging days, do you feel like you were able to move the ball down the field to some valuable purpose? Were your talents applied to achieve more significant or satisfying results than you could have achieved alone? That is the power of being part of an excellent team and a wonderful organization. That feeling fosters engagement, and an engaged workforce—not just a satisfied one—is the goal.

Bringing People with You

Focusing on employee engagement is about bringing people with you and helping to manage change. One thing we can certainly agree on is that we've experienced over the last few years is change. While we are quite intimate with change in healthcare, it is fair to say that it's been very challenging lately. We've been tested—a test of our leadership, processes, and systems and our lives.

I reference change throughout this book as we talk about each principle. However, it is worth highlighting here again as it relates to employee engagement. I'm going to spare you the graphs and statistics and summarize this simply and symbolically, as one healthcare human to another:

The violent storm came. It raged. We got knocked down. Most of us got up to be stronger, better, and wiser. We not only got up, but we showed up and continue to do so for those we serve and to honor the memories and legacies of those who didn't get back up. Our emotional, intellectual, and, yes, spiritual connection to our teams, our work, and our organizations are probably stronger now than ever. You've led, perhaps by experience and training, gut and instinct, or all of the above. But here you are, at this moment, trying to get better.

Take a moment. You're remarkable for that, and you need to hear it. So does every employee in your organization.

So how do we take this momentum and continue to change—not for the sake of change, but to create massive and significant change? Leaders often start change initiatives knowing more about the change than those they lead. Change does not happen in the dark. This is all about shining that light. To effectively lead through change and engage employees meaningfully and sincerely, a leader must be able to place themselves in their people's shoes and keep in mind the adage that it is important to meet people where they are, not where we wish they were!

The first step to personal change is understanding. You must understand where your people are on their personal change journey so that you can determine the most appropriate way to guide, support, motivate, and incentivize them to change.

I had a friend who had a triathlon on his bucket list. I went with him to meet his trainer. My friend has a fantastic spirit, but he's not an athlete. He doesn't go to the gym. He doesn't ensure he gets in 10,000 steps a day. The only thing he jogs is his memory. He would be a champion of competitive Netflix surfing rather than actual surfing. But props to him for dreaming big!

So, on the way to meet his trainer, he picks up a pizza for dinner. He brings it into the meeting because he doesn't want to leave it in the car. As she's looking him over and eyeballing the double-sausage pizza, his trainer asks, "Would you say you're into fitness?" and without missing a beat, he says, "I'm into 'fitness' this whole pizza in my mouth, but other than that... no."

Needless to say, she realized she had her work cut out for her. She had to meet my friend where he was, starting from level 0. But she did. Without judgment or condescension, she moved him up and over. He got serious. He made progress. He finished his first triathlon proudly at number 61 of 100 triathletes. And we all celebrated with a double-sausage pizza.

Look at your team. Some are well-prepared and might even help you take the lead. Some might need a little extra incentive or inspiration. Some will need a lot of extra encouragement, and inspiration. And yes, some will "tap out" and decide this isn't for them. That's a good thing. All of it is. You'll become a better leader for the journey, and they'll become better for the growth.

Psychological Safety

Harvard Business School professor Amy Edmundson first introduced the term "psychological safety" in the 1990s. She coined this phrase after researching the error rates of high-performing medical teams versus low-performing ones. Initially, Edmonson expected to find that higher-performing teams made fewer mistakes. However, her findings revealed that the better teams reported higher error rates. This was not because they made more mistakes but because they were more willing to discuss them. Think about that one for a moment!

Considering Principle 5 and the emphasis on employee engagement, psychological safety is very important. Foundationally, the significance of psychological safety lies in its ability to foster and truly drive employee engagement.

Think practically about the connection between psychological safety and engagement.

An engaged employee feels a deeper connection to their work. They speak up when they see an opportunity to improve things. They share a different perspective when approaching a problem. They are willing to stretch out of their comfort zone and take a risk to try something in a new way. Psychological safety drives that vibrant culture we talked about in Principle 1—a culture that manifests shared values and principles and where people are free to be authentic in what they see and say, do and don't do, and what they think and believe.

> In a nutshell, psychological safety is about being able to show and employ oneself without fear of negative consequences to self-image, status, or career. It is a feature of the group environment, not a matter of personality. A shared belief that the team is safe for interpersonal risk-taking—and it is determined at the group level.

Have you ever watched that TV show that chronicles air disasters? As a person who spent much of my life on the front lines of patient safety, I see profound parallels. I recall one heartbreaking story where there was an airplane crash with tremendous loss of life, yet there was no engine failure or weather anomaly. The whole crash came down to a small error the captain made that the co-pilot was too afraid to mention.

Why? Because of the culture of their airline as a whole and the micro-culture of that small working group in the cockpit. The co-pilot and the captain were highly trained, so there was no lack of knowledge or education. But there was a lack of psychological safety.

I felt judgmental of this co-pilot at first. Then I remembered, as I investigated issues as a risk manager, how often things went wrong because someone was afraid to speak up. While certainly this concept affects safety, it also touches most of what we do, and when people feel "safe," we are all the better for it.

Fostering a culture of psychological safety is the sacred duty of a leader who can humble themselves enough to know they can't possibly have all the answers and to find within themselves the patience to listen to those they are privileged enough to lead and be present. That alone will take you further than you can imagine.

What are some ways to create psychologically safe spaces?

- **Invite participation/Listen to what people have to say.** Convince your team members that their voices matter. This means paying attention to what they have to say. We must all recommit to the lost art of listening with intention. Asking for feedback and input is one of the key signs of an actualized leader. It demonstrates humility. Giving lip service to issues or sending seemingly sincere emails about how "we care what you think" will fall short if we aren't genuinely listening as leaders. In a culture where social media makes "stars" of folks spewing 30-second sound bites to cater to an increasingly distracted audience, many of us—myself included—have fallen prey to this listening deficit. It points to an idea, usually attributed to Dale Carnegie, that we are turning into a culture that focuses on being "interesting" over being "interested."

- **Ask purpose-focused, open-ended questions.** For example, "What could we do immediately that would impact our current challenges most and create a positive shift?"

- **Ask for feedback.** Just ask. Ask for feedback on training, communication, agendas, and ways to improve and impact work. Create easy pathways for people to share.

- **Encourage all voices:** Encourage employees who typically stay silent during meetings to share their perspectives. As we've often heard, "still waters run deep," and that quiet teammate who doesn't say a lot may have more to offer than we realize. Use your judgment but find ways to elicit and encourage the voices of people who are not outspoken/extroverts. For example, you might say, "Sophia, there were a lot of people bouncing ideas around in the meeting. You are a great listener, and I noticed you were deep in thought while everyone was talking. I wanted to hear from you. What are your thoughts about all of this?"

- **Embrace disagreements:** A psychologically safe environment does not mean everyone always agrees. It is just the opposite. Psychological safety empowers employees to speak candidly and exchange ideas freely in productive disagreement. Help your people shed their defensiveness to allow candor to be productive.

- **Appreciate and recognize:** Give out praise and appreciation in heaping measures. That which gets appreciated gets repeated.

- **Provide constructive feedback:** Ensure that feedback is constructive and not personal. It will be ineffective if it is a "gotcha" and doesn't come from a place of empathy. Make it as conversational as possible. It's fine to have your opinion as a leader. Just leave the "door open" in the discussion. Example: "What are your thoughts about moving the patient intake desk back to its original place? We've received a few complaints internally and externally about its proximity to the bathroom. I know you felt the new location would be an improvement. I'm open to giving that more time, but do you think we should reevaluate?"

- **Encourage people to be encouraging:** The feedback that discourages people from speaking up or sounds dismissive, like, "We've already tried that," "How could you make such a mistake?" or "That's such a dumb idea," makes people feel embarrassed and fearful to share. One could say, "We've agreed to treat each other's ideas openly and respectfully. Let's stay true to that agreement so we all have a place at the table!"

Remember this. Psychological safety in healthcare cannot be hoped into place. It takes vision, humility, planning, and commitment from the leaders and their teams. It's not just about being nice to each other, although that never hurts. When leaders take the time to round individually with their employees and engage in other intentional actions that promote constructive two-way dialogue, it fosters respect for the unique voices and perspectives of the team. This dialogue assures that the team feels heard and respected, which ultimately goes a long way toward creating a culture of excellence.

Employee Engagement Survey and Employee Retention

You need to know your starting point to get from point A to point B. An organization-wide employee engagement survey is an essential tool to help gain direction. However, it is important to remember that the key is not in collecting the data but in how well you share the data with the staff, take action based on that feedback, execute the action plan, and confirm the impact with employees.

As Derek Sivers once said, "If more information were the answer, then we'd all be billionaires with perfect abs." High-performing organizations assess engagement across the entire spectrum and identify what they need to build up and what they need to rebuild. A formal annual engagement survey serves as the benchmark, with other informal efforts taken throughout the year to ensure alignment.

Employee Engagement Surveys measure and assess your employees' engagement and identify areas of strength and weakness for your department and organization. They give you a real-time look into where you are now and where you may be going.

So, imagine this scenario: Your organization conducts a survey and finds out that employees struggle to see how their roles fit into the overall goals, vision, and strategy. Thinking through how to close the gap, one solution could be to educate managers on how to have one-on-one chats with their employees to help them connect the dots between their roles and the company's goals. This kind of effort across the organization could make a big difference in employee engagement.

But think about the value of knowing this information. You might never have known about this gap if you hadn't asked the right questions in the survey.

The quality of your questions determines the quality of the information. Or said more simply, the better your questions, the better the information you get! And that information helps you know what to do next.

Because we have found that when people feel like they matter and their ideas count, they get more involved. That's what makes the whole team successful.

When we stay focused on that and listen to each other, we can't help but win. That then gives you a specific direction. When people see that their needs are met, their voices are heard, and their opinions carry weight, they become more engaged. That is the foundation upon which the success of our entire organization stands. We can only succeed when we are laser-focused on that, guided by the team's voice.

The Employee Engagement Rollout Process
So, we have established the importance of employee engagement surveys and data. But conducting the survey and getting the results back to you is only part of the process! What is essential is to ensure you use the data to improve things.

So, what do we recommend for the rollout process?

First, it is an excellent opportunity for the CEO to lead this process and inform everyone what's planned for the survey results and rollout. After the survey is completed and the results are gathered and analyzed, senior leaders can review the data together and agree on actions to engage leaders better. This aligns actions and role models the process for all leaders before leaders share results with staff. It is crucial that you meet with and train your leaders to understand and communicate the data. After that, your leaders can share the results with their teams and develop a plan of action for their teams based on their results.

But it doesn't stop there! You can rate how well the meeting went in each department, make a 90-day action plan, and have your CEO follow up with everyone.

It might seem like a lot, but trust us. It's worth it. We've been doing this for years and found that the implementation process outline on the next page is a sure way to get the feedback and actions you need to ensure your engagement is on point and moving in the right direction. And all of this provides a seamless process to prepare and lead you easily to the next survey cycle.

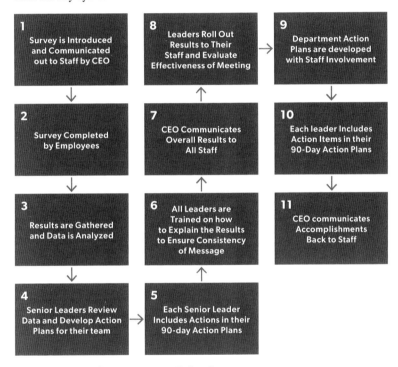

Figure 5.3: The Employee Engagement Rollout Process

In conclusion, if you take nothing else from this chapter, please take this: The level of engagement you achieve among your team will mirror the engagement your patients and all those you serve demonstrate. What you learn from an employee engagement survey is like taking glass cleaner to a smudged window. It will not only clear things up but also shines more light and helps everyone see better what is inside!

Retaining Your Employees

Let's explore five key retention strategies that foster employees' long-term commitment. These strategies not only maximize an employee's potential during their first days and months but also create and nurture meaningful connections and relationships along the way.

Retention Key 1: Orienting and Onboarding New Employees

Have you ever gotten off to a bad start? Maybe you get a patient from another area, and when you walk into the room, their arms are crossed, and they're not looking thrilled. Those first few minutes are an uphill battle. Or maybe you met a person for the first time and innocently said something that unintentionally offended or irritated them. No matter how much you apologize and backpedal, they're just not going to add you to their Christmas/holiday card mailing list.

How we start often determines if we win. Watch an athletic meet or race. Sometimes those are won by fractions of a second. The competitor who jumped off the starting line and got off to the best start most of the time has a better chance of winning if all things are equal. What starts well often ends well.

The ways we orient and onboard or start new employees have certainly changed and evolved through the years as we have studied and learned more about employee retention and what is most meaningful to our teams. Benefits of an effective orientation and onboarding process include:

- Improved employee retention

- Reduced mistakes

- Better engagement and a positive attitude

- Better communication between the supervisor and the new employee

I can't imagine that any of that would be surprising to any of us. Yet, at Huron, we often see organizations struggle with the onboarding process. I remember at one organization where I coached, they were very transparent about their onboarding process being a little lackluster. In fact, the CNO and the H.R. V.P. both called it their "on-BORING" process. Besides being a silly play on words, it let me know we had some work to do.

Onboarding is the process by which new hires integrate into an organization. It includes an initial new-hire orientation process and an ongoing introduction to an organization's structure, culture, vision, mission, and values.

The Society for Human Resource Management (SHRM)

A crucial stage of the onboarding process is the orientation. During orientation, human resources and other leaders address employee benefits, system logins and passwords, and review health and safety procedures. There is usually time to be introduced to senior leadership and tours to help transition into the company.

Yet, while *orientation* is an essential introduction to the company, it is just that—an introduction. Too often, this is where organizations stall. A comprehensive *onboarding* process works from the perspective that the organization must do all it can to fully equip the employee for maximum performance for the organization—and maximum fulfillment of the employee.

The risk of losing an employee within the first year is high. Research statistics vary, but a range of 10-30% is typical. One organization I recently worked with stated that as many as 40% of newly hired employees leave almost immediately after they start!

This is why we encourage onboarding new hires at an organization to be a strategic process that lasts at least one year. Not only does this affect the bottom line due to the costs of bringing new employees on and training them, but losing a much-needed team member affects workload, and, to be blunt, it hurts.

We are emotional beings, and having someone leave us feels bad. We are investing in these new hires— our time, money, knowledge, and hearts—to create team members who want to stay with us, support us, and are loyal to our culture.

An effective orientation and onboarding program is vital to supporting new employees and additions to your team from the start. It allows you and your organization to:

- Foster an understanding of the organizational culture, mission, and values.

- Welcome and facilitate successful adjustment to the new job.

- Help individuals understand their roles and how they fit into the organization through a culture of transparency.

- Shorten the learning curve so they can achieve role objectives. Show them you want them to be successful.

- Build a foundation of knowledge about the organization while encouraging them to be curious and to ask questions.

- Develop positive working relationships.

- Reduce anxiety by providing guidelines for behavior and conduct so the employee isn't left guessing. While a new job can be exciting, we all know those first few months can be daunting. Surround them with support in all ways.

- Establish expectations for them and what they should expect from others. It is helpful to remember that what is left unclear will always be assumed.

The return on investment (ROI) is huge when you get off to a good start with your new employees. Show people as early as possible that their decision to trust you with their career, time, and ability to provide for themselves and their family was wise. Here are a few ways to ensure you get new team members off to a great start during onboarding.

ONBOARDING TIPS AND BEST PRACTICES		
Before They Arrive	The First Day	The First Week
• Send a handwritten note from a senior leader or their direct manager to the employee's home to welcome them. • Prepare their workspace and have it cleaned and stocked with supplies. • Place a welcome card on their desk/locker/workspace. Have it signed by the people they will work alongside. • Place their name marker in their workspace or locker.	• Meet with the employee at the start of their first day to discuss the following: – Their personalized onboarding plan so they know the schedule and there are no surprises. – Their specific role and why it is critical to the functioning of the department and organization. Let them know they are valued and here because they are an asset to the team.	• Schedule a time to meet at the end of their first week. This is an excellent practice for tying up loose ends and checking in on any improvements that might be made. • Schedule 30- and 90-day check-ins with the new employee. Be sure to explain the "why" behind meeting with them at these times and also share the questions you will ask so they can prepare.

ONBOARDING TIPS AND BEST PRACTICES

Before They Arrive	The First Day	The First Week
• Post their picture on your communication board. • Schedule time to spend with the new employee on their first day. • Schedule IT to provide equipment and computer training as appropriate. • Assign a mentor, preceptor, or buddy who is engaged and helpful. • Prepare an assignment for them to complete to give them a sense of accomplishment and importance.	– Departmental goals and policies. Set the expectation up front that those are taken seriously. – "Unwritten" department rules or customs. Many skip this step, but it's essential. It also makes new people feel like they are part of the team. • If appropriate, have lunch with the new employee and invite their mentor or buddy to join. Make this casual. It is stressful being new, and it's great to have a meal where they can feel like they can exhale. • As appropriate, introduce new employees to staff, supervisors, managers, and key leaders. Manage them up and manage up the team to show the organization's culture. People want to work in a positive and supportive environment. • Walk with and acquaint the new employee with the facilities, work area, communication boards, etc. Try to see it all through their eyes. (As a new employee, I remember someone telling me that the elevators on the left were faster than the ones on the right.) • Meet with the employee at the end of their first day to recap the day.	• Schedule monthly employee rounds. • Welcome and introduce them at a team huddle or department meeting and have them share a bit about themselves with the team. PowerPoint slides of their family, pets, travel, etc., allow a great backdrop for a fun introduction. People will often leave an organization because they don't feel like they are treated like a person. Help them to share a little of who they are. It matters.

Figure 5.4: Onboarding Tips and Best Practices

Experiential Onboarding

As the title suggests, the onboarding process should be an experience, something memorable and engaging. Whenever I am asked what this looks like, I recall an organization I coached with a phenomenal method called the "Cheat Sheet." Their two-day orientation might have had 40-50 new employees for each cycle. Before lunch on day one, they would ask them to fill out a form.

It asked questions like: What's your favorite color? Do you have a favorite hobby? What's your favorite snack? Do you have a sports team that you follow? These forms would then be collected and shared with the managers of the new employees.

So, let's say you said that your favorite color was purple, you love peanut butter cups, and your hobby was pencil art. Your new manager makes a quick run to the store, and when you come back on day two, guess what's sitting at your seat? A purple mug, a bag of peanut butter cups, a sketchbook with a couple of pencils, and a handwritten note about how excited they are about you joining the team and making a difference.

Imagine what that would feel like for a new employee. This "cheat sheet" gives a manager ideas about what is meaningful and important to that employee. It allows for that welcome gift moment and gives the manager a meaningful and specific way to reward and recognize the employee later. Talk about dual purpose.

The tasks of onboarding and orienting new employees are relatively cut and dry. Making those tasks into an experience is where the magic happens. The example above makes the experience specific to the employee, which turns up the level of engagement to 11—try it!

Retention Key 2: The First 90-Days

Think about the last big decision you made. Perhaps you purchased a car or signed a mortgage or lease for a new home. If you are like most people, underneath the excitement is a subtle yet nagging buyer's remorse. Did I make the right decision? Should I have chosen the other one? Did I need that extra bedroom? Should I have gotten the extended warranty? Did I spend too much?

Likewise, new employees might ask themselves the same kinds of questions. Is this the right job for me? Will I like the work environment? What are the people like? Will they like me? Will I like them?

The best leaders hire the right people and support them to have a successful first 90 days. According to a report by Jobvite, about 30% of new hires quit their jobs within the first 90 days. While 43% say that their role doesn't meet their expectations, 34% report that a specific incident drove them away, and 32% blame company culture.

Most people want to work for an excellent organization where leaders and their teammates are accountable. We may lose some highly talented and valuable people if that doesn't occur. Therefore, training and expecting employees to uphold organizational Standards of Behavior and align their behaviors to these standards is essential. (We'll talk about that more in Principle 6: Be Accountable.) Hiring people who are excited and skilled to work in an organization that adheres to living the values and reinforcing a positive culture is equally important.

Remember that your new employee might compare their first few weeks of work with you to their last week at their previous job. And what usually happens to an employee during the last week? They get a party. Maybe a cake. Maybe a plaque. And a lot of hugs, well wishes, and reaffirmation. They look around at all those familiar faces and think, "I'm going to miss these people!"

Now they are in a new place where nobody knows them. There haven't been any parties thrown for them, and they haven't received a plaque and probably not a hug. And the cake was a distant memory. So, what can help?

To set a positive stage for a new hire, hold 30-day and 90-day meetings. These are additional checkpoints during this important onboarding time. Too often, when leaders ask to meet with employees, they share bad news or identify a problem that needs to be corrected. That's why connecting intentionally, building relationships, and having regular conversations with your new employees are essential. By letting employees know up-front that these meetings will occur, leaders can reduce that anxiety and reinforce the idea that these check-ins are business.

> 30- and 90-day meetings are one-on-one conversations designed to retain new employees.

Don't forget that you can learn from these meetings as well. New employees are an excellent source of information and ideas. They bring a fresh set of eyes to how your department operates. Spacing meetings at the 30- and 90-day marks is a great way to capture this valuable information at different stages in your new employee's experience.

It's crucial, then, to set different objectives to reflect the new employee's progression. At 30 days, you want to establish a relationship for effective feedback and gather information to apply before the 90-day interview. At 90 days, you want to further build your relationship and provide follow-up and feedback on what was discussed in the 30-day check-up.

Too often, we hear from new employees that the honeymoon is over after about a week. A military veteran healthcare worker told me that being new in her organization was like the big send-off right before being loaded into a troop transport plane, parachuting behind enemy lines, and being left to fight your way back. Not the look most of us are going for!

30-Day Meeting Questions

Here is what we suggest as good 30-day questions to ask:

Question #1: Now that you've been here for a month, how does what we do compare to what we said in your interview?
This question provides insight into the authenticity of the organizational culture reviewed during the interview.

How do your behaviors stack up against your stated values when that employee took the job? You may hear a perceived discrepancy. For example, "When I was hired, I heard the job was from 8 to 5. But now you're asking me to work different hours."

Be open and receptive to whatever feedback you receive. If the employee raises a question, listening and talking about it is key. If these concerns or issues are not addressed early when they can be handled easily, they become bigger issues that lead to more complicated resolutions. (Better to deal with a single burning tree than a raging forest fire.)

It's also critical that the leader not accept "fine" or "okay" as an answer to their questions. Dig deeper. Ask for specifics. When a leader demonstrates sincere interest and listens with compassion and the goal of learning instead of lecturing, they show the new employee that they matter. When they feel that they matter, they show up like they matter—with authenticity, confidence, and their whole self. It starts them off well.

Question #2: What are we doing well?
This question inspires new hires to recall what they like about the role, processes, and work environment.

We've all heard of complaint departments, but most have never heard of compliment departments! What you give energy to is usually what is empowered. Starting early with this positive question is a great way to set the tone and helps build connections and relationships.

Question #3: Are there any individuals who have been helpful to you?
This question identifies values/mission-driven employees who have invested in the new hire's success and gives you an opportunity to reward and recognize them.

For example, if they say, "Kairo was super kind to me and always answers my questions," then make sure that day, if possible, you tell Kairo what was said. Why? Because Kairo now feels great to be complimented by you, their leader, but also feels good about the new employee. It creates an emotional connection.

And if a new employee says, "ICU here is the best I've ever seen," then pass that on to the ICU. How do you think the new employee will be treated by the ICU the next time they transfer a patient? Good. This gives the employee a chance to build that relationship, and as a newer person on the team, this is a significant win for all.

Question #4: At your previous job, what are some things you saw that could make us better?
This question demonstrates value for the new hire's input with a fresh eyes perspective on inefficient processes and workflows.

This may be my very favorite question to ask a recent hire. People often get annoyed or even offended when a new person says any version of, "That's not how we did it at my last job." In fact, the reflexive reaction may be, "Well, if it was so good there, why are you here?" or "Well, you're not there anymore, and this is how WE do it."

Other industries see this in a whole different way. And if we are wise, we will too. Many industries, like car manufacturers and tech companies, have people sign non competes or non-disclosure agreements. These forbid those employees from sharing anything if they take a job elsewhere because the companies don't want their competition to have access to their processes, tools, or ideas to give them a boost.

Yet here we are, with no such legal obstacles in place, and we tell someone who maybe can share a better way of doing things, "Nope. Keep it to yourself!" As the old saying goes, "If you do what you've always done, you're going to get what you always got!"

While we may not be building a high-tech system or supercar, we are doing something much greater: Saving lives. What if that other organization has figured out an answer to one of our problems, something that has caused harm or creates stress for our teams, and right in front of us is a person who knows exactly how to get that done for us, but we just don't want to hear it?

If a new hire shares ideas or ways they did things, be respectful and listen with an open mind. Maybe they're not bragging; perhaps they're just trying to make us better. And if they haven't volunteered anything, ask them that question early on in their employment—before they get too ingrained in the new system—so you can harvest that opportunity for process improvement.

Question #5: Is there any reason you feel this is not the right place for you? Is there anything that might cause you to want to leave?
This question provides a pulse check for how the employee is adjusting to the new role and allows managers to identify potential concerns for retention.

This question may be uncomfortable, but its power is in how direct it is. I've witnessed this process, and the new employee answered a few times, "Yes." Those are some startling and unsettling moments we all have as leaders. And as challenging a conversation as it is, afterwards, when the issues were addressed, the leader was able to find common ground and create a trust to keep those new employees on the job.

90-Day Meeting Questions
The purpose of the 90-day meeting is to continue to build the employee/leader relationship, provide feedback on the answers and suggestions obtained during the 30-day meeting, and demonstrate commitment and support for the new employee.

So, use the same questions at both the 30-day and 90-day interviews. But, in this interview, add two questions to the list.

Question 6: Do you know anyone who would be a good fit for our organization?
Ask this question, as referrals are an effective way to identify new employees!

Question 7: As your supervisor, how can I help you?
This question demonstrates your commitment to the employee's success. At this juncture, the employee should feel comfortable telling you about the support they might need to develop.

In summary, these are vital questions to ask both at the 30-day and 90-day interviews. It's not only a fantastic way to reduce employee turnover within the first quarter of that employee's tenure and get off to a good start, but it also serves you as a leader. The more real you can be as a leader, especially at the starting line, the more authentic your team will be with you and then you will see some real results at the finish line.

One hospital has greatly succeeded with 30- and 90-day re-interviews with new doctors. The process improvements allowed them to harvest great wins for the staff, they identified some frustrations for the physicians that were easy fixes, and leaders were especially pleased to hear physicians express their preference for that hospital when choosing where their patients would receive care. Physicians are under tremendous pressure now more than ever. Anything we can do to support them as we bring them on board and make their lives easier and more efficient is a win/win for us all.

30/90-day meetings are so effective at driving results across the pillars that they should be considered a must. They're easy to put in place and easier to maintain. You need, at most, a pad and pen, a few minutes, some compassionate listening, and a willingness to follow up.

It's not a lot to give, but you certainly get a lot in return.

Retention Key 3: Leader Rounding with Employees

> "To soar to what is possible, you must
> leave behind what's comfortable."
>
> *Cicely Tyson*

Sometimes we get comfortable with what we do. Taking a minute, resting, and recovering are all good things, but when we always lead from a place of comfort—never daring to stretch, push, or challenge ourselves—we don't get very far. Some leaders find the idea of rounding uncomfortable. I know many of the ones I coached did. And that's good.

I knew if they were uncomfortable and I could show them impact and progress and empower them, they'd find that on the other side of that discomfort was something worthwhile, new, and invigorating. When Huron first introduced the concept of leader rounding with employees, we boldly said we believed it was the #1 action to drive employee engagement. Twenty years later, we still say the same. And most likely, 50 years from now, we will as well.

If there are only a few things you take away from this book and begin to do stat, one should be leader rounding with employees. Often just putting this in place is enough to move the dial on engagement.

Why is leader Rounding with Employees so important?

Here are four powerful reasons that illustrate why rounding is so essential.

1. **Employee rounding helps leaders understand what matters most.** Excellent leaders don't just assume things. They are curious enough to want to learn.

    Recall the Huron study we referenced at the beginning of this principle. It found a big difference between what healthcare workers want and what leaders think is necessary. Surprisingly, leaders only got six out of the top 10 things right (See Figure 5.1).

    Do you think leaders missed this because they didn't care? I don't think so. They based what they thought mattered to their employees on their assumptions or personal biases.

    One of the most effective ways to discuss important matters with your team members is through leader rounding with employees. This approach lets you connect personally with your employees and understand what they value. By engaging in regular conversations and asking certain questions, we build stronger relationships with our team members and create a transparent and safe space to find out what is important to them.

2. **Employee rounding improves retention.** Most healthcare employees do not leave an organization because of pay, benefits, or because they want to leave the industry. Gallup's "State of the American Manager" states that 50% of Americans have left a job to "get away from their manager at some point in their career." Also, according to Gallup, "52% of voluntarily exiting employees say their manager or organization could have done something to prevent them from leaving their job. Over half of exiting employees (51%) say that in the three months before they left, neither their manager nor any other leader spoke with them about their job satisfaction or future with the organization."

    Think about what that means from a human standpoint. An organization thought highly enough of someone to spend the time and money to hire and train them and trust them with actual human lives, but not high enough to talk to them, check in with them, and make sure they were doing okay.

    That's like saying you love someone enough to ask them to marry you, live with you, and trust them with your ATM PIN, but not enough to find out what they like for dinner, what makes them feel special, where they want to go on vacation, or their favorite color. Some organizations create these professional relationships with people and feel like it can all be done on autopilot.

3. **Employee rounding increases engagement.** Rounding for outcomes builds trust between employees and leaders, which directly impacts employee engagement. When you have regular, purposeful, and outcomes-based conversations with your team, you show you are engaged, which in turn engages them.

4. **Employee rounding improves the patient experience.** Highly engaged healthcare employees are also willing to go above and beyond for patients. When we feel valued, we give value. When we feel cared for, we care more. When we are engaged, we create engagement all around us.

Making Rounding Matter

You might look at this evidence and think, "I'm good on this one. I talk to my employees all the time. I high-five my staff so much I have callouses!" I understand that leader visibility is a thing, and it's good to be visible, but that is not enough to create a culture of inspired excellence. Visibility is no substitute for engagement, communication, and connection.

You might even say, "Why do I need rounding? My team and I talk all the time!" That's sort of like saying, "Why do I need exercise? I lift things all the time—forks, coffee cups, my cat, and donuts."

It's not the same.

Lifting, when one is exercising, is deliberate and structured to become stronger and fitter. There is a specific process to fulfill those goals; it is an intentional action. Simple conversation is great, but it is simply that. It doesn't fix problems and empower teams. It's not a planned or intentional activity with a structured process to reach a goal.

So, how can you use this time in the best way to maximize the benefit for your employee and the organization?

Employee rounding is when a leader purposefully visits direct reports on a regular frequency with the intention to:

- Engage and listen.
- Build and maintain relationships.
- Reward and recognize exceptional performance, care, or service.
- Gather information.

- Identify processes that are either successful or require improvement.

- Be a more efficient leader.

- Become a more intentional leader.

As I've said before, we only have so much time and energy (as anyone who has ever worked a double shift can attest to), so we want to manage our time and energy to create better outcomes across the spectrum of all we do. That's where intention comes into play.

Think about a sailor on a sailboat. If she drops the sail and lets the boat bob around, the tide may move her along, but she isn't in control. But if she wants to get from Island A to Island B, she will have to assess the wind, set the sail, and make adjustments as needed, taking intentional actions to make that journey.

Rounding should be very intentional about what you're doing and what you are trying to get out of that exchange. You're setting your sails to get to where you intend to land. At Huron, we have learned that employees need these purposeful conversations, especially during times of disruption. Wouldn't it be the same for anyone you care about in life? If a loved one was struggling through a challenging time, wouldn't you get closer to them and listen to find out how you could make things maybe even a little better? That's the spirit of rounding, which is needed now more than ever.

With everything on your plate, you may feel you don't have time to do a bunch of employee surveys. I agree. Rounding on employees isn't a survey but about making time to have outcomes-based conversations. It takes intentional action to proactively address things while they are manageable flame-ups instead of raging infernos. One takes a cup or two of water to extinguish within seconds or minutes. The other takes fire trucks, helicopters, and a week or two of major effort.

For every five or 10 minutes spent on rounding for outcomes proactively, you may save yourself hours later. I know I did when I was a leader of a large department, and the leaders I coach also see this return on investment.

The Steps of an Effective Employee Round
STEP #1: PRE-ROUND—GET ORGANIZED
Don't rush into the conversation without taking time to review and prepare.

- Recall any personal information about the employee you know from working with them or the last round that you can now reference.

If you've rounded before, this is why a rounding log (we will get to that in detail in a bit) is so great. If they told you during the last rounding session that they would chaperone their son's field trip to Washington, D.C., it would be amazing to open by asking about that. It shows interest and respect. It also makes both of you more comfortable with the more outcomes-based questions.

- Review what you talked about last time you rounded with the employee. By doing this, you are showing what they said mattered. People want to be heard.

- Review the stoplight report. We will describe that shortly, but for now, it is a tool a leader uses to connect what has or hasn't been implemented since the last rounding session and helps the employee see the status of important things to them and others.

STEP #2: ROUND—THE CONVERSATION

	Element	Sample Key Words or Questions
1	**Concern and Care** Make a Meaningful Personal Connection.	*"How are you and your family doing?"* *"How is the new house/school/puppy, etc.?"* *"How was the first day of kindergarten for your son?"*
2	**Positives** Ask What is Working Well.	*"What's working well?"* *"What has been a positive experience with a patient or co-worker?* *"What good news have you heard these days?"* *"The new supply system has been up and running all quarter. Tell me something that's working well for you or the department since we started using it?"* *"What are you grateful for right now?"*
3	**Recognition** Harvest People to Recognize.	*"Is there a team member/physician I can recognize and why?"* *"Is there anyone who has been especially helpful to you?"* *"Who is doing a good job, you'd like to see recognized?"* *"What department/area/practice has impressed you lately?"*

Element	Sample Key Words or Questions
4 **Systems** Solicit Ideas for System Improvements.	*Are there any systems you want to improve? What are your ideas to fix them?"* "*What processes can be improved to make your work more efficient?"* "*What ideas do you have to help the unit improve quality or safety?"*
5 **Resources** Discuss What Resources They Need.	"*Do you have the resources (tools, equipment, and information) you need to do your job or care for patients today effectively?"*
6 **Follow-up** Follow up on What You Have Learned and Update Stoplight Report Where Appropriate.	"*Thanks for helping me make this a meaningful rounding session. Here is what I learned today and will follow up on this week."* Of course, use your version of this in your voice, but the key here is that you show appreciation for them giving you their time and assure them you will follow up on anything that needs your attention.

Figure 5.5: Key Elements of a Rounding Conversation

Also, if applicable, discuss quality, safety, or other area-specific topics and welcome any "tough questions." Soliciting and responding to tough questions is covered in Principle 8: Communicate at all Levels.

"Ice, ice, baby."

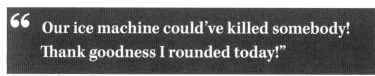

> **66 Our ice machine could've killed somebody! Thank goodness I rounded today!"**

Bonita, one of the nurse leaders I was coaching, yelled this at me as I walked past her office with her co-lead, Liem. The two of us backtracked into Bonita's office for an explanation.

"I was rounding on Amy, one of my respiratory techs, and she told me that when she was walking with Lonnie from phlebotomy, Lonnie suddenly lost her balance, and Amy caught her right before she fell. Amy said a few patients and visitors have almost wiped out over there!"

Shocked at hearing this, Bonita was even more surprised to understand the culprit. "Amy said the ice machine leaks, and everyone was so used to it they just throw towels underneath it, but sometimes the towels get so soaked the water creeps around and forms puddles! Well, I would never have found this out if it weren't for that Huron conference you sent me to, Rich, where we talked about asking questions during rounding about safety concerns that staff may have just accepted!"

Bonita confirmed the ice machine situation, then called facilities management. They just had to change out a rubber O-ring to fix the leak. Bonita was shaking her head in disbelief when Liem spoke up and admitted he'd known about the issue but, like everyone else, had gotten used to it.

Bonita reassured him, "We all get used to certain things, and unless someone helps us see it differently, we keep going. I get it. I probably passed that ice machine and towel pile twice a day and didn't think of it, either. We were lucky no one slipped and got hurt. Thankfully I found two other simple fixes elsewhere in the department when rounding with others that could've led to safety issues. I'm glad I asked."

Liem shook his head and reflected on how a faulty O-ring was the cause of the Challenger space shuttle disaster. "I'm not at all saying the two are even close to being the same," he clarified, but we all understood the larger message about how such a small thing led to such a big disaster.

We stood there for a moment, grateful that, in our case, asking a simple question prevented someone from suffering. Because that's what we are all in this healthcare life for, isn't it? To minimize or prevent suffering?

I can't encourage you enough to ask your team about safety when rounding and help them become re-engaged with the impact of the little things. What do they see? What should we see? Where are the "leaking O-rings" in your department?

There's something I would emphasize when soliciting positives, ask something like: "What are you grateful for right now?" It could be about work, or it could be about their life outside work.

I remember having a tough time with my oldest son when he was in elementary school. He had a learning disability and was struggling a bit personally and academically. So, I doubled down on staying close to him and communicating more. Whenever I picked him up from school, I always tried to be positive and ask, "How was school today?"

I'd always get the same answer—the things that went poorly or didn't go well. That is important to deal with, but it felt like that's all we did. What you give energy to is what grows. One day I decided to try a new approach and instead asked, "What's something that happened today that you're grateful about?"

It took him a minute to reset. But we needed a reset. "Well, you know math is hard for me, Dad, but today the teacher asked a math question, and I knew the answer, and I raised my hand, and she called on me… and I got it right! And Dad, the class cheered for me! I guess I'm grateful for that!"

That might sound trivial to some of you, but for those of us who have struggled academically or had kids who have, you know that these small victories are meaningful. We spent the whole 30-minute car ride talking about that math question, how he knew it, how he felt, and that his friends were proud of him, and we may or may not have gotten ice cream as well.

That was the question I used to "round" on my little boy moving forward until one day… I forgot. I was a bit distracted when I picked him up one day after a long shift at the hospital, and I probably just asked the age-old, "How was school today?" He was quiet and said, "Dad, you forgot to ask me what I'm grateful for."

I apologized, and he went on for the whole ride about some things that he was grateful for, that he was looking for and expecting all day. He told me every day he looks for things to be grateful for, and suddenly, he was finding them.

That's the thing about this question. When we know we will be asked what we are grateful for, we start to look for it. Guess what happens when you spend the day looking for something? You typically find it. It's how the mind works. I encourage this question because it opens a whole new way of finding the positive.

STEP #3: POST-ROUND—FOLLOW-UP

Remember that the round isn't complete until the follow-up is done. Proactive and intentional follow-up is crucial to earn trust and create a strong culture. It is easy to finish rounding on an employee and quickly get pulled to another task. However, get into the habit of pausing after the round to reflect on what you heard and observed. Ask yourself:

- What did I learn?

- What will I do with this information?

   – Who will you reward and recognize based on rounding?

   – What are barriers/issues, etc., you need to resolve?

   – Is there anything to add to the stoplight report?

Close the loop and take appropriate steps to address these questions. Information without action doesn't get you that far. You may need to reward and recognize a staff member, check on some supplies, or make a phone call. Also, document and update the rounding log. Give yourself these quick wins. As a leader, it feels incredible to learn about an issue and fix it asap. It feels even more incredible to hear from a manage up and be able to share it right away, creating that goodwill between you and your team. I always say don't wait on good news, especially in environments that crave it, like healthcare.

Rounding Tools—Don't Round Without Them!

If you were a lumberjack, you would need to know the reasons and best practices for cutting down a tree, but you'd also need some tools. Without the saws, axes, etc., you couldn't do much "logging."

Rounding is no different. You have to know the "how" and the "why," but there are a few tools of the trade, two critical tools—the rounding log and stoplight report.

These two tools work together to help leaders consistently close the loop and take action after rounding. They are your saw and your axe.

Rounding Tool #1: The Rounding Log

> What is a rounding log? It's a document that contains the questions and conversation points you use during rounding, with space for you to note answers and record feedback from your conversation with staff.

You might question whether it is appropriate to take notes as you round. It may feel very formal or like you aren't giving them your full attention. That's a reasonable concern. However, taking notes during a conversation sends a very positive message. It lets the person know what they say is important and that you value their input.

Think about when you go to your healthcare provider. In their assessment of you, they ask what medications you're on, what surgeries you've had, about your allergies, etc. Now, wouldn't you be a little concerned if they didn't document it? I mean, if a server in a restaurant doesn't write down my order and they accidentally bring me sparkling water instead of still water, I'll survive. If my healthcare provider doesn't write down that I'm allergic to something and prescribes something that might cause anaphylaxis, maybe I won't.

It is already second nature for healthcare professionals to document things because, as many of us learned in our training, "if it isn't documented, it isn't done!" That holds here. You might say, "This conversation is important to me, and I don't want to forget what we discussed today. I will take notes as we talk so I remember what I need to follow up on after our conversation." Documenting the conversation shows your respect and value for their words, especially when they see you take action on what they said.

Below is an example of a rounding log.

Name: Area:
Employee: Date:

STEPS	COMMENTS	
Relationship building/personal connection		
What's working well?		
Who can I recognize and why?	Who?	Why?
Do you have the tools and equipment to do your job?		
What ideas for systems or process improvement do you have?		
What can I do for you?		

SUMMARY

- Who will you reward and recognize based on rounding?
- What are barriers/issues, etc. you need to resolve?
- Is there anything to add to the stoplight report?

Review findings with next level leader in one-on-one meetings.

Figure 5.6 Rounding Log Example

Rounding Tool #2: The Stoplight Report

Gathering and keeping conversation notes in the rounding log is only one step. If all your healthcare provider did was to document, "patient complains of severe lower back pain, bloody urine, and has a history of kidney stones," shook your hand, left the room, and didn't do anything else, well, that would leave you wondering what happened.

So, it is crucial that the information your team shares with you when you round with them has a follow-up and follow-through component. Communicating BACK to employees what you've heard and what you are doing with that information is necessary. And you can do that with a stoplight report.

> What is a stoplight report? It is a way to show your team the progress and actions taken based on feedback, especially the two questions regarding tools and equipment as well as systems and processes. If you will, it is a living document that is updated regularly as you gather new information and take subsequent actions. It is displayed in an area where the team can always see it.

Here is the breakdown and an example:

- **Green:** These items say, "Work is complete." These things have been addressed based on two questions asked during rounding, and green communicates that the issues have been addressed. What a great way to harvest much-needed wins and show the team their input is valued and acted upon.

  - Issue: "We run out of routine office supplies nearly every month: tape, staples, paper, and toner for the copier."

  - Resolution: "Andrea is assigned responsibility to inventory and re-supply weekly, and we have approved an increase in the monthly supply budget to cover necessary items."

- **Yellow:** These items show "Work in progress." Documentation should provide steps completed and an estimated resolution date. If the date is unknown, state when the next update will be provided.

  - Issue: "Two chairs in the staff lounge are broken and unsafe."

  - Status: "We have temporarily borrowed two chairs from other departments and ordered replacements. They are on backorder, and we have a delivery date of July 8. If that changes, we will update as needed.

- **Red:** These items show "Can't complete at this time, and here's why."

  Be sure to explain WHY and, if possible, an alternate solution.

  - Issue: "There isn't enough staff parking."

  - Explanation: We do not have the physical space or land to build additional parking lots or garages. It is encouraged to continue using the offsite parking, free shuttle, or carpooling. We are unable to resolve this issue for the time being."

While no one likes to be told no, sometimes that is the reality. Being honest about the no serves two purposes. First, even though it is not always appreciated, the honesty behind it eventually is. Your team will have more respect for you than if you pretend to care and never fix the thing, leaving it for someone else to address down the road. Second, we all love being real in healthcare. As a leader, it becomes tiring to hear the same old complaint. Conversely, as a team member, you become tired of bringing up the same issue. A well-explained "no" allows everyone to move on from it, let go of the anxiety of false hope, and move to acceptance.

Below is a sample completed stoplight report for you to review. Note that we also speak to stoplight reports in Principle 8, and you can find some additional dos and don'ts to using this powerful communication tool.

GREEN = COMPLETED			
DATE	IMPROVEMENT ITEM OR RECOGNITION	RESOLUTION	DATE COMPLETE
4/25	Clarification of ER Tech duties is needed.	The Job Description is reviewed with CN and communicated to staff.	7/14
4/25	An additional refrigerator is requested for staff use.	Refrigerator was ordered and installed in the breakroom.	7/1
5/2	Create new "code blue bags" with essentials for code patients.	The bags are complete, and the supply closet is stocked. (Thank you Jamie!)	7/8
6/2	Need more tele packs.	The hospital purchased additional packs, and is in use.	7/8
7/22	Raheem from security offered fast support when a violent patient was striking out at staff.	A group thank you note was sent to Raheem's home address with a $10 Starbucks gift card.	8/1

YELLOW = IN PROGRESS			
DATE	IMPROVEMENT ITEM	STATUS	UPDATED
3/27	Need a better flow model for BH admissions.	Working with BH Dir. & ED CN. The target deadline for model changes remains 8/31.	7/31
5/2	Better handoff on admission is needed.	Pilot in process. Staff report improvements. Pilot completion is pushed back two weeks to 8/14.	7/31
6/22	More continuity is needed during triage processes.	A multi-disciplinary task force was formed to review the current triage process. All ambulance patients will go to a bed unless there are zero beds. This protocol starts on 8/4.	7/31
6/22	Need a Focused Assessment with Sonography in Trauma machine—ED specific.	FAST is being reviewed as an option by the task group. The idea has merit, but it may not be the right time now—the final decision will be made by 8/15.	7/31
6/22	More IV poles are needed.	The hospital purchased a bulk supply. Expect delivery by 8/30.	7/31

RED = CAN NOT DO			
DATE	IMPROVEMENT ITEM	EXPLANATION	UPDATED
5/25	Raise for paramedics and increase per diem rate.	Financial constraints across the hospital have put a hold on all future increases until further notice.	7/31
6/1	Too many patients in the hallway.	Lack of space requires the unit to continue using the hallway to bed patients.	7/31
6/1	Request for more monitors for hallway patients.	The purchase of additional Dash monitors is not feasible due to current budget constraints. This item is added to next year's budget/capital expense.	7/31
5/21	Meditech documentation system—not user-friendly.	No plan for change as we remain committed to the Meditech platform. More training is being provided.	7/31

Figure 5.7: Completed Stoplight Report Emergency Department Example

It is one thing to make a stoplight report and another to keep it current. Update your stoplight report at least once a month or at the very least once a quarter. Remove anything in the green that has been completed and communicated. Update items in yellow, especially if a date or timeframe is given. Remove anything in red once you notice people have stopped bringing it up in rounds.

This stoplight report is a reflection on your leadership. Accountability starts inside before it can be expected outside. Embrace it, because it will make you a better leader and your department a better place to work, all through transparent communication.

Rounding Tips for Success
Tip #1: Hardwire the process.
Make it non-negotiable, or it may not get done. Many leaders have found great success when they schedule specific rounding appointments or block time on their calendars for this activity. Some leaders find it helpful to post rounding times so staff can schedule themselves. Learn to create a cadence by completing two or three a day; whatever fits your staff levels and needs. I have had days where I rounded on 10 staff, and I have had days where I rounded on zero. Give yourself some grace. Just don't give yourself excuses. Find what works and do that. If your organization commits to rounding—and they should—it will become a must-have part of your culture.

DO YOU REALLY HAVE TIME NOT TO ROUND?

Let's address the elephant in the room. Your time.

Without a doubt, we are in the middle of some of the most disruptive and challenging times in healthcare. And because of this, it is easy to let rounding slip when disruption occurs. We might lose focus or avoid asking people to do one more thing. It feels there isn't enough time for you to round or ask your staff to stop their work for this conversation.

In fact, we feel the opposite is true. Organizations who have kept a strong commitment to this practice even during times of disruption and workforce challenges prove it is time well spent.

When workforce challenges seem too much, and you don't feel you have time to round, here are some important reasons to consider to stay committed to this practice.

- **Employees want a relationship with you.** Rounding with employees builds relationships, shows you care, and shows you value them. During times of disruption, your relationship with them matters more than ever.

- **Employees need efficiency.** Remember that rounding with employees creates efficiency for busy employees. It is proactive way to handle problems BEFORE they occur. It addresses the tools they need to do their job, the obstacles that might be in the way, and how you can help them.

- **Employees need encouragement.** Harvesting recognition during rounds and sharing it with your employees gives people hope and encouragement when their world might be spinning.

- **Employees appreciate intentional conversations.** Rounding is not about doing more, but doing something better. Think about it. You are already having conversations with your employees. This is about taking conversations you are already having and making them more intentional and purposeful. They pave the way for meaningful and relationship-building discussions to show people and their well-being matter to you.

- **Employees need people to stay.** Also remember how much more time it takes to replace an employee if they leave—the time you spend posting replacement positions, interviewing, hiring, and training. Rounding with employees saves time in the long run and leads to a more engaged and stable workforce.

Tip #2: Use your own words.
Rounding is a framework, not a script. As we said in rounding on patients, use your voice; be you! Even a framework can be adapted and personalized. Like every new skill, it may feel a little formal at first, but you'll make it your own after a while.

Tip #3: Proactively manage the round.
Some people may need more of you. If you need to redirect a conversation that starts to stray, that's okay. If there are deeper topics that need deeper conversations, schedule those. Also, set up the situation well at the beginning. Call the interaction a "round" and let them know the intended duration. You might say, "I commit to keeping our round brief, about 10 minutes or so. Your time is valuable to me, so I will keep us focused." After a while, the team will get used to this, and it will flow easily.

Tip #4: Actively manage engagement.
Use key words to convey the importance of staff's opinions and input. Let them know you need their help to create a culture of recognition and confirm they are instrumental in identifying issues and barriers (processes/systems to improve). Also, when employees do not actively

engage in discussion, remind them of the purpose and ask for help. Feel free to reschedule if they remain disengaged and ask them to prepare for a meaningful conversation in a day or two. The key is no opting out!

TIPS FOR ROUNDING DURING CHALLENGING TIMES

Location Change. During the disruption, be flexible on the perfect "location" for your round. Remember rounding should not be a formal sit-down meeting in your office. Save time by meeting in the hallway, a vacant room, or in the break room—anywhere that allows for a private conversation. It saves time for you and the employee.

Delegate Responsibly and Cautiously. Remember the primary goal of rounding with your employees is to build and foster strong relationships with them. Delegation may seem like a quick fix, but in reality, when you delegate you are giving up an opportunity to build and grow your personal relationship with someone. In times when delegations are necessary, delegate only to other leaders on your team who are skilled and trained in employee rounding. Consider delegating a large group or section of your direct reports and rotating groups monthly. For example, divide your group between leaders on your team. To ensure effectiveness, add a leader/charge nurse collaboration meeting to bring back any trends from rounding to ensure the leadership team is aligned and addressing needs from each round.

Build Your Leader-Rounding Employee Muscle. Sometimes the hardest part of a task is getting started and taking that first step. Here are a few suggestions to start the process and get to the frequency needed for great results.

- Set a reasonable frequency goal and timeline: Define an initial goal for the frequency of rounds and establish a timeline for increasing frequency until you can meet the best-practice guidelines.

- Commit to your daily goal: Whatever the initial number of rounds you decide on, commit to meeting that goal daily. Increase the number of rounds gradually as you feel comfortable until you reach the best-practice frequency.

Tip #5: Keep it personal and individual.
Employee rounding is not a group activity. As tempting as it may be to walk into the employee lounge during lunch and power round with

a group, that is not what is intended. Rounding is meant to build 1:1 personal relationships and allow every singular voice to be heard. Rounding with an individual one at a time creates a more valuable and meaningful connection.

Tip #6: Timing is everything.

If you begin a rounding discussion and it is clear that person can't focus on anything positive (what's working well, someone to recognize, etc.), it's probably not the right time to round. Instead, listen empathetically to the challenges the person is facing, help them think through solutions as appropriate, and state that you'll come back the following day/later in the week to continue the rounding discussion. Prompt them if they still can't identify anything positive or someone helpful. Show them you're serious about these two questions. It's possible that some of your team may not be so easy to round with or might push back a bit. That's okay. You're up for the challenge.

> ## 66 Don't give up on Barb.

Barb was the staff member who truly taught me the value of rounding. Not because she was so awesome to round with, but because she made it hard for me. When she saw me approaching with my rounding log in hand and my "I'm going be the best manager ever" smile on my face, she rolled her eyes at me harder than a 14-year-old being told that they can't hang out at the mall with their friends unless a parent is at least 10 feet behind them.

Whenever I asked, "Is there anyone in the department that has gone above and beyond that I can recognize?" she'd smirk and say, "Everyone. We are this hospital's hardest working department, so yeah, everyone." Awesome.

Finally, one day I wised up. After I asked that question for the umpteenth time and Barb gave me her snarky answer, I opened the other notebook in my hand, with the names of every staff member listed in alphabetical order.

"Great! So, let's go through them all, and you can tell me specifically what they did. Let's start with the As—Acevedo? Adams? Adderly?"

She knew I had called her bluff. Before I could move to the Bs, she yelled, "Bonelli! Desiree Bonelli!"

"Oh, awesome, Barb. What did she do that impressed you?"

"Well, the other day, there was a large family here, and they were upset, and I was worried things were going to escalate. But Desiree entered the room and connected with a few family members. By the end of the night, everyone was smiling. She does that a lot. So, yeah, Desiree should be managed up."

At first, I wanted to revel in the smug satisfaction that I finally got Barb to cough up a compliment. But the sincerity of what she said and how she said it was touching. I thanked her and told her that coming from someone like her, who had such high standards of caring for her patients, meant a lot.

I immediately found Desiree and shared with her what Barb had said. Her smile was like a bright summer day! She went and found Barb and gave her a big hug.

In martial arts, there's a saying: "A black belt is simply a white belt that never quit." The same holds here. Don't give up on the "Barbs" of your team. They need you. Even when rounding gets tough, keep at it. Don't quit.

Don't Forget to Round with Physicians and Clinical Providers

Rounding is not only for direct reports. Physicians and other clinical providers appreciate the chance to connect with a leader and have personal time to share their experiences. Use the same framework, but be aware of the five key drivers of physician engagement:

- **Care Quality.** Physicians want to know their patients receive high-quality care and a top-notch experience. Let them know you share this expectation. Ensure procedures and processes are consistent and reliable to ensure safety during an episode of care. Encourage your organization to invest in leading practices and new technologies that lead to better outcomes. Share quality data consistently so physicians know where the organization is trending. Make sure to listen to their input and discuss solutions collaboratively.

- **Efficiency.** A physician can lose hours a day if departments run inefficiently or if the clinical staff is not prepared with necessary information when that physician returns a call or is left on hold. Some organizations have partnered with their physicians and asked them to create a wish list of what they'd like staff to have on hand or know when they call to check on their patients. Standardized processes and support training around evidence-based medicine relieve stress, give physicians enough time to engage with patients, and facilitate improvements that reduce firefighting.

- **Input.** Ask physicians for ideas about what they believe is working well and where they feel the organization can improve. Model curiosity by speaking 20% of the time and listening 80% of the time. Consult with physicians before implementing changes that impact care quality in their area of expertise. We often listen with our own biases, which might cause us to miss out on a great opportunity, so never squash an idea immediately, even if your initial reaction to it isn't positive. Be open, be interested, and be compassionate.

- **Responsiveness.** Promptly fix the issues you can and follow up on things that will take longer to resolve. Our physicians often manage complex processes and deal with difficult issues, and part of their reality is enacting quick and timely resolutions. So, they will appreciate it if you discuss issues transparently. Close the loop one-on-one or create a stoplight report to share updates more broadly and proactively.

- **Appreciation.** Physicians are no different than anyone else, and they value a thank you and acknowledgment when things are going well. Celebrate milestones such as tenure, published articles, committee memberships, children's graduations, birthdays, etc.—often. Recognize positive behaviors, efforts, and results in team meetings, one-on-one, and company communications (e.g., newsletters, updates, etc.). Encouragement increases positive momentum, and initiative should be praised, not discouraged. Physicians are great resources as partners, healers, and teachers. The majority take great pride and derive much personal satisfaction from sharing knowledge. Embrace and celebrate that.

66 Doubting to Believing.

One of our leadership coaches, Faye, had an outstanding experience moving a physician leader from doubter to believer. Faye had the opportunity to partner with the chief of emergency medicine in a large healthcare system. Their job was to address sagging employee engagement in the face of a high census and limited staffing.

Faye shared that the chief was more than a bit skeptical about conducting "fluffy rounds" with his busy team of providers. She proposed that he do three rounds before he made his final decision. There's an old saying: Sometimes you have to taste the soup before you pour it down the drain. Faye was never one to quit easily and knew he might like the soup if he gave it a chance.

The first round went well and took about six minutes. The staff physician was eager to share, openly appreciative of the chief's time, and welcomed further opportunities for 1:1 dialogue. Afterward, the chief admitted, "All right, I get it now. I thought I had regular interactions with my team. But our quick conversation surpasses anything I'm currently doing for engagement and retention. I'm committed to doing this."

The soup was better than he thought!

This chief went on to hardwire the practice and served as a champion with his peers and chiefs of other service lines. It resulted in a huge win regarding engagement survey results and a better place to work for the providers. So, before you let any of your physicians dump out the soup, offer them a bowl, put a spoon in their hand, and let them get a taste. Just wait; they'll come "round" for more!

Retention Key 4: Stay Interview and Retention Conversations

Too many organizations have employees with one foot out the door, and we, as leaders, have no idea. Survey after survey shows that many workers across all fields actively search for job opportunities elsewhere. A quick internet search will show that at least one of the causes of quitting a job is poor communication.

An inspired leader doesn't wait for signs of trouble. They are forward-looking and future-facing, and they know that success is all about the team. The higher the team performs, the higher the organization can go. So, inspired leaders stay close to their teams and create a culture where communication is frequent, meaningful, and purpose-driven. We call these communications "stay interviews" or "stay conversations."

Stay interviews aren't new but are coming up more often as employers ramp up retention efforts during periods of record turnover. For years, Huron taught about having specific conversations with high performers to show them their value and ensure they are inspired and encouraged enough to keep that value invested in your organization. Stay interviews use that same concept and purposefully help people playing job "hokey pokey" get BOTH feet back in!

> Stay conversations are one-on-one conversations designed to learn more about the employee, including their passions and career goals, what they value in life, and what they need to be more successful and engaged in their role. Effective stay conversations are two-way exchanges that reach the heart of the individual's needs, motivations, and engagement drivers.

The goal of these stay conversations is three-fold yet simple: re-recruit, recognize, and retain your high performers. They not only build but strengthen relationships.

I knew a guy who was an engineer, and his main job was assessing bridges in his state. He told me most bridges don't show signs of issues in their first few years. That's why you must regularly check on them to ensure they are stable, dealing with stress well, and have no apparent cracks, or they will collapse.

Sound familiar? A relationship might be great at first, but over time stressors may begin to wear away at it and, if they are not dealt with early and well, will lead to a collapse. The "waters" of healthcare can often be troubled; we need to make sure our bridges are okay.

Now, stay interviews are intended to be informal conversations. However, that doesn't mean you shouldn't be prepared. Here are four critical elements of the conversation:

- Offer sincere thanks and specific appreciation for their effort and work. They need to feel valued. It is worth repeating that saying things like, "You're doing a good job!" is okay, but saying things like, "You have received more letters of thanks from patients and their families than anyone else in this department this month. The theme of all of them is that you are a kind, present, and professional caregiver. Dr. Achebe emailed me today and said she never worries about the world whenever you have her patients. That is so amazing. I am grateful to have you on this team," is much more individual, meaningful, and encouraging of similar future behavior.

- Talk about why individuals are so important to an organization. When people feel part of something bigger, they understand and appreciate the organization. And their impact on the organization gets way bigger when that happens too!

- Explain where your organization is headed and what steps are being taken to achieve those goals. This kind of information is incredibly motivating for high performers who want to be involved in the process and feel like they're making a difference.

- Ask them for input. Let them know you want to retain them and give them time to share their thoughts and ideas. My dad would say, "Tell me your ideas without worrying if I agree. Assume a 'yes,' and if it is a 'no,' you at least practiced using your mind, which will serve you in life because many people are out of practice!" Ask if there is anything you should be doing better and what they need from you, including any areas where you, as a leader, can improve.

Some creative ways to stimulate conversation and input might include:

- What excites you about coming to work?

- What are you most grateful for?

- Do you feel good about the impact of your work?

- What do you want to do more of at work? Less?

- What should we do more of around here? What should we do less of?

- Do you see any waste of resources that we can fix?

- Are there any obstacles to your engagement or growth that I can address?

- Have you thought about transferring or leaving? If so, what are the reasons? (Yes, ask this direct question! I've shared this already, but I cannot tell you how many wins have come from this question. Be prepared. Your goal as an excellent leader is to retain your high performers, but if they aspire to greater than what you can provide, be big enough to help them achieve those. Be brave enough to ask this question and humble enough to hear what is said.)

- Do you see a future for yourself at the company? How are things the same or different?

- What would you do differently if you were a manager for a day?

Remember, people will only honestly share how they feel about work if they feel a sense of psychological safety—that they can speak freely without fear of retaliation and know their feedback will be fully accepted. Be vulnerable and tell them how much they mean to you and the organization. Doing so allows you to partner with your best and brightest to become even better and brighter. As author and researcher Brene Brown said, "Vulnerability is the birthplace of innovation, creativity, and change."

Retention Key 5: Senior Leader Rounding

> Senior leader rounding occurs when an executive, individually or in partnership with other leaders, systematically and purposefully connects with departments and patients throughout the organization regularly.

66 I'M KIND OF A BIG DEAL…"

I worked with a senior leader many years ago who felt she was very visible to the organization. When coached on senior leader rounding, she responded, "Everyone knows me! I don't think this is a good use of my time. My picture is plastered all over this place."

And it was. There were newsletters and posters, even a billboard or two plastered with this leader's picture. She was visible, and her immediate colleagues said she was a lot of fun to work with. But much like with Faye's story earlier, I needed this leader to "taste the soup." So, I got her to agree to some senior leader rounding. She smiled at me and said, half-jokingly, "This is going be easy… I'm kind of a big deal around here."

We rounded first on the emergency department. As a former E.D. leader and spouse of a former E.D. nurse, I can confirm that folks in the E.D. can be… direct. The leader introduced herself to a nurse and made her rounding request. The nurse replied, "I've seen your picture on billboards! Did you know your picture is on a bus bench outside my apartment building? I've never met you before, but you're clearly a big deal!"

The senior leader froze. The moment was not planned and in no way was the nurse being shady—her energy, demeanor, and posture were very warm. But the message was heard. We rounded on three other nurses in the E.D., two techs in the lab, one respiratory therapist, and one person from patient access. They all recognized this leader's face. Yet none of them had ever heard her voice, seen her in person, or knew much about her.

She was highly visible and yet somehow also invisible. This leader was extremely kind, very personable, compassionate, and, as I said, fun. But you can't tell that from a picture on a bus bench.

Over time she fell in love with senior leader rounding. She loved it so much that she asked her board to include it in her evaluation metrics. Even better was that her staff fell in love with rounding with her.

She was one of those people that have a scary good memory, and while she kept logs, she would see someone in the hallway that she rounded on and remember to ask them about their friend who had been sick or their daughter who went into the Air Force, or the restaurant they recommended. She created connections and learned much about what was happening in her organization. She was able to send personal letters to people for recognition. She was able to fix problems, procure equipment, and even was invited to a wedding! All because she got off the billboard and got into the hallways.

She told me she felt like she was in a rut and that senior leader rounding "Saved my career. I will do it until the day I retire."

She was kind of a big deal.

Don't ever assume that a title creates connection—leaders make it their business to connect. As the great athlete Michael Jordan reminds us, "Earn your leadership every day." Senior leader rounding is important for senior leaders to do just that.

Senior leader rounding is a powerful and proactive tool for senior leaders to connect, recognize, and reward specific staff members. But it's not just about patting people on the back. Effective senior leader rounding will:

- Build relationships.

- Reward and recognize teams and individuals who are doing their jobs well.

- Create a two-way dialogue between executives and department team members, and patients.

- Role-model leadership and rounding behaviors.

- Obtain a pulse of the organization.

- Celebrate wins.

- Support and advocate for the department leaders by reinforcing and aligning key messaging.

- Harvest best practices.

- Eliminate the we/they mentality. Rounding with the front-line director/manager helps fulfill this purpose well.

Stoplight Report, Rounding Logs, and Scouting Reports

Three tools are used as part of the senior leader rounds to set them up for success.

- **Stoplight Report:** Senior leaders can review the latest stoplight report. It will allow them to anticipate tough questions around the "red light" issues and be supportive of the local leader. Also, they can be prepared to manage up the green and yellow on behalf of that leader.

- **Rounding Log:** Document your findings in a log for follow-up on items as appropriate.

- **Scouting Report:** Provide a department summary regarding what is happening in the department before they visit. We call these scouting reports. They summarize such things as recognition opportunities, personal bright spots in employees' lives, improved department results, anniversaries, birthdays, and questions the team might ask. When the round is scheduled, ensure the area leader provides the completed scouting report at least 48 hours before the round. With this expectation in place, senior leaders should feel comfortable canceling the round if no scouting report is provided.

Here is an example of a scouting report:

Senior Leader Scouting Report

Date:	August 5
Senior Leader:	Juanita Martinez
Dept/Unit:	Med Surg – 2 North
Unit Leader:	Brian Matthews

Area Specific Information	**Comments** *(enter information/notes here)*
1. Accomplishments of the Dept./Unit	• 0% turnover in the last six months • We are performing better than budget; staff commitment to efficiencies with inventory have made a difference
2. New Tools or Equipment Purchased	• A new copy machine was purchased for the unit • EMR rollout in the Department has been flawless; staff are positive and open to coaching
3. Employees to Recognize (may include employees from ancillary services as well)	• Randy Smith, RN (13 yrs.): 7 positive comments from patient surveys in this quarter • Lisa King (2 yrs.); became a grandma (1st time) • Joe Smith, CNA (22 yrs.) mentors new CNAs
4. Employee Engagement (employee engagement initiatives / scores / wins / issues)	• Decision to delay the renovation of employee break rooms across the organization
5. Tough Questions or Issues (common issues or concerns brought up by employees)	• Decision to delay the renovation of employee break rooms across the organization
6. Patient Experience (recent scores / wins / issues / patient experience initiatives)	• Patient survey results for "friendliness of staff" at >85th percentile for three consecutive quarters
7. Provider Activities or Issues (wins / issues / who to recognize and why)	• Recognizing Dr. Smith—he is a role model for how to use the electric medical record *with* patients for staff and other physicians

Figure 5.8: Senior Leader Scouting Report Example

Leadership Tips for an Effective Senior Leader Round

We at Huron have learned much about Senior Leader Rounding over the years. Here are some tips and insights to consider.

We at Huron have learned much about Senior Leader Rounding over the years. Here are some tips and insights to consider.

- Model behavior: We can't emphasize enough how important it is for leaders to lead by example. CEOs should round on their senior leaders just like they want their leaders to round on their direct reports. The way the CEO rounds sets the tone for everyone else, so it's crucial to get it right.

- Team with the leader: Senior leader rounding is a team effort. If you're a senior leader, ensure before entering an area. Get a scouting report from the leader of that area so you know what to expect. Preparation helps you avoid any surprises and lets you know what issues need to be addressed and which staff members deserve recognition.

- Harvest ideas: Another great tip is to look for good ideas to harvest. If someone is doing a great job with something, like electronic medical records, take the time to recognize their success. But don't stop there! Ask them what they're doing that works so well and how the organization can get others on board.

- Follow-up: Make sure you follow up with people after you've rounded. Let them know that you listened to what they had to say and that you're taking action where appropriate. Solid follow-up helps build trust and shows that you're committed to making things better.

- Let the leader capture wins: The senior leader's role is not to be the hero of the day. You want it clear that you didn't magically come across this information but that the team leader shared it with you. It creates a win for all. For example, as senior leaders round, they can manage up items in the brief and stoplight report. They can give a leader credit for getting those additional monitors or new desk chairs that were requested. Senior leaders can manage up a leader as they provide rewards and recognition. Say things like, "Margie shared how helpful you've been as a preceptor. She said your last three precepts have become some of the highest performers here! Thank you for helping to create our next generation of outstanding team members!"

- Thank you notes: We will discuss thank you notes in Principle 9, but these rounds will allow the senior leader to send a handwritten message to the employee's home for great work that they notice or hear during the rounds. This level of personal engagement and recognition creates an outstanding culture of recognition that starts from the top.

- Highlight department successes: Discuss performance highlighted in the department communication, such as successful fall reduction, infection control, or decrease in employee accidents. It is also a great time to reinforce the goals and outcomes the department is set to achieve.

- Scheduling: Determine a round schedule and put it on the calendar as a must-do. Make it known to anyone who can add to your calendar that this time is nothing less than sacred, and only the truest of emergencies should interrupt it.

- Hardwire: Set a time for an executive review of findings and actions taken from rounds across all senior leader rounds.

66 Uncovering the water wells."

I recently heard an awesome CEO talk to his team about the importance of senior leader rounding.

When he was the CEO of a hospital near a large army base that also had a hospital, he connected with the general of that base and hospital leaders to create relationships. As the CEO got to know him better, the general shared a story about the impact of "keeping your team's voices in your ears."

One day the general was making the rounds of the base and talking with his other officers and enlisted soldiers. He noticed that on one of the training fields the drill sergeant was going back and forth on a golf cart carrying large water dispensers to ensure the soldiers stayed hydrated in the hot sun.

The general stopped the sergeant and asked if this was the best use of his time. The sergeant shared that he had inquired about running some pipe to get the water closer to the training grounds but was told the cost was too high. Recent deep budget cutbacks were already causing a lot of stress on the general. He began the arduous process of trying to move money around to get this problem fixed, but he kept running into walls.

The next day he was rounding with his team, one of whom was the groundskeeper. The general mentioned the issue with the water and expressed how frustrated he was about this. The groundskeeper, who had been there for many years, scratched his head and said, "Well what about all the water wells?"

It turned out that when the first round of cutbacks had happened years earlier, the many water wells in the fields were covered up and capped off. In the intervening years, the grass-covered over the wells.

The general was shocked. "Do you know where these wells are?"

Fairly confident that he did, the groundskeeper and the general took off immediately to the training field with shovels in hand. After digging some test holes, they found several of the wells and used some stored supplies to re-tap into them, purge the lines, and provide clean, cold water for the soldiers to use.

We often accept a problem because "that's how it's always been." Still, if we are open and humble enough to have conversations with our team—often through rounding—many times we will find they are untapped reservoirs of valuable information. No one thought to ask the groundskeeper for input, while he had the fix ready to go all along. Maybe you have a few "covered water wells" in your organization?

Principle 5 Summary

There is a science as well as an art to employee engagement, and what you've just read gives you a lot to work with. Ultimately, it all comes down to ensuring that as leaders we are doing all we can to provide our teams the environment, tools, and culture they need to be their best, feel their best, and give their best. People get into healthcare for big reasons: they are driven by a higher purpose and crave meaning and affirmation in the work they do. The work is hard—sometimes even heartbreaking—and we would be wise to remember that even the toughest among us still need reassurance, support, and inspiration.

In many ways leaders are artists. While you may not be creating a painting or a sculpture, I would argue that making someone feel valued and engaged is the highest form of art. It is making life better for your teams, patients, organization, and, yes, you. Your masterpiece awaits!

PRINCIPLE 6:
BE ACCOUNTABLE

Commit to Individual Accountability to Achieve Organizational Goals

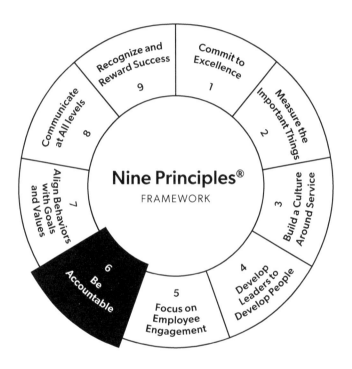

"Ninety-nine percent of all failures come from people who have a habit of making excuses."

George Washington Carver

Retired U.S. Navy SEAL Jocko Willink talks about "extreme ownership," where leaders accept responsibility for everything that happens under their watch with no blame or excuses.

This idea of accountability is not only an essential nutrient in our diet of "inspired excellence," it is a non-negotiable part of our success. Principle 6 focuses on creating a sense of ownership within the organization. It begins with a decision we make as leaders to hold ourselves accountable for what we think, say, and do, thus modeling the behavior we want to see all around us and setting the standard we want others to follow.

Leadership accountability leads to organizational accountability. It is an inside-out process. Someone can be "held" but can't be "made" accountable. Accountability is an internal decision, a conviction.

This chapter is about creating a culture where people are inspired to be accountable for their actions. They make that choice, and they own it. These are places where people have a deep connection to their work and live the organizational values, engage with their teams, accomplish organizational goals, and consistently innovate for success, not because they are told to, but because they've learned the skills and developed the mindset where there is now an internal drive to do so.

Remember this: People support what they create.

The human spirit wants to feel like it is a part of something bigger, memorable, and meaningful. It is creating something that naturally breeds ownership. It draws us to work more efficiently and effectively because we participate in it. You don't want it to fail because you feel that if it fails, you fail.

As far as you are concerned, I know that is not an option. Your reading this shows your ownership, commitment, and sense of accountability to excellence for you, your team, and your organization.

So, this chapter focuses on what it takes to be an accountable team member and leader. It links being accountable to standards of behavior, describes the characteristics of employees who are owners of their work, and reinforces the significance of hiring people who align with the organizational culture. We will also learn the impact of peer-to-peer conversations and highlight how these tactics inspire innovation.

Being Accountable— What Does it Mean?

> "Have patience. All things are difficult before they become easy."
>
> ~*Saadi*

A culture of accountability is easy to write about but more challenging to establish and maintain. As I've often said, just because it is "easier said than done" doesn't mean it is not worth doing. Often doing the difficult things upfront can offload the weight. In other words, it isn't easy until it is not. Or, the more accountable the culture you create as a leader now, the easier your job will be and the better outcomes you will achieve in the long run.

> Accountability is being responsible and answerable for one's actions and decisions. It involves taking ownership of one's responsibilities, obligations, and commitments and being willing to accept the consequences that result from them.

Accountability doesn't refer to the big things— essential meetings, key presentations, or an extensive system rollout. Accountability lives in the simple activities of our day-to-day work life and the systems and processes your organization implements to be successful. It is what you write in an email, how you carry yourself when conducting a meeting, follow through on feedback during rounding, and communicate with your team based on their performance. It is about making sure that what you say and do aligns with your closely held values.

What that all means is simply this: A culture of accountability starts with you.

Innovation

Let's not forget the impact being accountable has on innovation. New ideas, even radically new thoughts, are most likely to be generated when psychological safety—feeling safe to dream, explore, and even fail—is a characteristic of the workgroup. It is also beneficial to have systems to encourage and reward innovative ideas.

Generating innovative thinking takes more than a "suggestion box." For several years Huron worked with an organization that required two "Bright Ideas"—submitted and implemented—as part of the annual bonus payout. Adopt/adapt your own strategic approach:

• Develop a "Bright Ideas" program.

• Create an "Innovation Club."

• Develop a structured reward system for implemented ideas.

Renters vs. Owners

If you "rent" the outcomes or culture, you aren't as invested as you would be if you had a sense of emotional and intellectual "ownership." Like I said in a previous chapter, if you were to describe the best performer or speaker you ever saw, you'd say, "They OWNED that room!" No one says, "HEY! You need to take rentership of your actions!"

Note that this is not literal nor disparaging the renting of physical items or property. This is about mentality. If you prefer, you could also think of it as observers versus creators. You may be pretty involved with a thing you casually observe from a distance, but you will be strongly involved with something that you've closely worked on and created.

You will see the word "ownership" often in this chapter because it is tightly tied to accountability. We refer to owners as those who see themselves as co-owners or co-creators of the organizational mission and goals. They develop a sense of individual accountability to see that things get done at the highest performance levels. Owners strive for excellence in their personal and professional continuous improvement process.

> **❝ My hospital—My signature.**

Glenda, a housekeeper at the hospital for more than 24 years, was turning over a room one evening when I stopped to visit her while making night rounds. Her attitude was so positive, and I thanked her for that and how she carried out our mission each day.

She said to me, "It's the baseboards."

I wasn't sure what she meant. "Baseboards? Tell me more."

"The signature I leave in every room for our patients is clean baseboards. I guess you can say it's my thing. A clean room is a safe room. When someone enters a room, it looks, smells, and feels clean. They feel safe. Especially with all the germs and viruses out in this world these days! I love to clean, and I love my job and this hospital. If I were sick, I'd want clean baseboards, and I want our patients to have them, too."

If that wasn't enough, Glenda shared that she lived in the same neighborhood as the hospital and walked to work daily, even in rain or snow. Every day she walked up to the hospital, she looked at the big green letters on top and thought, "That is my hospital, and those are my baseboards."

As I walked away, I wondered if I ever looked at the shining neon logo on my hospital the same way Glenda did. She saw it as a reminder that what she did and where she did it mattered. Her work made a difference.

What is the "signature" you leave at your work every day?

Standards of Behavior

Principle 6 is all about being accountable. But let's be honest. Unless we determine and communicate what's acceptable and what's not, it will be tricky for people to know how to be accountable.

This is why Standards of Behavior are so important.

> Standards of Behavior are specific actions and behaviors every colleague will commit to, role model, and perform.

I also can't help but think about how standards of behavior make the definition of culture we discussed in Principle 1 come alive. Standards will direct what we see and say, what we do and don't do, and what we think and believe. They make your mission and vision come alive and help drive the outcomes across your pillars.

Standards of behavior allow you to be very specific about what good behavior looks like and spell out the behaviors we expect individuals to exhibit at work. They address how we interact with people and what we all agree to live by when working together.

Why are Standards of Behavior so Important?

Well-defined and effectively executed standards of behavior play a crucial role in any organization, shaping its culture and bringing it to life. Also, they are not meant to give people more to do or a document of rules to follow. They are intended to make work easier.

They do this because they define what "right" looks like in your organization. They set the bar to know how to effectively reward, recognize, and hold performance conversations as needed. Think about it this way. Without standards of behavior, you're leaving it up to individuals to decide which behaviors align with your values, and it may not all be moving in the same direction.

These standards of behavior provide a unified approach to reward and recognition, allowing everyone in the organization to acknowledge and appreciate others for living up to the standards. Recognition from leaders is undoubtedly essential, but peer recognition can be equally significant. As the saying goes, "what gets recognized gets repeated," "what you honor will become habits," and "what gets complimented becomes commonplace."

Also, they provide an outward sign of the organization's mission, vision, and values. They aren't just words on a sign in the elevator but are living, breathing concepts demonstrated by what you say and do. (There is that culture definition again!)

By defining specific behaviors that every person is expected to perform, whether working with patients, families, colleagues, or the community, these standards provide clarity and leave no room for ambiguity. They set a bar that says, "If you don't do this, you are outside of who we are and what we believe."

This framework helps to recruit and retain employees by attracting excellence. Excellence naturally attracts excellence. Just as athletes want to play on a team that is most likely to be the champion, people want to work in an environment where people's behaviors are aligned. People don't want to feel like they must be the "hall monitors" but want to work where people's behaviors are productive and everyone works with the same energy and intentions.

Back to being accountable, which is the essence of this principle, these standards drive ownership and accountability. We can "own" what we are when we know what to do. Standards also help to manage performance by providing a guide for productive coaching and performance conversations with the team.

Test Your Standards of Behavior

Want to know how to spot strong and effective standards of behavior? They typically have four crucial similarities. Those characteristics are: Specific, Observable, Applicable, and Realistic. And what do you know, it spells "SOAR" to help you remember. Let's break each down a bit further.

S: SPECIFIC – *Is the standard of behavior specific, clear, and unambiguous?*

A standard with specific actions has much greater success than one unclear or general. Ask yourself, "Would all colleagues know exactly what to do if they read the standard of behavior as it is written?" If not, dig a little deeper to define and describe the behavior.

For example, let's say you want a positive attitude standard. Instead of just saying that, think about what specific actions show a positive attitude. Maybe something like smiling and greeting people in the hallway using the 10-5 rule (eye contact and smile at 10 feet, verbally acknowledge at five feet). Or asking others, "What can I do for you today?"

These actions are meant to be specific and show a positive attitude in a way that everyone can understand.

O: OBSERVABLE – *Is the standard of behavior easily observed?*

Standards should describe the actions you want to see, hear, or observe someone doing instead of describing a general feeling or desire.

For instance, if a standard states, "I will demonstrate pride within the organization," it is essential to note that pride is a feeling and cannot be observed. Instead, the standard might read, "I will maintain a clean and organized environment by picking up trash and ensuring that the organization is tidy throughout my daily activities." This way, when someone picks up trash while walking down the hallway, it is evident that they are living up to the standards and demonstrating their pride in the organization.

A: APPLICABLE – *Does the standard of behavior apply to 100% of the people in the organization?*

You want to create buy-in, which requires organization-wide participation from everyone; volunteers, contractors, and the CEO.

We all understand that certain standards might be more specific to a profession, job, or team and that departments can have specific standards for their area. However, the goal is that the organization-wide ones are for all to foster a sense of unity and shared responsibility.

For example, "Escort people to their destination" is something every colleague could do. However, standards such as "Make sure the room is clean before you leave" or "Caregivers will round hourly on all inpatients" would only apply to those who are part of patient care.

R: REALISTIC – *Does the standard of behavior have an outcome you can expect to achieve?*
This one is a little tricky. The best standards of behavior require you to stretch a bit to achieve them. However, standards should always have an outcome you can expect to achieve, given the skills, motivation, and values of your colleagues and organization.

While stretch goals can be beneficial, it is important to exercise caution when setting standards or goals that may be unattainable for the majority. It is crucial to remain realistic and establish standards that outline the appropriate behaviors expected of colleagues. These realistic standards should create a culture that looks and feels like what you'd want if someone you loved dearly were being cared for or working there.

Examples of Standards of Behavior:
Here are some sample standards of behavior for you to reference. Think about the characteristics (Specific, Observable, Applicable, and Realistic) as you review.

Caring and Compassion:
- I will assist patients and guests in finding their destinations and walk with them if possible.

- I will use the 10/5 rule—when I am 10 feet from a guest, I will smile and make direct eye contact, and when I am within five feet, I will verbally greet the guest.

- I will introduce myself and tell people not only my job title but my experience as well.

- I will use a person's name during conversation as soon as I have heard it or as it is written.

- I will introduce other staff to patients when a hand-off occurs and explain that the staff person will provide excellent service.

- I will discuss issues directly with co-workers and not go to other people unless the issue cannot be resolved.

- I will be mindful and respectful of others' time and schedules. Meetings will start and end on time.

Elevator Etiquette:

- I will pause before entering elevators to allow guests to enter and exit first. If a patient is being transported, I will wait for the next elevator to respect privacy.

- I will speak softly in elevators and hallways and never discuss patients or private/confidential information in elevators or other common areas.

Telephone Etiquette:

- I will answer the phone saying, "Good morning/afternoon/evening."

- I will make every effort to answer calls within three rings.

- I will smile when speaking on the phone to convey a pleasant tone.

- I will return voicemail messages within 24 hours or the next business day.

Facilities:

- I will do my part to keep our hallways and other areas in our workplace tidy and clean by picking up trash.

- I will park only in designated staff areas, avoiding spaces reserved for patients, visitors, and physicians.

Quality and Safety:

- I will wash my hands—wash my hands—wash my hands.

- I will correctly identify patients at every encounter.

- I will always ensure I have the RIGHT patient in the RIGHT place for the RIGHT procedure with the RIGHT equipment.

- I will perform a "time-out" with the team before every procedure.

Privacy:

- I will knock on a patient's door before entering.

- I will close curtains or doors during exams and procedures.

- I will provide a robe or second gown if the patient is ambulating or in a wheelchair.

- I will keep patient information confidential and never discuss patients and their care in public areas.

Figure 6.1: Sample Behavior Standards

Signing a Standards Agreement— Being accountable from the start

All job applicants should be required to sign a Standards agreement before they are considered for hire. You want to hire people who align with the organizational culture. Most people who struggle in new positions don't align their behaviors to what is expected because they were unaware and were then surprised by those expectations. When organizations develop and use the standards to hire people, new hires can hit the ground running.

Remember, this stuff is like a magnet for high performers! They need to work somewhere that wants the best from the best. When we bring a new team member on board, we want them to understand who and what we are as a culture and to "agree" to be a part of that. On the surface, this may appear to be a transactional thing. But it is meant to be an act of creating a clear statement of togetherness. We are signing a page to say, "We are on the same page."

Human nature shows that people want to live up to an expectation. We will all meet our "expectations" of ourselves. It just depends on what expectation is placed before us. Asking prospective employees and contracted staff to sign the standards of behavior is no small thing. You are setting the expectation that they agree to behave in accordance, harmony, and agreement with the values of your culture. Think about it. Don't you have certain expectations of how people will conduct themselves in your home? Perhaps it is your "standard of behavior" that your family removes their shoes before entering the house, washes their hands before meals, doesn't use profanity, allows the dog on the sofa, closes the door when they go outside, recycles, etc. So, if your kids were having a friend sleep over and stomping around the house in their dirty sneakers, grabbing at food with unwashed hands, and "cursing like a sailor," you might have a thing or two to say about that!

We commonly establish "standards" in various ways for our homes. We ensure family members understand and agree to these standards and hopefully communicate them to others who visit our home. Our work "home" is no different.

Behavioral Standards Commitment Statement

The employees of <organization name> have developed a set of behavioral standards to establish specific behavioral expectations all employees will practice while at work.

By incorporating these standards to measure overall work performance, <organization name> clarifies that these behaviors are mandatory for continued employment, not optional.

I have read and understand the <organization name> Standards of Behavior and agree to comply with and practice the standards outlined within.

_____   _____

Signature of Applicant   Date

Figure 6.2: Sample Standard of Behavior Signing at Application

Tips for Successful Behavior Standards

Here are a few tips we have learned for creating and applying effective standards of behavior through the years.

Start with the mission or value statement. The mission and value statements represent what your organization is trying to achieve. The standards describe the behaviors that can effectively express the mission and values of your organization.

Involve employees and colleagues in writing the standards. As you develop standards of behavior, bring a group of high and middle/solid performers together to lead the charge. This group, often called the "Standards Team," should include those who work directly with patients, families, and other employees. Together, they work to draft and refine the standards. Also, employees are more likely to accept, embrace, and act on standards that their peers developed. So even though many organizations may have similar standards, each set is unique to their specific needs and values. Your standards reflect what's most important to your organization, and involving those closest to the action will make sure they represent your organization well.

Update over time. Your "Standards of Behavior" is a living and breathing document. With that in mind, standards are dynamic and are reviewed and updated as needed. Perhaps a standard did not work as intended and needs to be changed or dropped. Add a new standard if needed. For instance, years ago, we didn't use mobile devices like today or conduct meetings virtually on camera. So it might be appropriate to add an electronic device or virtual meeting etiquette standard to ensure that we are fully engaged during interactions and meetings. The key is keeping standards current, and an annual team review is a great way to keep them fresh and updated for you.

Roll out with appropriate energy. After the standards have been developed and endorsed by senior leaders, they are ready to be presented to the organization. How your organization rolls out the standards can affect how they are received. If the rollout is casual and low-key, people may perceive the standards as such. However, if the rollout includes everyone, is endorsed by senior leaders, and is presented with some fanfare, it will help ensure that all employees know their importance. Some organizations choose to be very ceremonial in the rollout process. Some hold an employee forum or a company-wide meeting to introduce the standards. It helps to create inspiration and a culture that values and upholds these standards.

Hardwire standards into critical processes. One crucial way to gain traction is to hardwire the standards of behavior into current conversations and interactions with staff. Bringing standards into key processes will increase and accelerate ownership and accountability. For example, have applicants read and sign your standards, as discussed earlier. Also, integrate them into your performance management, reward, recognition, and coaching processes.

Sign and commit to the standards. Ensure every employee and senior leader signs the standards as part of their agreement and commitment to working for the organization. Sometimes pledges or banners are made for everyone to sign to show commitment. It is incredible how much more seriously people take these behavior guidelines when signing on the dotted line.

Reinforce the standards. Create communication and activities over time to help "keep the standards alive" and use them in the organization.

The goal is to find ways to boost awareness of the standards. Getting people to think about how standards apply to their daily work is vital.

Ways shown to be effective in communicating and keeping standards alive include:

- Standard of the month

- Employee forums

- Staff huddles

- Meeting agendas

- Reward and recognition

Include vendors, physicians, and contracted employees too. The standards of behavior can include anyone directly connected to the organization. There are ways to leverage those relationships—they should be aware and held accountable to exemplify your standards. Vendors, for example, generally have some contractual relationship, or at least a check-in, with the organization before they can be in your facilities. Use this touchpoint to make them aware; to hold them accountable when they are there. The same thing is true for non-employed or contract physicians through credentialing. You have the same opportunity for touchpoints to hold them accountable for awareness and potential performance.

Selection—Hiring People Who Align to Your Culture

> "My biggest mistake is probably weighing too much on someone's talent and not someone's personality. I think it matters whether someone has a good heart."
>
> *Elon Musk*

Accountability sounds like all "tough" and no "love," but in a way, it is both. Whatever you define as a "good heart," let's agree that someone who is not only good at their job but also at kindness, compassion, integrity, and self-growth is worth investing in. I would say who you hire, takes you higher.

Hire well, be methodical, and you will reap the rewards many times over. On a lighter note, think of it like this: Pick your employees like you'd pick your plastic surgeon—make sure they both make you look better than you did before you met them!

Individual accountability starts even before the first job day for new employees. This is why hiring the right people who fit the organizational culture is so important. You want to give new hires every opportunity to connect to the work profoundly and have the framework for individual accountability. Why? If they're successful, then **you** are successful.

The destinies of the new hire and the organization are tied by the string of who you are and what you say and do. Selection is critical to building a culture that exemplifies and sustains excellence. To hire the right people, you ensure job descriptions align with job competencies rather than tasks. You include standards of behavior to emphasize culture. You then ask interview questions aligned with job responsibilities and standards to assess the right fit.

It has often been said that you are a reflection of the people you surround yourself with. As we mentioned in Principle 5, a critical skill for leaders and staff is ensuring you have an excellent system. Look at how your applicants are screened, interviewed, and either selected or rejected to fill a position. Use the gift of your team to ensure that there is a diversity of opinions and angles from which each new prospect is viewed. In short, take advantage of all means available to you to establish a relationship with someone who can feel comfortable in your organization and serve as a long-term contributor to your goals.

Peer Interviewing

Again, people will support what they create. If they are part of "creating" the team, they will be much more supportive of the team. Think about how you felt about something you built or created—a cake, a shed, a painting, or that furniture that takes 78 hours to assemble?

I learned long ago that while I had some acumen when assembling things (furniture aside), it may take a team for the best results. Sometimes as leaders, we don't see the complete picture. Sometimes we need a little help.

66 The Glass Slipper.

Her resume was on point! As soon as I read it, I knew she would be "the one." We needed a few new nurses, and my team was knee-deep in the interview process. My manager was screening the candidates, and few had advanced to the peer interview process. I noticed that the one I KNEW was the chosen one, the Golden Child, the frosting on the cake of our future team, wasn't on the list.

As I stood before my manager, holding up the resume like some rare archaeological find that would forever change the course of history, I said, "Estelle, what about Autumn?"

I got her famous look. The one that lets you know you are in the middle of a minefield and better be ready for the boom. "Not going to happen, Rich!" she said.

I was thrown. In my deepest and most convincing "I need you to make all my department director dreams come true" voice, I said, "But Estelle, her resume is amazing. She has more qualifications than almost anyone, and she's been a nurse for a long time. Look where she went to school. Look where she's worked."

Estelle looked me up and down and said, "I know you think this one is Cinderella, but I am telling you she's one of the stepsisters. No way."

I still wasn't convinced. I told Estelle I wanted to meet Autumn. Estelle must have been confused, or maybe she didn't see what I saw. I wanted her to "fall" for Autumn as I did! (pun intended)

So, I scheduled a meeting. Autumn was 15 minutes early, dressed sharply with a big smile and great eye contact. I thought to myself, "See? She is already showing what a rockstar she is! Oh boy, was Estelle wrong about this one!"

We started talking, and all was going well. She answered my questions; seemed sharp and professional. Then I showed her our standards of behavior. This was the moment, the glass slipper was in her hand.

"I find these types of things silly," she said. "I am a master's-degree-prepared professional, and I often must care for people who probably don't even own a book, much less a degree. So, I would never sign something like this. I expect that when someone hires me, they understand that as an adult who must deal with all sorts of people, I can't be expected to be told how to behave. It should be up to me how to behave. This is for people who see the world through rose-colored glasses. I see the world for what it is. I'm here to save people's butts, not kiss them!"

The glass slipper was not a good fit.

I don't recall most of the rest of the interview, as I was now trying to figure out how to tell Estelle she was right without admitting I was wrong. Autumn left, and Estelle was in my office before I could say, "Bibbidi-Bobbidi-Boo."

"So... how was Cinderella?"

Deep breath (time for some individual accountability). "You were right about Autumn."

Estelle leaned forward, "Wait... what? I am sorry it is so loud out there. I am not sure I heard you?" (She was not going to let me off easy.)

"I said... you were right about Autumn. She is not a good fit for us."

Estelle grabbed my hand and said, "I guess it is wintertime for Autumn, huh?"

We both had a good laugh. Winter had come, for sure! Also, for my ego. I needed to listen more to my team.

We hired a fabulous nurse named Georgia, who had fewer degrees and years of experience than Autumn but brought a lot more to the team and was an absolute joy to work with.

Thank goodness this "fairytale" had a "happily ever after." And I owe that 100% to the team I had around me.

Peer interviewing is powerful because the peer interview team ensures the candidate is the best person for the job and the best person for the culture. They know the culture, helped create it, and ARE the culture. Wouldn't you rather know about a poor cultural fit before a person is hired?

Also, if an employee has been part of the peer interview and the new hire is brought on board, they already "know" each other. That's a great thing for the new hire, isn't it? This is compassion in action—helping someone feel welcomed with a familiar face before they've started their first day!

Remember, many people leave a job within the first 90 days. From research and what Huron has seen working with hundreds of organizations, those people didn't feel "welcome" or "part of" an organization. Peer interviewing gets everyone off to a good start.

So, who should make up a peer interview team? Usually, a human resources representative will screen the candidate's skill set and share standards of behavior, the leader of the department will interview the candidate and make the decision whether to pass a candidate on for a peer interview, and then a peer interview team made up of high performers who exemplify the standards, represent a diverse cross-section of the organization, have some tenure, and are voluntarily part of the process conduct their interview.

It should be made clear to members of a peer interview team that this is a form of recognition—they're on the team because they are high performers. Ensure you show gratitude to them for taking the time, doing the work, and caring enough to improve your workplace. Take them to lunch, write thank you notes, give gift cards, flowers, or whatever they enjoy. Lavish these folks with good things. Remember, they are helping you to build a dynasty!

Behavioral-Based Interviewing Questions

In the interviews, you want to determine how a candidate would handle certain situations. Your standards of behavior can be used to create workplace situations focused on individual accountability. The candidate's response helps assess their cultural fit. Behavioral-based questions are open-ended, so candidates must respond with a specific example or story. Use language such as "tell me about a time when…" instead of "what would you do if…" so the candidate recounts real-life situations, not hypotheticals, and can describe how they behaved.

Best Practice Update: Behavioral-Based Interview Questions

Behavioral-based interview questions are used to identify the candidate's depth of experience in specific job skills, sometimes referred to as competencies. How the candidate answers these questions highlights their past behavior and indicates their ability to succeed in similar situations. There are many competencies, but here are a few examples:

- **Patient experience:** Describe when an angry patient or family member confronted you. How did you handle the situation?

- **Adaptability:** Give me an example of when you had two import-ant projects competing for your time. How did you manage this?

- **Initiative:** Tell me about when you identified a new or unusual approach for addressing a problem or task.

- **Communication:** Give me a recent example that best shows your communication ability.

- **Conflict resolution:** Tell me about a time you had to resolve a conflict involving a team member, patient, or family member.

- **Integrity and honesty:** Talk about when you demonstrated honesty and integrity in a work situation.

- **Teamwork:** Talk about a time when you demonstrated excel-lent team member behavior. What was the situation, and what did you do?

Remember, this is all about creating a working environment where people feel part of something special. Peer interviewing is a way to share the journey of inspired excellence. Your team will be better, stronger, more resilient, and in more of a flow state once peer interviewing becomes the way you work. It is a way for everyone to become invested in the success of everyone around them.

Peer-to-Peer Accountability Conversations

"The price of greatness is responsibility."

Winston Churchill

In this shared voyage of "inspired excellence," the ship's captain can be no greater than the sum of the crew. If leaders are solely responsible for your organization's accountability, you won't even be able to get off the dock, much less sail to new worlds. A ship's crew must also hold each other accountable, as the captain can't manage every sail or wield every oar. A great captain can inspire and encourage a great crew. A great crew can inspire and encourage each other.

When people are sharing in accountability, they are also empowered. Most often, a challenging or uncomfortable conversation at work can best be done by a peer. It can be seen as less intimidating and create an even deeper dialogue and better response. It can be challenging to do and receive, but it is powerful.

To do this most effectively may require some training. In Principle 4, we shared the "Stub Your Toe" coaching conversation model. Here is an example of how you might adapt that concept for peer-to-peer accountability.

How to Structure a "Stub Your Toe" Conversation

1. Find a private place to talk.

2. Start positively to prevent the other person from becoming defensive.

   - "I value you as a colleague."

   - "I greatly respect the expertise you bring to our team."

3. Clarify your purpose to set expectations for the conversation.

   - "I saw/ heard something inconsistent with our <values, policies, or standards of behavior) and wanted you to be aware."

4. Connect your concern to values.

   - "I wanted to bring this to your attention because I believe that you would want to be aware." or "I felt I should let you know because I owe you the opportunity to see how this affects our team."

   - "I've known you a while and feel we trust each other, so I feel comfortable saying this to you. I believe you'd do the same for me, and I'd want you to do so."

   - "I am not perfect. None of us are, and this isn't about that. This is about who we all are and try to represent, and I want to share what I feel. I hope you'll hear it in the way I intend it."

The key here is, to be honest, compassionate, and direct, and not to make any "personal digs." Hold this conversation when not in the "heat of the moment." Most of all, be yourself. Your intention is not to show that you're "better." If you are not in a good place with this person or have had a past conflict, think about that. Are you the best person for this conversation? Is there another peer who may be better suited to do this? The goal is for this to be a "win/win" and ultimately help this person to be their best.

Sample Conversation

"Dr. Molina, do you have a moment to talk privately with me? I greatly respect the expertise you bring to our team. Have you ever heard of a 'Stub Your Toe' conversation?"

- **If no:** "It involves colleagues sharing a perception about something they saw/heard."

- **If yes:** "Great! I wanted to share my perception about something I saw/heard today."

"During our patient round with Mr. Lee, I felt your tone and body language were dismissive of me when I tried to interject my thoughts. You waved your hands toward me and said, 'That's not important right now.'

That's very different from how you usually communicate with me, and it made me feel a bit embarrassed. As you know, that's not in line with our core value of respect and teamwork, and I wanted to talk to you about this as I would want you to do the same if you perceived me communicating in that way."

What about their reactions, and how should they be handled?

In each situation, remember that the goal is to let your colleague know the observed behavior is concerning and merits reflection. While every interaction and every work relationship is different, you will find that the most common reaction is appreciation or respect for bringing the behavior to their attention. If that is not their reaction, don't try to downplay or enable the behavior. Doing so can diminish the value of the conversation.

Once you've had your say:

1. Pause for at least 15 seconds to let the other person reflect on what you said and allow them to respond.

2. If the other person becomes emotional, listen respectfully, say thank you, and end the conversation. What you said may trigger them or strike something within them that maybe they are aware of but struggle to deal with. Your goal here isn't to discipline them. Your goal here is to communicate.

Possible reactions and your responses:

- **Appreciation:** "I had no idea I was coming across that way. Thanks for letting me know."

- – YOU Show Gratitude: "You're welcome. I hope you'll do the same for me if necessary."

- **Denial:** "That's ridiculous! My tone was perfectly fine! You're exaggerating!"

  - – YOU Avoid Arguing: "I can see you've become upset, and that wasn't my intention. I just thought you'd like to know. Thanks for your time."

- **Deflection:** "Did you ever hear Dr. Lawrence talk to patients? Oh, that's right. He doesn't spend much time talking to patients; when he does, he's condescending and rude. But no one ever confronts him! Now I'm the bad guy!"

  - – YOU Stay on Message: "I can see you're frustrated with your peers, and if I ever have an issue with anyone else, I assure you I will talk to them as well, but I think we should stay focused on what just happened between you and me. I thought it was important for you to know how I felt. If you want to touch base later, I am very open to that. Thanks for your time."

- **Justification:** "I've been working for nearly 24 hours straight, and I'm tired. I might've been short, but I'm burning the candle at both ends. Cut me a little slack."

  - – YOU Don't Try to Fix the Root Cause: "I appreciate how hard you work. I'm sorry you're feeling tired, and I hope you get to rest soon. I wanted you to know because I value you as a colleague and our working relationship, but I could see that the patient felt as awkward as I did, and I know that wasn't your intention. We can talk later when you're feeling up to it if you'd like. Thanks for listening."

Again, this is not always easy. Some people may need training, while others may be naturally good at this type of communication. But can you imagine the positive impact this could have on your culture when you commit to it, every person feels equipped to discuss their concerns, and you are all in agreement to listen to each other?

Accountability doesn't start and end with leaders. Everyone can learn from anyone else on the team. You are all on the same crew, trying to navigate this sea as best you can. It is a shared responsibility for every "sailor" in your organization.

Principle 6 Summary

Principle 6: Be Accountable means we commit to individual accountability to achieve the organizational goals. We want to be that person that others can rely on. We want to be able to rely on others. To do so, we live by standards of behavior, act as co-owners of our organizations, and hire people with the skills to do the job and are a cultural fit. Remember, leaders must model these behaviors for their teams. Only then can we expect employees to be accountable for their behaviors and actions at work.

Accountability is not an easy destination to reach. And while it is certainly okay to visit, it is much better to make it your home. The old way of thinking about accountability is that it is merely a way to hold people responsible for their mistakes or errors. I hope what you take away from this chapter goes deeper than that.

Our view now of accountability is more about creating a culture of trust, co-creation, and ownership—not where people feel mandated to take ownership but empowered to do so. It is the kind of culture where leaders and their teams are all on the same page regarding the values, standards, actions, and behaviors they exhibit. It is also the kind of culture where the team feels confident enough to address lapses, to come together to rebuild, and where mistakes are seen as opportunities for growth and learning.

Being accountable isn't a form of confinement; it's a mindset of expansion. As Sigmund Freud once said, "Most people do not want freedom because freedom involves responsibility, and most people are frightened of responsibility."

Don't be like "most people"—be accountable and thus be free. It is a destination worthwhile to set your sails toward.

PRINCIPLE 7:
ALIGN BEHAVIORS WITH
GOALS AND VALUES

Apply Consistent Practices to Move Your Organization in a Positive Direction

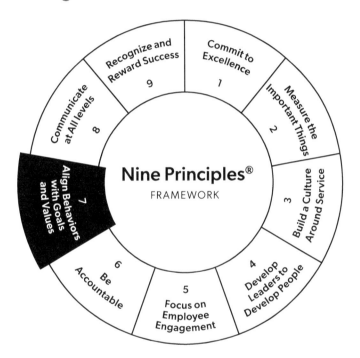

"A boat doesn't go forward if each
rower is rowing their own way."

Swahili proverb

66 0.0036 seconds.

It was the 2010 Winter Olympics in Vancouver. The German bobsled team led, with the U.S. underdogs, the "Night Train," trailing at the bottom of the competition. Because of the German team's long history of success, it was no surprise that the odds were in their favor.

It was the final heat of the competition, the U.S. against Germany. On the last turn, the underdogs took the lead and ultimately won the competition by 0.0036 seconds.

How did that happen? Pictures later reveal, on that final turn of the final heat, the second member of the German team leaned about six inches outside the rest of the team, causing their helmets to be misaligned. This slight lean caused the aerodynamics to drag just enough to slow them down.

By contrast, the photos showed the U.S. team's helmets in tight alignment. They won the race by 0.0036 seconds.

0.0036 seconds. Wow. And all because of the slightest misalignment.

Imagine losing a race by 0.0036 seconds! But isn't it incredible how even a slight misalignment could lead to a "loss?" I saw it illustrated that if you're traveling somewhere and you're off by just one degree, over time you'd miss your destination by a lot. Specifically, if you were on a rocket en route to the moon and were off by one single degree, that one degree would cause you to miss the moon by 4,169 miles—basically two times the moon's diameter.

Using that analogy, we can see the importance of alignment and how it can be the difference between a "moon landing" and being "lost in space."

"Agreement is the seed of action."

Abdul Baha

These days, leaders are pulled in more directions than taffy at a state fair! It can be challenging when striving to succeed, but we feel the push and pull of all that we need to do and know. Leading our teams to success isn't and should not be a solitary role. It not only "takes a village" but sometimes an entire continent!

When we agree, or, as this principle calls for "Alignment," we set ourselves, our team, and our organization up for success across the board.

That is a great place to start if "Agreement is the seed of action," as the quote teaches. If you've noticed a trend throughout this book, there continues to be a vantage point I am taking, (and frankly, we all should be taking), which is that of "why."

Any goal created must be viewed from the "why" and then supported by the "who" (or "what") so that the seed of agreement can be planted and success can begin to blossom.

Principle 7 is about setting, tracking, maintaining, and aligning your course, direction, and results. In this chapter, we will discuss individual goal cascade, result scorecard/dashboard, ongoing action plans, and accountability and outcome check-ins which drive the results and destination when used consistently and effectively.

Let's start with level-setting on what aligning behaviors is all about.

Aligning Behaviors

Aligning our behaviors with goals and values relies on an improvement mindset. We strive to achieve measurable goals and tackle any challenges that come our way, always knowing we can get better and better at our work. To improve continuously, we must challenge people to up their game to live up to their potential and be the change they wish to see in their workplace. People need to feel motivated and excited to not only do different but to be different. Improvement is an inside-out process, not an outside-in process; leaders should remember that.

Alignment doesn't just happen—just like wealth, fitness, a happy relationship, polite kids, clean laundry, or a stunning rose garden doesn't just happen. It takes intentional effort (actions) and strategy (planning) to create agreement among team members with different mindsets and historical experiences influencing their journey.

The Why and What of Alignment

Let's talk more about the why and what of alignment.

Alignment is defined as a position of agreement.

So, we see the definition, but what does it mean? Although it may be easy to talk about it philosophically, what exactly does alignment look like in actual practice? Simply put, we see alignment when team members act in a coordinated and collaborative fashion toward a clear vision or purpose.

It means team members have a shared sense of urgency to achieve a higher purpose, even when it means putting the team's goals above their personal ones. Alignment requires individuals to make an intentional choice to match their personal values with the mission of the organization.

Alignment and Accountability— The Dynamic Duo

In Principle 6, you learned how to foster your culture of accountability. Ownership is a beautiful thing! In this principle, we think more deeply about how it works with the concepts of alignment and performance management to foster organizational success.

Just expecting someone to be accountable on their own is like expecting the person in front of you to hold the door open for you. They may, and then you fly through. They may not, and you break your nose and spill your coffee. If we want anyone to support an initiative or strategy, they have to believe in it. And that means they have to feel it is the right thing to do.

People will follow a leader they have built trust with and see as authentic and self-reflective. This means when we talk about accountability as a leader, we first talk to ourselves about it. Consider asking self-reflective questions like:

- How committed am I?

- How much 'leaning' do I allow in my behaviors?

- What else do I need to support the strategy/objectives of my organization fully?

- Do I believe in this?

- Am I setting my intentions and staying true to them?

People will lean in a bit when they understand what to do. They will lean in often when aligned with the "why" and see themselves as part of the solution. It should feel somewhat personal. And really, when is healthcare not personal, at least on some level?

Your team wants to know how they fit in and contribute to the bigger picture. They're also wondering, "What's in it for me?" That's not self-serving. It's human nature and honestly enhances one's commitment to being part of a team. Establishing performance measures that are relevant and personal to each team member helps them understand their role and where they need to focus their efforts. This creates a sense of ownership and accountability, which is crucial for success.

> "Accountability is the glue that
> ties commitment to results."
>
> *Bob Proctor*

Accountability can sometimes feel scary, like someone's just waiting for us to mess up so they can point the finger and blame us. It's no wonder so many of us have negative associations with it! But that's why we have this whole principle of rewarding and recognizing good work—to help us overcome those old fears. See, accountability isn't about getting punished when we make mistakes. It's a way to connect our commitment to work with our desired results. It's like a bridge that helps us get from one side to the other.

Four Ways to Hardwire Alignment

Now that we see that accountability can be that bridge, let's look at four key strategies to help create and sustain accountable discussions to drive purposeful and meaningful outcomes throughout your organization:

Figure 7.1: Four basics for creating alignment.

The overall message is that communication and connection will go a long way toward making this all successful. Let's review each of the four elements in detail.

1. Individual Goal Cascade—Sets and Aligns the Course

Individual Goal Cascade

Each leader's list of goals, prioritized by weight for the 12-month performance year, sets a clear and focused approach to measure the work to be done.

These goals align with the overall organizational goals and are best used to support performance evaluations as part of the annual review.

It is a courageous, value-oriented organization that develops and commits to accomplishing measurable goals. Why? Because it shines a spotlight on how well the organization is living up to its mission.

Senior leaders set the strategic vision and direction of the organization. They answer questions about what the organization wants to become, how it can remain relevant, and what future success may look like (We discussed goals and planning in Principle 2: Measure the Important Things).

But what is next? How do leaders get individuals in the organization to align behaviors with these set goals and priorities? By developing department-level goals which align with and contribute to the overall achievement of the organizational goals.

Clear and measurable goals help a leader keep an eye on the essential focus areas for their business unit. Although this may make logical sense, it can be an emotional process. Ownership and accountability can be uncomfortable, mainly if outcomes are not at the level leaders initially thought. It becomes that much better when you have an accurate picture of what success looks like.

What are the benefits of cascading goals?

This process will promote the following:

- **Ownership and Accountability:** Leaders know precisely how they will be evaluated, what they own, and what they are accountable for achieving. This goes a long way toward reducing many leaders' anxiety during this process.

- **Team Focus:** Everyone knows their priority and focus areas.

- **Teamwork:** Once focused, everyone understands their part in achieving the organizational goals.

- **Objectivity:** Since goals are objective and based on measurable evidence, it creates a fair system to evaluate performance and clearly shows who is meeting their goals and who is not.

- **Development and Training:** If a leader is struggling in an area, it proactively allows you to provide the training and development they need to be successful.

How do you help ensure success?

To create measurable goals that move results and support the overall strategic plan, consider the following:

FIVE EFFECTIVE GOAL-SETTING TIPS

1. Set organizational/pillar goals.

2. Cascade goals to all levels of leadership and ensure alignment.

3. Set common and shared goals.

4. Ensure senior team alignment and equity review.

5. Prioritize—use goal weights for appropriate focus.

Let's dive further into each of these five areas now.

1. Set Organizational/Pillar Goals:

Effective goal cascading starts with organizational goals, not individual ones. In working with organizations, Huron finds hundreds of goals that could be placed on individual leader evaluations. However, when we look at them all together, there are typically eight to 10 key metrics that an organization wants to achieve in each performance period.

These eight to 10 goals are often informed by the board of directors, system leadership, or the organization's strategic plan, and organized under categories or headers called "pillars." These are the organization's key strategies; from them, subset goals are cascaded to all levels of leadership. Individuals typically carry between four and eight goals. This allows for prioritization and focus on the most critical things with weights, which we will address later in the chapter.

Remember, in Principle 2 we described the pillar framework as a structure that helps "hold up" the organization's mission, vision, and values and serves as categories for your organization's goals. A pillar framework typically includes service, people, quality, finance, and growth. Often a community or philanthropy pillar is added.

However, your pillars should align with your organization's unique culture and focus on ensuring long-term sustainability and acceptance. That's why Huron may help organizations with goal "templates," but those are merely launching points for an organization to make their own. Even when going your way, it's often helpful to see where others have gone as a guide.

Note: This includes a sample of measures often found in each pillar. Your organization will want to select from these or other goals unique to your organization. Select no more than 8-10 each year. For simplicity, we've not included numbers/percentages in the graph below to keep it generic, but you'd want to ensure the goal is specific. For example: "Improve operating income by 10%," "Increase employee engagement to 90%," or "Reduce no-shows by 50%." In other words, goals should have a measurable bar to strive for.

SERVICE	• Improve Patient Perception of Care by Service Line (i.e., CAHPS®, ED Overall Rating, CGCAHPS, Hospice CAHPS, etc.)	• Improved Interdepartmental Satisfaction Survey
PEOPLE	• Increase Employee Engagement • Reduce Employee Turnover	• Increase Physician Engagement
QUALITY	• Improve Overall Core Measures • Decreased Preventable Readmissions • Decrease Infection Rate	• Decrease Hospital-Acquired Conditions • Reduce Length of Stay • Improve ED Throughput • Improved Culture of Safety
FINANCE	• Improve Operating Income • Decrease Cost Per Adjusted Discharge	• Reduce Accounts Receivable • Increase Days Cash On Hand
GROWTH	• Increase Volume • Increased Revenue • Decrease Left Without Treatment	• Reduce No-Shows • Increase Average Daily Census • Increase Market Share

Figure 7.2: Sample pillar goals

2. Cascade Goals and Ensure Alignment:

Please close your eyes for a moment and imagine you are hiking along a beautiful river when suddenly, it begins to rain. You notice a waterfall at the top of the mountain. The mossy rocks along the mountainside cause the water to shift and split off into smaller streams before joining back together at the mountain's base to flow into the river.

You won't necessarily see but probably know that when the water in the river is heated by the sun, it evaporates and rises into the air. Then the water vapor cools and condenses to become droplets which form clouds. At some point, those clouds grow heavy enough to fall onto the mountaintop like rain, creating the cycle that repeats.

This incredible environmental process illustrates how goal cascading works. It flows down and up. It's all connected. The clouds are as much a part of this as the mountain, which is as crucial as the stream and as important as the waterfall. It's all about the flow!

3. Set Common and Shared Goals:

After the organizational goals are defined, the senior leadership team should consider how they will accomplish them and who is responsible for performing the work needed to achieve results. Should team members share the same measure and outcome to increase focus on a centralized outcome, or should the unique differences between areas of the organization be considered to ensure relevance and buy-in from the team?

When writing goals, develop guidelines to outline team member expectations. Additionally, consult subject matter experts to help write standardized measures that streamline and simplify the writing process for those goals expected to cascade through the organization. This is a team effort, so involve some of your high performers, who are often great "goal ambassadors" for the organization.

4. Ensure Senior Team Alignment and Equity Review:

The senior team begins the goal-cascading exercise and assesses the 8-10 organizational measures for their area of responsibility and span of control.

Remember, less is more when setting annual performance goals. Leaders should have no more than eight goals. Five to six is ideal. Pace yourself. This is a marathon, not a sprint!

Once goals are selected, they are prioritized, assigning weights that total 100% for that leader based on how significant each goal should be for the leader over the next 12 months. We discuss the concept of prioritization and weights later in this section.

Now it's time for the equity review—the final step to ensure senior leader alignment and validate that the right leader has the right goal at the right weight. This exercise should be conducted with all members of the senior team present. This clarifies what each member is working on for the year and allows members to validate they have the appropriate counterpart to support them.

This is key to the success of an organization's goal-cascading effort. Upfront collaboration prevents having to walk things back later, slows progress, and creates insecurity throughout the organization. This step sets the pace and tone for the cascade of goals to the next leadership level. An example of the equity review worksheet follows.

Pillar	Entity's Goal Description	CEO (Org Goals)	CNO	CMO	CFO	COO	VP HR
Finance	Increase Net Operating Income to budget or higher.	15%	10%	10%	20%	20%	20%
Growth	Increase Inpatient admissions compared to budget.	10%	10%		10%		
	Increase Outpatient Revenue compared to budget as measured by Finance Department records				15%	15%	
People	Increase employee engagement to 90th percentile as measured by annual survey.	15%	10%	10%	10%	20%	20%
Quality	Reduce Average Length of Stay (ALOS) to 4.85 days or less.	10%	10%	20%	15%	15%	
	Achieve Value Based Purchasing Rollup measures.	10%	20%	20%		10%	
Service	Maintain overall Emergency Department patient engagement at 90th percentile.	10%	10%				
	Increase CAHPS® in 6/8 composites at 80th percentile.	15%	15%	10%		10%	15%
	Increase physician engagement to 85th percentile as measured by annual survey.	15%	15%	30%	10%	10%	10%

Pillar	Entity's Goal Description	CEO (Org Goals)	CNO	CMO	CFO	COO	VP HR
	Other department/ cascading metrics. Examples: AR Days, Door to Doctor, Productivity, Patient Safety Measures, Physician Engagement				20%		35%
		100%	100%	100%	100%	100%	100%

Figure 7.3: Goal weighting example

Measures for senior leaders are typically long-term measures. As you cascade goals to other leaders, some short-term measures may be appropriate to include.

5. Prioritize—Use Goal Weights:

The weighting of goals is where the real magic of this process comes in. In Huron's experience, if a leader has eight unweighted goals, they will achieve six well, and not the other two. Six out of eight isn't bad, right? But what if those two missed goals are vitally important? Evaluating a leader as "good" for achieving or exceeding goals can also message to the organization that it is okay to miss two goals entirely.

Weighting is a vital part of the goal-cascading process. Weights allow leaders to focus on the most critical items as they develop implementation plans. If everything is a priority, then nothing is a priority, which is a recipe for failure.

Not every leader's evaluation will look the same, even when their goals are aligned. As a guideline for weights:

10%	20%	>30%
Awareness	Focus	Urgency

Intentionally selecting weights informed by the senior team and discussed between a leader and a one-up empowers leaders to use their critical thinking and own their success throughout the year. That's the undercurrent of this whole cascade. When people feel "ownership" of their success, they become more successful.

Weights on common goals may vary based on how far a leader may be from the goal compared to their peers. Here are four questions to ask yourself when selecting weights for individual leaders:

- **Leader contribution:** Is the leader an influencer of success, or can the leader directly control the outcome?

- **Leader skill set:** Is this measure an area the leader needs to develop the skill to support?

- **Historical performance:** Has the leader historically struggled in this area, and if so, how can you help them to rise above that struggle?

- **Strategic influence:** Does this measure heavily influence the organization's strategic plan?

When weighting goals, it is also recommended that no weight be less than 10%, and the weight of all goals equals 100%. Organizations often follow the 1-2-3 Guideline to promote focus and balance urgency across measures. Ideally, a leader should have one goal at 30%, two at 20%, and three at 10%.

Prioritization matters in evaluating leader performance. Cascading goals is far more effective at driving results when objective goals are prioritized via weighting. Using heavy weights with evaluation metrics is one of an organization's most significant levers to move performance among leadership team members.

2. Results Scorecard/Dashboard— Tracks the Course

A results scorecard/dashboard users performance data to track progress toward meeting the annual goals. It monitors performance—monthly, quarterly, or sometimes annually—to ensure leaders know where they stand on each goal.

I once overheard someone say, "I love being surprised. Unless it's a letter from the IRS, a spider, or a flat tire."

The scorecard prevents those "unwanted surprises" and keeps everyone in the "transparency zone." You have seen this referred to as a "monthly report card" in Huron's work. But we've adapted the name a bit to allow for timing flexibility and customization to meet your organization's needs.

The key is that this scorecard serves as a reminder to review performance regularly (monthly, quarterly, or annually). With patients, we know how critical it is to monitor their vitals. The same is valid here. We monitor the organization's vital signs by aligning behavior to what the vital signs tell us we need to do.

At any time, leaders should be able to communicate to their team or senior leadership where they are progressing toward a goal. This journey requires not only momentum but also navigation. In other words, it's great if we are "moving," but what is our position? Are we on course?

Establishing a scorecard can sometimes be frustrating as leaders will want to understand when the data is available for a given measure, who holds the source of the measurement, and how the data is being reported. Understanding these qualifiers before setting the goal ensures a leader does not lose precious time waiting for the data to become available during the performance period. Leaders/team members with similar goals should continually represent the data on their scorecards. This ensures consistency in messaging and language across the teams regardless of which leader reports on the measure.

Tracking and reporting progress throughout the year is essential. Below is an example of a monthly scorecard. Many organizations color-code their scorecard to make the tool more visually compelling. Red = decline from baseline; Yellow = progress toward a goal; Green = goal achieved. For "visual learners," that can be helpful. Plus, it does trigger some emotional/psychological responses when we see the colors we often associate with "go" or "stop."

Pillar	People	People	Service	Quality	Quality	Finance
Goal	Decrease Overall Annualized Employee Turnover score from 24% to 20% or lower as measured by Monthly Turnover Report	Increase Overall Employee Engagement score from 4.03 to 4.10 or higher as measured by Annual Employee Engagement Survey	Achieve 3 of 5 service lines at or above the 70th percentile as measured by patient experience surveys by end of FY18	Increase Year-To-Date Sepsis Bundle Compliance percentage from 74.6% to 80% as measured by Monthly Safety Report	Reduce Hospital Wide HAI rate from 2.13 to 1.96 by year end as measured by Monthly Safety Report (CAUTI, CLABSI, C. Diff, MRSA, SSI Colon, SSI TKA, SSI CBGB)	Increase Operating Margin from -1.65% to +1.00% as measured by monthly YTD financial reports. YTD Operating Marfin entered monthly
Goal Weight	15%	15%	30%	10%	20%	10%
Jan.	22	4.03	4	82	2.65	2.03
Feb.	23			81	2.01	1.98
Mar.	22			80	1.63	1.87
Apr.	22		4	81	1.87	1.93
Jun.	21			83	1.75	1.95
Jul.	20			82	1.73	1.97
Aug.	20		4	83	1.77	1.99

Pillar	People	People	Service	Quality	Quality	Finance
Sep.	21			83	1.8	1.98
Oct.	21			83	1.74	1.92
Nov.	21	4.12	4	81	1.77	1.89
Dec.	20			80	1.77	1.99

Figure 7. 4: Scorecard example

3. Ongoing Action Plan—Navigates the Course

> "When it is obvious that the goals
> cannot be reached, don't adjust the
> goals, adjust the action steps."
>
> *Confucius*

This quote hung on my wall in my office at the hospital. I looked at it often, as it helped me realize that when I felt frustrated with my goals, it was more likely frustration with what I was or wasn't doing. Goals guide the actions we need to take to achieve great things.

Monitoring progress is, of course, essential, but simply monitoring a heart rhythm during a cardiac arrest isn't going to save a person's life. We also take intentional steps to make that happen! This is where an action plan comes into play. This, in conjunction with the goals set and the scorecard, helps people navigate throughout the year and know exactly where to focus next steps.

> An action plan is a tool to put specific actions in place to achieve goals.

Huron has often referred to this as the "90-day action plan," but again, it has adapted the name to allow for flexibility and customization to meet your organization's needs. It may vary in timing depending on the action. Maybe it is for 30, 60, or 90 days.

Think of this action plan as your GPS. You plug in a destination. No matter how far or complex, the GPS provides each step or turn needed to get there. The GPS also might "recalibrate" to reroute you around a bad accident or traffic jam. All in all, the GPS helps to make the trip more enjoyable and efficient for you.

Like a GPS, a good action plan will help you navigate effectively and hopefully improve the journey. It helps leaders find the best route for the next 90 days (or some other time). And step by step, the action plan will take you to your destination/goal.

Many experts don't talk about excitement, passion, or inspiration around setting goals, as it doesn't sound "serious" enough. But you know what is "serious?" Not hitting an infection reduction goal. Not preventing a fall. Not preventing a sentinel event. Not preventing employee injuries. In healthcare, we passionately pursue our goals because we "have to hit that number" and because we are making someone's world better.

An effective action plan:

- Helps leaders stay focused on the priorities on their plates.

- Establishes smaller incremental goals and actions throughout the reporting period to make the goals feel more achievable.

- Reduces the anxiety of guessing where you are and what to do as the next steps.

- Encourages productive conversations and dialogue around current goals throughout the year.

- Builds a partnership among leaders as they review, establish, and achieve results together.

- Prevents surprises for leaders.

- Maintains alignment with organization and department goals.

- Allows leaders to hold up the mirror on what's in place to achieve their goals and results.

- Prevents last-minute scrambles to align efforts to achieve annual goals.

- Allows the opportunity to coach leaders and keep track of progress all year, pinpointing skill gaps and training as appropriate.

Elements of Effective Action Plans

So, what are the critical elements of effective action plans? The actual form or wording may look different from organization to organization or from using a software performance management system. Regardless of the format, the following six elements are consistently part of an effective action plan.

ANNUAL GOAL	Identifies the overall **improvement metric** you are expected to achieve over the next 12 months.
SHORT-TERM GOAL	Identifies the **portion of the annual improvement metric** you are expected to achieve in the designated time frame.
ACTION STEPS	Identifies what behaviors, processes, or tasks you will complete to help you achieve your goal.
LEVEL OF AUTONOMY	Identifies what you and your direct supervisor have agreed upon regarding your **autonomy to move forward** with these action items. (Do they need to check in with you?) • 1 – Full speed ahead • 2 – Full speed ahead, but keep your supervisor informed before you move forward with this action • 3 – Do not move forward without prior approval on this action
RESULTS	Identifies what portion of your action items you have **completed** and the **impact** you see because of your actions.
STATUS	Identifies the **status** of your committed action items (completed, on target to be completed by the deadline, or behind schedule).

Figure 7.5: Key elements of an action plan

Now, let's put it all together. Below are two examples of action plans. Note the elements included in each. This, for example, is a paper-based tool.

PILLAR	People Q1
ANNUAL GOAL DESCRIPTION	Decrease turnover to 16% by Q4, as reported by HR. Baseline = 18%
90-DAY GOAL	Maintain turnover below 10% in Q1

ACTION STEPS	Train the leadership team on effective leader rounding with employees at the Q1 Leadership Development Session.	Implement leader rounding with employees throughout the department by the end of Q1 2023.	Observe 100% of leaders' competency in leader rounding by 3/30.
LEVEL OF AUTONOMY	1	2	1
RESULTS	Completed training at January LDI. 100% of department leaders are in attendance.	Created and distributed a standardized template to all leaders. 100% compliance achieved.	70% of targeted leaders were observed to date. The remaining 30% to be completed by 3/30.
STATUS	On Target		

Figure 7. 6: Sample action plan

Tips for a Successful Action Plan

- Confirm that a direct supervisor has approved an action plan before it is considered final. This ensures alignment with what is expected to be accomplished within the quarter.

- Plan proactively for the next quarter's actions. Example: A Q2 plan should be updated and approved by the direct supervisor before the last day of Q1. This will help communicate what will be done in the next 90 days to sustain improvements or what is being modified to improve results.

- Update the results of the action plan monthly at a minimum to stay accountable for accomplishments in the quarter, and communicate progress to the one-up supervisor. A leading practice is to update the plan a few minutes each week.

- Set timelines for actions within the quarter instead of identifying all action items to be completed by the end of the quarter. This helps avoid procrastination and manage time more effectively.

- It is crucial to utilize action steps that incorporate impactful key words to achieve desired outcomes. Words such as train, coach, validate, observe, implement, and complete are far more effective than continue, encourage, keep trying, discuss, attend meetings, and similar phrases. By incorporating powerful key words, you can drive results and ensure success.

- Use weighted goals to determine what action items should be focused on first.

  - Goals weighted at 10% should not require a lot of time or require much improvement.

  - Goals weighted at 20% identify items to be intensely focused on to improve results.

  - Goals weighted at 30% or more identify an area of urgency. Action steps should be completed in a timely manner and discussed often with a one-up leader to remove barriers and celebrate success.

- Confirm that every action item in the plan will be time well spent to help achieve your goal. More is not always better. One or two key behaviors that will drive a positive change are much better than a list of 10 things that will not significantly impact the results or overwhelm you and you'll skip them.

4. Accountability/Outcome Check-Ins— Checks the Course

The course is set, you have a scorecard in place to track it, and you have action plans written to navigate it, but all this effort will lead nowhere if it is not communicated regularly and consistently. This is why accountability/outcome check-ins are vital to aligning behaviors and goals.

> An accountability/outcome check-in is a structured agenda-based meeting led by the direct report with their one-up leader to focus on priorities and report progress on goals.

This check-in is where you discuss the goals and align or realign behaviors based on that discussion. This check-in keeps results moving in the right direction and ensures individuals progress toward their goals.

You may have called these "monthly meetings" or "monthly check-ins" in the past. Note that we have adapted the title because what is most important is ensuring that a meaningful and structured check-in specifically focused on outcomes is calendared appropriately. So it might be monthly, bi-weekly, or maybe even daily, depending on the need and urgency of the outcome.

Accountability/outcome check-ins help ensure appropriate time is spent outside of day-to-day duties to deliberately focus on what the leader needs to achieve their desired results. This meeting is a safe space for the direct report and leader to solve problems, recognize success, and correct course as needed.

This check-in turns the usual leader-led meeting upside down, requiring the reporting leader to create the agenda, prepare in advance, and lead the meeting. Essentially, they present an update on their area of responsibility or book of business. This allows the more senior supervising leader to take a more thoughtful, mentoring, guiding role in the discussion. The model is used in any setting in which leaders lead leaders. This connects well with Principle 4: Develop Leaders to Develop People.

Many of us have had that experience where we believe we are on the right track and are full steam ahead, and then we are shocked to learn our leader is concerned that we aren't hitting the mark. By the way, that mark may have never even been on your radar! This check-in also ensures everyone sees the same blip on the radar and moves together in transparency and accountability.

We win when we know where we are going, why we are going there, how we are getting there, and who we need onboard. We keep winning when that remains in focus. As one of my favorite cartoon characters, G.I. Joe, always used to say, "Knowing is half the battle!"

Principle 7 Summary

The often-quoted author Jim Collins once said that building a visionary company requires 1% vision and 99% alignment. Talk about variation in "weighting!" But reflecting on that advice really speaks to this chapter's heart.

When actions, behaviors, and goals are aligned with values, we enter a whole other realm of excellence. Our view changes from what we see in front of us to what we can see beyond us. This brings about more than mere transactional "change" but a transformational shift.

Cascading goals upstream and downstream, establishing a clear and transparent scorecard and dashboard that leaves no doubt as to where we are and where we are going, having a dynamic and ongoing action planning process with open and honest dialogue, and leveraging accountability/outcome check-ins all help build that bridge between where we are and where we aspire to go.

We reviewed how to apply consistent practices to align and move the organization positively, highlighting individual goal cascades, results scorecard and dashboard, ongoing action plans, and accountability/outcome check-ins. Each of these components is important to successful alignment and accountability.

In the end, as defined in this principle, it is about applying these practices not once, occasionally, or when it is convenient but consistently.

Remember that even in the most challenging of times, under the most trying of circumstances, many people have achieved greatness through perseverance and consistency. I do not doubt that what you've read can help you achieve that.

PRINCIPLE 8: COMMUNICATE AT ALL LEVELS

People know why what they do matters.

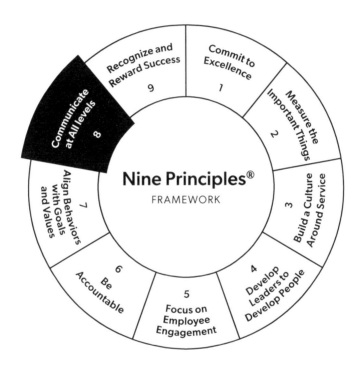

Recognize and Reward Success
9

Commit to Excellence
1

Measure the Important Things
2

Communicate at All levels
8

Align Behaviors with Goals and Values
7

Nine Principles®
FRAMEWORK

Build a Culture Around Service
3

Be Accountable
6

Focus on Employee Engagement
5

Develop Leaders to Develop People
4

"The single biggest problem in communication is the illusion that it has taken place."

George Bernard Shaw

66 Well, this isn't what was supposed to happen."

The CNO was pacing back and forth, talking to herself. "I mean... I'm sure they'll all be here soon. It's fine. I need to calm down."

All I could do was watch.

I had been brought in to speak at a large hospital in California. The original plan was two sessions on a Thursday, but I was asked to add one on Wednesday at the last minute since I would already be in town. I love doing what I do, and I was all in, despite the proposed 3 p.m. time slot.

In my experience, that was not a time that worked for most hospitals in getting much attendance. My pushback was met with assurances that "we are different" and that, somehow, they would let people know about the added session. It seemed I was right to worry about the time and the "somehow." Because now here we were. The CNO and me on Wednesday at 2:52 p.m. And...

No

One

Else

Was

There.

The CNO looked at me and said, "Well, this isn't what was supposed to happen."

Of course it wasn't. But I noticed this team had communication issues right out of the gate. For example, three people emailed me to schedule a pre-call to discuss the agenda, topic, and logistics but didn't cc each other. Also, they created two very different agendas for Thursday with different times listed, which they had sent out to the entire hospital—and then had to retract, correct, and resend once I notified them of the mistake. After several calls and many emails later, we seemed ready to go.

Then came the request for the Wednesday session. Given my experiences to date, I sent the team a message along the lines of: "Since this is a last-minute add-on and there have been a few communication issues, we just need to make sure that this new session day and time is shared with the leadership and that they communicate this throughout the organization using multiple avenues so that folks know all about it..."

I was trying to say as professionally as I could that I lacked confidence in their communication capabilities and, short of pulling out all the stops with robocalls, door-to-door visits, and an airplane sky banner, I encouraged them to have a plan so I didn't end up talking to myself at the Wednesday session.

Back to that. It was too late at this point for robocalls and airplanes. Instead, the CNO went old school and called 10 leaders in a panic. We then went around the house and rounded up as many people as possible. By 3:30 p.m., we had a total of... five people.

The team felt terrible, but I reassured them I didn't care if there were five or 5,000; I was there to do my work and serve people. Still, it should have been 10 times that amount, at least.

Here's the good part: the five attendees were super engaged, and we had a good time. The better part? My two sessions on Thursday were standing room only, with over 120 people in each session! So, we got to make a difference for 240 plus five people. For that, I am grateful. But had communication been better, that might have been 345.

It doesn't matter if we are discussing scheduling a seminar, surgery, infusions, physical therapy, staff meeting, regulatory inspection, employee forum, sharing data and outcomes, policy changes, or a new hire interview. If communication is not done well at all appropriate levels, you will, at best, miss your intended audience and possibly have a hot mess on your hands.

As an epilogue to this story, I was invited back to this organization over a year later. They had been working with some of our incredible Huron coaches on their communication structure and systems, and things went very well. We had four sessions over two days, all of which had over 100 people each, and none were at 3 p.m. They applied many of the concepts you'll read here, and they "got it."

So, how do we communicate effectively at all levels without using robocalls or airplane banners? Read on.

How often do we assume we've communicated 100% clearly and found it was an illusion? Here's what is probably a very relatable example. Let's say you had been chatting on your cell phone for several minutes, telling your friend a juicy story. You're suddenly startled when your phone starts vibrating and ringing in your hand. When you look, you see it's a call from the person you thought you were talking to! The call had dropped, but you didn't realize it. You were communicating—it just wasn't being received. It doesn't matter if we "feel" we've been communicating. If the "reception" isn't there, then what's the point?

If leadership—especially excellent, meaningful, and inspiring leadership—is an art, then communication is the paintbrush with which we bring that art to life. It is the tool by which we learn, grow, improve, mentor, and effect meaningful change. Human beings have a dual need to be understood and valued. What makes great leaders genuinely stand out is that they are great listeners.

As we delve into communication, it is pretty easy to fall into that trap of only focusing on what is being said and how to say it. We tend to overlook the importance of listening for feedback or affirmation. So, in Principle 8, we will also shine some light on the receptive side of the communication coin.

At this point, you have certainly noticed the thread woven into the fabric of most of the principles we have discussed. AIDET® Communication Framework, rounding, leadership fundamentals, and measurement are all significant components and are influenced and fueled by communication. That said, we may repeat a few things in this chapter from previous ones because, as adult learners, sometimes we need to hear things a few times.

Bruce Lee once said, "Repetition is the key to mastery." If you ever watch any of his films, you can't help but be in awe. As my kids are both martial artists, I know that to be "average" takes thousands of kicking and punching combinations practiced over time. Just imagine the number of repetitions of kicks and punches a legend like Bruce Lee must have done, the repetitions of swings and serves champions like Venus and Serena Williams must have done, or the repetitions of practiced free throws and dunks for a Kobe Bryant or Michael Jordan?

To be "world-class" at anything, especially leadership, we will have many repetitions. Musician Pablo Casals, who John F. Kennedy awarded the Presidential Medal of Freedom, once said, "We can only retain what we keep repeating." These are wise words to consider as we continue to weave this tapestry of excellence with our communication thread.

The Impactful Sequence: Why–What–How

Leaving the "why" out of communication is like leaving the apples out of an apple pie. It is the connector to purpose, meaning, and success. Your teams won't be moved by "what" you ask them to do, but they will be moved by the "why" as it speaks to their inner spirit and ignites that spark of that more profound calling in our healthcare DNA.

Start with "why" when communicating new processes, changes, and news. It reduces resistance and anxiety for the person making or implementing the change. Rather than feeling they are being given yet another thing to do, they are instead moved to see it as a meaningful way to do it.

For example, if you told someone to push a button as rapidly as possible in a minute, they'd probably do well. If, instead, you told that person that for every button push in a minute, you'd donate $25 to their favorite cause, my guess is you would see a significant difference. Healthcare workers have that internal drive—our "why"—to do what's right to comfort, heal, and save lives.

 Once they know the WHY, their values can't allow them *not* to do it.

It seemed simple when the research first came out that supported giving aspirin to patients presenting to the emergency room for acute MI. Although this new practice wasn't easy to implement, the data overwhelmingly showed it was vital for better patient outcomes. And even though it was tracked, too many organizations reported their results were nowhere near where they needed to be.

Many in healthcare were shocked. I was running an ED around this time and thought we were great at letting our team know what they had to do and how to document it. So, what was the problem? Why were we also falling so short? Holding up the mirror, perhaps too much time was spent explaining WHAT to do and HOW to do it instead of WHY.

Sure enough, not only in my ED but across the spectrum, once clinicians understood the outcome achieved (saving lives!) when a little pill was given at the right time, the WHAT and the HOW took care of themselves. Many staff developed better processes because once they knew the WHY, they were even more motivated by the values and convictions of that inner calling to achieve the desired outcome.

Manage Up: Position Yourself and Others in a Positive Light

We briefly touched upon and defined the concept of "managing up" in Principle 3 when we discussed rounding, but it's worth giving a little more "love" to it here. It's a great place to start with this principle as it touches many aspects of what inspires excellence and what makes a great place to work... great.

There are several "managing up" or "manage up" definitions we see. In some organizations, it refers to *making your leader's job easier, managing your leader, or approaching your leader when bringing up problems or getting buy-in.*

We use the terms *manage up* and *managing up* differently.

> Managing up is positioning someone or something in a positive light.

Managing up will help you to:

- Gain trust and support.

- Reduce others' anxiety.

- Create more autonomy.

- Enhance your professional presence.

- Re-recruit team members and promote engagement.

When do we manage up?

Most leaders know the importance of managing in their role. But to quote one of my favorite movie characters, Morpheus from the movie *The Matrix*, "... sooner or later you're going to realize, just as I did, there's a difference between knowing the path and walking the path." As a leader, you'll want to actively look for those opportunities to manage up on your journey, not passively wait for them to cross your path.

So, where can you find them? When things are going well, you have great news to share, or fantastic results to broadcast. When you mentor a new hire and want to build their confidence. When you have a solid performer and want to encourage them to step up their game, or a high performer you want to retain. When there is a need to build trust or solidify relationships.

Here are some specific ways to proactively walk the path:

Manage up your leader: Leaders are often overlooked for managing up because some of us think it looks like we're trying to be the "teacher's pet." Also, many people assume leaders don't need managing up for themselves. But study after study shows that leaders, especially in healthcare, suffer from burnout and feelings of insecurity as much as front-line staff. Let them know you appreciate their investment in the team with a thank you card. Please email them to let them know you were impressed with a speech they gave or an action they took. Usually, people only communicate with a leader when they have a complaint or an issue. No matter the person's title, a little manage up can be a big deal.

Manage up staff, physicians/providers, or other departments: We covered this well in the AIDET® Communication Framework in Principle 3, but in addition to managing up staff/departments/physicians/providers to people we serve to reduce anxiety and create a positive impression, you can do the same to other staff/departments/physicians/providers. If you're meeting with other leaders and the lab, facility operations, or volunteer department did some good things, give them a manage up in front of the leadership team. If you're passing by one of the surgeons and you were super impressed with the way the new anesthesia tech interacted with your team, let her know! Manage up that staff person or department before the senior leader rounds so they can show their appreciation and create goodwill that benefits everyone.

Manage up the organization: The best marketing, advertisement, or public relations asset for an organization is the people working there. You are a walking billboard when you are out in the world buying groceries, getting a flat tire fixed, or playing with your dog at a dog park in your uniform, name badge, or t-shirt with your organization's logo. Hopefully, you work there because you respect, value, and maybe even love the place. So, if it comes up in conversation, manage it up! You may be the reason that person chooses your organization over another.

Remember, when you're a leader, you are being watched. You are more influential than you think. We've talked about culture a lot in this book. Culture comes from within the organization, and when you manage up—sincerely, authentically, and transparently—it is seen, felt, and has an impact.

Be the leader who isn't afraid to lift others, knowing everyone benefits. Be the leader others seek to imitate. Be the light others are drawn to. As you've heard said by basketball coach John Wooden, "The most powerful leadership tool you have is your example." The example you set as a leader is more powerful and memorable than you may realize.

We/They Phenomenon

"I would switch your weekends, but you know how Matt has been since he became manager... he forgets what it's like to be 'one of us.' It's not worth the drama. Sorry."

"If it were up to me, I'd order the extra beds. Trust me, I fought hard for it, but Administration never gives in when it comes to money."

We have all probably done this at one time or another—positioned ourselves or our team favorably at the expense of others. This "we/they" dynamic is usually not intentional and often stems from the well-meaning effort to "soften the blow of the no." It is also the subconscious expression of some version of: "I don't want you to dislike me/be mad at me/hold me responsible for this or that answer/thing," so it's easier to blame "them."

The problem is when we have a culture of we/they it undermines success. While you may not be the "bad guy" in one sense of that scenario, what you are doing is undermining the other part of your team. If you are a leader, it also undermines your authority and respect for your role. You make them look bad, and in essence, that hurts everyone.

> **66** **WOW! That's a lot of chairs!"**

Ruth-Ann had been the outpatient director for 20 years; longer than the hospital had even existed. She and three other employees worked in a trailer on the hospital construction site. Ruth-Ann always joked, "I am older than the dirt here," as she showed you a framed picture of her standing next to dump trucks carting in the dirt for the building's foundation.

She was loyal. Sometimes to a fault. She was great at teaching skills, knew where everything was, and was a fierce patient advocate.

Unfortunately, she was also very good at "we/they" because she valued being loved by her team. Whenever the staff had an issue or a request that needed approval that was out of her scope, she'd always set the stage.

"Well, you know how the administration is, they're not like us, but I'll fight for this, don't you worry!" If a request were approved, she would return triumphantly and claim, "I let them know if they didn't give us those IV pumps, I would quit! They knew I wasn't playing around, so they gave in!"

But even in instances of "no for now," she maintained an adversarial stance. For example, once, her staff asked for extra chairs for the waiting room. The senior leaders had just budgeted a remodel of the waiting room and decided to order some brand-new chairs to match the new décor, but they were on backorder, so they asked for a bit of patience.

Rather than tell her team they would have to wait a few weeks, Ruth-Ann told them their request had been denied. Of course, the team rallied around her, both in shared indignation and in not wanting one of Ruth-Ann's infamous lines—"I might get fired for this, guys, but here goes nothing"—to be realized.

A few days later, the CEO did some senior leader rounds on the team. Ruth-Ann was delayed in a meeting, but he felt comfortable enough to round based on the information the manager had provided. Yet he was a little taken aback when one of the staff asked, "So, why can't we get chairs for the waiting room?"

"Oh, those should be here in about three weeks," he responded. "We know you all take pride in the department rather than piece it together. We will try to get the matching waiting room chairs all at once. We used the colors and ideas you submitted last year; you'll love it!"

In walked Ruth-Ann. The CEO apologized for stealing her thunder about announcing the waiting room remodel because the staff asked about the chairs. Ruth-Ann changed about 15 colors in 30 seconds and stammered, "Chairs are good... I like chairs!"

The CEO could read a room and saw what was going on between Ruth-Ann, who looked like she was about to pass out, and the confused staff. He was also compassionate and liked to coach his leaders. He somehow moved the subject along and then met with Ruth-Ann later one-on-one.

To her credit, she owned up to the blame game. She took account-ability for not wanting to tell her team "no" because she worried they'd be angry. Was he angry with her?

No. Instead, they had a real heart-to-heart about leadership. The CEO offered her some time with an executive coach, who helped Ruth-Ann see how "we/they" was like a nerve block for surgery—it might make things painless at the time of incision, but it eventually wears off, and then the pain makes itself known.

Because of the insight she developed, Ruth-Ann decided to transfer into a different role where many of her strengths could be better utilized. She later told me, "This is the best I've felt coming to work since the days of the trailer!" She helped train the incoming director and made sure to emphasize, "If there's one thing that I've learned, it's that there's no 'we/they,' there's only 'us.'"

After the new waiting room was complete, "they" asked Ruth-Ann to cut the ribbon for its opening, which she did. And after everyone cheered, she said, "Wow, that's a lot of chairs!"

There sure were!

To once again quote former U.S. Navy SEAL commander Jocko Willink from his book, *Extreme Ownership: How US SEALs Lead and Win*: "Leaders must own everything in their world; there is no one else to blame." That mindset is not easy to establish and takes effort and commitment, but it nonetheless makes us the type of leaders we genuinely want, and our teams need us to be. "We/they" is an easy trap to fall into. Take "extreme ownership" for the betterment of all involved. And where appropri-ate, manage up others—position individuals and departments in a positive light.

As leaders, we want to do the best job we can. We want to win. We want everyone to win. Awareness and training can help stop the "we/they" phenomenon and foster ownership.

- Explain the *why* of the decisions that are made. If you're unsure of the why, find out to accurately convey the information.

- Take ownership: explain what you *can* or *can't* do.

- Imagine your leader and other leaders are listening to you when you speak. You do not want to position yourself positively at the expense of making anyone else look poorly.

- Be transparent without pointing a finger. You can do both. It might sound something like, "I understand how you feel. I am disappointed too. I know our administrators considered every fact when making this hard decision. Although we may have liked to see a different decision, I trust the decision. They often have information or context none of us have, and I am confident they made the best decision for the organization."

In the story earlier in this chapter, I loved how Ruth-Ann coached the incoming director, who would take over her department: "There's no 'we/they,' there's only 'us'."

Words to live by for sure.

Answering Tough Questions

If you are a leader, you have ALL the answers, right? Sometimes it feels as if we are expected to. I get it. But we know better. Yet we've also met those people who think they have ALL the answers. While applauding their confidence, we must be wary of their arrogance. Part of being an excellent and inspired leader is being humble enough to know what you don't know and to be able to give yourself a little grace around that.

If you are asked a question and genuinely don't know the answer, stand in your truth, look them in the eye, take that grounding pause, and own it. You may not feel you gain "points" when you admit you don't know something, but I'd challenge you to think differently. You gain "points" in this game of life and leadership when you are authentic. Ultimately, you will find an opportunity to grow and be better than ever.

There is often a belief that a tough question—one that goes a little deeper or asks more of the person for whom the question is being posed—is "disrespectful." A well-posed and meaningful "tough question" may be needed. Albert Einstein famously said, "We can't solve problems using the same thinking we used when we created them." I would say: we can't create change by asking the same questions we've always asked.

> Tough questions are challenging topics that center around sensitive information, diverse circumstances, longstanding unaddressed issues, or where there could be misinformation or gossip.

Even when we recognize the value in tough questions, it doesn't mean we are comfortable with or good at addressing them. If we don't prepare ourselves and the leaders around us with the skills to answer tough questions, we might see them revert to "we/they" platitudes or, worse, unintentional misinformation.

The key to answering tough questions is planning and training. By anticipating possible questions and harvesting them from staff members during rounding and other conversations, you and your fellow leaders can work together to prepare practical answers. You want to minimize surprises as much as possible, but they still happen. There are some helpful ways to navigate this.

Five Steps to Remember When Answering Tough Questions

STEP 1: PAUSE AND GIVE YOURSELF A MOMENT.

Sometimes "inaction" is more powerful than action. Often as leaders, we think we need to "answer fast" or risk sounding or looking like a deer caught in the headlights. But pausing allows you to process, collect your thoughts, and not react emotionally. Sometimes a tough question can hit a "button" or "trigger," and your first reaction may not be the most constructive.

ASK YOURSELF:	EXAMPLES:
• Do I hear the question correctly?	•"Thank you for your question. Would you mind if I took a moment to grab something to take notes?"
• Am I feeling an emotional or negative reaction to this question?	
• Can I put that aside, pause, and take in this question from a logical and objective place?	•"Let me take a moment to think about this because I want my answer to be as thoughtful as possible."

STEP 2: UNDERSTAND THE "WHY" BEHIND THE QUESTION.

It is okay to ask for clarification or even definitions. Someone may ask a question using subjective terms, and you want to demonstrate respect for the questioner and their question. Validate your assumptions before you launch into a response. Another pause is okay here.

ASK YOURSELF:

- What questions should you ask to understand the employee's question further?
- What is the underlying issue(s)? What is the motivation driving the questioner?

EXAMPLES:

- "I just want to make sure I am clear on what you're asking, out of respect for your question. So, your question is (repeat)... is that correct?"
- "Before I answer that, can you clarify what you mean by 'delayed'? When was it communicated that it would arrive, and how long was the delay?"

STEP 3: DETERMINE WHAT INFORMATION YOU NEED TO PROVIDE THE BEST ANSWER.

Suppose you don't have the information you need to be comfortable to answer honestly and transparently. Your team will respect you more when you acknowledge that and commit to getting and sharing that information within a specific time frame rather than giving a long and meaningless speech.

ASK YOURSELF:

- Do you have all the facts you need to provide a credible response?
- Does the response you have in mind address the underlying questions you've uncovered?

EXAMPLES:

- "Thanks for the question. I have some ideas, but I'd like to get more information before I answer."
- "I truly don't know the answer to that at the moment. May I have time to think about that and get back to you?"

STEP 4: UTILIZE YOUR RESOURCES.

Utilize the resources and contacts you have on hand to answer tough questions. People realize that "smart people" don't always have the answers, but they know who to go to when they don't.

ASK YOURSELF:

- Is there someone with additional expertise that you can bring into the discussion?
- Can I ask for help without passing the buck or creating a "we/they" situation?

EXAMPLES:

- "I honestly don't have all the information to give you a solid answer, and I don't want to answer for the sake of answering. Let me research a bit, and I will get more information from finance."

ASK YOURSELF:	EXAMPLES:
	•"Let's meet with Jamie in human resources, an expert in this area."
	•"I don't know the answer to that question, but I know someone who will. May I send them an email and get back to you?"

STEP 5: DECIDE HOW BEST TO COMMUNICATE THE ANSWER.

No two questions or situations are exactly alike. Some tough questions are more sensitive and need to be shared individually; some merit an answer in a group setting. The bottom line is that it is wise to pause and consider the question and the best method of communication.

ASK YOURSELF:	EXAMPLES:
• Is this a topic best answered in a one-on-one conversation, or is it a topic for the whole group?	•"I'll bring you answers to these questions after our team meets Tuesday. I believe I will be able to have more details for you then."
• Would understanding be improved if you had visuals or printed material for staff to reference?	•"Let me look into this question, and I will meet with you tomorrow."

Best Practice Update: Tough Question Exercise

This exercise provides a structured method for leaders to respond effectively to questions and speak in a unified voice. It also helps leaders connect staff to the "why," so they are more likely to buy into making the change successful.

Tough Question Exercise:

Directions: In a small group of leaders, identify the tough questions you anticipate or solicit them in advance from your team. With each question in mind, ask your executive team to work through these questions, explore the issue, and develop a unified response.

What is the tough question or issue?

What questions should you ask to understand the employee's question further?

What is the underlying issue?

What is your best response (key words) to the employee's question or issue?

What leader competencies and information do I need to address this question?

How should we best communicate this message?

Figure 8.1: Tough Question Exercise

Tough questions can be one of the most demanding aspects of being a leader. They are also one of our greatest gifts, as they open up authentic dialogue and help us build our communication muscles in ways that the easier questions do not. They can be uncomfortable, but the conversations that come from them are real. "Real" isn't always comfortable, but it is, for sure, what is needed in leadership. "Real" is powerful and always wins in the long run.

You can say, "When the questions get tough… the tough get real."

Tools and Techniques for Effective Communication

We love tools and tactics in healthcare. As a nurse, it was a great day when we got to unbox a shiny new device that would improve our care. Sure, there was always the learning curve, but once you got the hang of it, you were on cloud nine.

Most of us enjoy the excitement of new "tools." Think back to when you were a kid and got a new pair of sneakers. What about the new pencils, pens, or that box of crayons you got at the start of school? So, how can we talk about communication without giving you some new "crayons" to color your life and new "sneakers" to run circles around everyone else?

The first thing to realize is that what worked 20 or even three years ago will probably not work as well now. Things are changing fast. People are overloaded with information and have many things — positive and not-so-positive — competing for their attention.

Forbes magazine published an article about the role of communication in retaining employees. In it, the author stated, "If there's one thing we can take away from the pandemic, it's that openness to flexibility has meant that many businesses can not only survive hardships but can also thrive during them. We should translate this same openness to how we communicate internally, as the traditional methods of face-to-face meetings or to-and-from emails may not cut it anymore."

Communication has changed and will continue to do so.

Think about our personal lives. Have you ever video-called, texted, or Face-Timed a loved one... *from another room?*

No? Just me?

I bet some of you have. So, these changes in how we communicate are making their way into the very fabric of our lives.

Let's talk about some ways to "communicate," most of which are relatively simple, maybe even familiar, and some we've touched upon already but deserve a little extra attention.

Communication Boards

Communication boards remain a key vehicle for communicating with large numbers of people.

> Communication boards are placed in departments, units, and other staff-based locations throughout the organization. They allow for consistent distribution of material based on the pillars of your model of excellence.

And a communication board is an easy thing to maintain and visualize. Think of them as the "Billboards on the Highways of Our Workplace!"

In some organizations, one team or department provides standardized information for the boards, designating what should be placed under each pillar or critical focus area. If your organization does not have such a group, think of information that would be helpful, relevant, timely, interesting, and even inspiring to your team, and create your communication board structured under key focuses or pillars.

In some organizations, one team or department provides standardized information for the boards, designating what should be placed under each pillar or critical focus area. If your organization does not have such a group, think of information that would be helpful, relevant, timely, interesting, and even inspiring to your team, and create your communication board structured under key focuses or pillars.

Tips

- **More pictures, less text.** Help your team members quickly identify important concepts with pictures, icons, and graphs versus text-heavy printouts. Think about those highway billboards. No one is going to read details zipping by at 70 mph. Try to keep words to a minimum.

- **Keep current.** Validate that boards are kept current and consider assigning responsibility for each section to a high-performing team member. Utilize your team's strengths and get them engaged as "Keepers of the Board" (KOTB) in cooperation with your organization's brand/design standards.

- **Engage users.** Challenge your KOTB to make the content engaging, creative. and exciting. Maybe you have someone who is artistic or crafty. Let them use those talents! Set them free to use all the rhinestones and glitter they want! It'll bring some much-needed sparkle to the environment and maybe even some smiles. Like my artist friend Gabriel used to say, "Less bitter, more glitter!"

- **Validate their value.** Ask individual team members to walk you through the content displayed. What are their key takeaways, and what actions should they take? Don't make it only an "information board" but truly a "communication board," which means there should be a discussion. If it means enough to you to engage with it, your team will also see it has value for them.

On the next page is an example of a department communication board for you. Notice it's simplicity as well as it demonstration of the above.

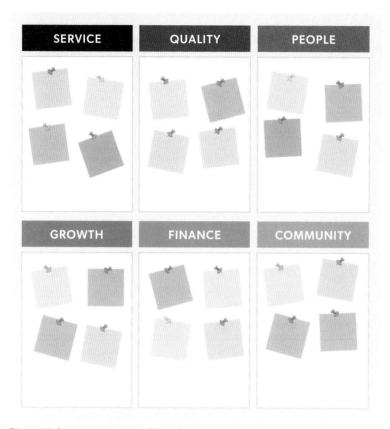

Figure 8.2: Communication Board Samples

Communication Calendar

Here's another idea to ensure consistent messaging in your organization. This idea came out of the COVID-19 pandemic which was forcing radical changes in practice and policy seemingly daily. One organization Huron works with decided to create a new form of communication: a communication calendar to ensure a consistent message was delivered throughout the organization.

Every leader participated and had actions to take that were detailed in the calendar. Resources were made available in print and recorded audio files. Their senior leadership says this adaptation of their usual communication processes played a significant role in keeping the rumor mill in check and reducing anxiety across their workforce during significant disruption.

		WEEK #1		
Themes		Rounding Self Identification as Healthcare Hero Thank a Hero		
Description	Daily Senior Leader Communication or Action	Tip of the Day		
		Audience ⬇	Resource ⬇	Action ⬇
Monday	Daily business / organizational update	All Employees	Healthcare Heroes tip (row 3) - printable with 2 tips	All can print Leaders print and share in huddles Post in unit/area
Tuesday	Daily business and/or organizational update	All Employees	How to Meditate (rows 30-31) printable	All can print Leaders print and share in huddles Post in unit/area
Wednesday	Daily business and/or organizational update Share commitment to rounding	Leadership	Maximizing Rounding – printable (row 26)	Round with employees; leaders share in huddle
Thursday	Daily business and/or organizational update	All Employees	What is Mindfulness? (row 33) Download Mindfulness app (row 25)	All can print Leaders print and share in huddles Post in unit/area
Friday	Daily business and/or organizational update Share tip and personal example (can be text or video)	All Employees	Healthcare Heroes tip Rocket Man video (row 7) Printable sign	All can access Leaders can stream and role model Share in huddle Print document and share in huddles Post in areas
Ideas for Senior Leadership	Create hashtag campaign like #healthcarehero Have employees take a picture w/ healthcare hero signs (fun activity)		Top Executive: Commit to role model and require Senior Leader Rounding	There are no "just A's" in Healthcare (7 MINUTES)

Figure 8.3: Communication Calendar Example

Staff Daily Huddles

If you have ever watched a team sport, you are familiar with the huddle concept. This is when the team gathers around their coach to receive the play, discuss strategies for scoring, get motivated, clap, line up, and prepare to enter the game. The huddle concept, for us, is designed to be a moment to have clarity around what's happening on the "field" and get "pumped" before we "get back in the game." While we may not be trying to score touchdowns, we are going for something much more meaningful: saving lives and healing our fellow human beings.

So, whether conducted in person, via Zoom, Facetime, or other advanced technologies, the essence of a huddle remains the same—to inform and align the work of a team and increase productivity, accountability, and outcomes.

Let's define a staff huddle.

> The daily huddle is a simple and efficient standup meeting at the start of each workday or the start of each major shift. These huddles typically last between 3-5 minutes, never exceeding seven minutes. Following a standard agenda, the huddle aims to enhance team productivity, accountability, and outcomes as individuals begin their shifts.

Many non-patient-facing departments adopt this practice and hold weekly huddles for the same purpose. The cadence is up to you; some teams do it twice per shift, and some non-patient-facing departments do it daily. Whatever works for your team is what is best!

Standard Agenda Items:

While huddles may be a common practice for you, the quality of the content discussed during these meetings is where leaders can make significant improvements. Ensuring that the huddle is productive, informative, and engaging for all participants is essential. By doing so, leaders can foster a sense of unity and collaboration within their team, leading to better outcomes and increased success.

Huddles work best you follow a standard outline or agenda every time. This allows the huddle to run efficiently and staff to anticipate the information they will receive as they begin their shifts.

DAILY STAFF HUDDLE AGENDA

Date: _____ Dept./Unit/Area: _____

AM Huddle Facilitator: _____

PM Huddle Facilitator: _____

WINS from yesterday's rounding (1 minute)

_____

_____

WOW Stories (<1 minute)
(Connect to purpose stories, patient/family compliments)

_____

_____

Review Patient Experience and Safety Results (2 minutes)

Our patient experiences goals are: _____

Our current performance is: _____

Our safety/quality focuses are: _____

Our current performance is: _____

Focus for the Day (1 minute)
Key Word Examples to use today (e.g. managing up, key elements of AIDET or Hourly Rounding); Safety Issues (high risk patients, recent events, priorities to reduce risks)

_____

_____

Questions/Comments from Team (1 minute)

_____

_____

Acknowledgments (<1 minute)

_____

_____

Promotions, birthdays, babies

_____

_____

Positive Call to Action

_____

Figure 8.4: Sample Daily Huddle Agenda

Huddles are a great forum to support process improvement, information updates, quick rewards, recognition, and connecting to purpose. It is not for problem-solving—use another forum for that. The trick is to keep huddles brief, engaging, and focused on the essential actions for that shift, day, or week.

- **Wows, wins, bright spots, or connections to purpose:** Kick the huddle off by focusing on positive and bright spots. This is the perfect time to highlight department and personal wins to recognize and reward behaviors and achievements. A great idea is to allow your team member to contribute something positive, share a story, a joke, or something lighthearted to set a positive vibe.

- **Announcements:** The huddle provides a consistent forum to share critical information for staff awareness and keep everyone in the loop. Share important information with your team, such as upcoming deadlines, training sessions, and meetings. This will ensure everyone is aware of what's happening in your department. These announcements may include:

    - Safety risks and how to mitigate them

    - Operational updates

    - Process changes

    - Specific patient population checks

    - Other safety and quality information

Stoplight Reports (Again!)

We have mentioned Stoplight Reports before, but some of these tools apply to different principles in different ways. (See Principle 5).

When communicating at all levels, Stoplight Reports are an excellent way to communicate the things that are completed, in progress and what cannot be done and why. We recommend reviewing updates to the Stoplight Report during daily staff huddles as well.

GREEN = Completed	YELLOW = In Progress	RED = Cannot do at this time and here's why
2/13- 4x4 gauze pad par increased to 3 boxes. (complete)	2/12- Need more 4x4 gauze pads on par cart	
	2/12- Process idea regarding multi-d rounds. "Can the bedside RN be notified when it's time for their patient's rounds?" 2/20- **UPDATE**: Charge nurse group developing plan for notifying bedside RN when time to discuss their patients in Multi-D rounds.	

GREEN = Completed	YELLOW = In Progress	RED = Cannot do at this time and here's why
	2/12- Need two more bladder scanners on the unit.	2/13- Due to cost of each bladder scanner, we will request during capital budget planning in November. Unable to purchase now. **Will develop process for sharing with another unit until capital budget process timing later this fall.

Figure 8.5 Stoplight Report Example

Staff Meetings

Staff meetings are certainly timeless in concept, even though they may look different with remote workers and associated technologies. Using the pillar structure, you can help your agenda stay focused, balanced, and organized across all the essential areas of your team.

Inviting leaders or staff from other departments to share success stories, teamwork examples, or compliments is a great way to keep the meetings lively and connect your team to others across the organization.

If your department is 24/7, you will conduct multiple meetings to allow all team members to participate. It's a big commitment for you as a leader, but well worth your time to engage every team member. One creative way to do this is to make allowances so that you can shift your schedule around for the meeting. Perhaps one day you come in a little later or stay later to engage the night shift or come in earlier and leave a little earlier to do the same for the day shift.

I found this to be a good thing, personally. I worked the night shift for many years, so it wasn't a big stretch to get into that schedule for a few days, and I loved the change of energy and "vibe" as a leader, being with my night and evening teams. They seemed to, as well. Maybe because I brought coffee, bagels, muffins, fruit, cookies, and donuts, but a leader striving for "inspired excellence" must never be above a little healthy, well-meaning "incentivizing."

You can utilize the "huddle" sample agenda as a guide for your staff meetings. You would lengthen the time for each topic and perhaps add some time for problem-solving, which we discussed should not be part of the huddle model. Huron's coaches have compiled some great resources for meeting models on our website/learning lab that we invite you to explore since they are continually updated to reflect new learnings in the field.

Executive Leader Daily/Weekly/ Monthly Communication Virtual Broadcasts and Recordings

Depending on the organization's size, the executive leader may not have regular direct contact with all employees. In these instances, executive leader virtual broadcasts are an excellent option to create connection and visibility. They are especially effective in the face of significant disruption or crisis as they allow for a rapid response and can reach a broader audience.

Create your broadcast or recorded content with a "people first" attitude. Be heartful, use your authentic voice, and remember it doesn't matter if you're communicating about a construction project, a crisis, or reading a list of the names of new hires; you are giving of yourself when you communicate. If you haven't already, you will find that when you "give" of yourself, you get a lot in return.

Remember:

> "The fragrance always stays in the
> hand that gives the rose"
>
> *Hada Bejar*

Here are several suggestions when scheduling executive leaders' virtual broadcasts:

- **Be Authentic.** This is one of those repeating themes that could be a whole book itself. The more "real" a leader is, the more people will find them credible and the more forgiving they will be when things aren't going well. Part of being authentic is accepting your faults and strengths and being good with who you are, even while working on yourself. I speak on stage in front of people hundreds of times a year, and even after decades of doing so, I still get that pang of "less-than." Your "stage" may be a meeting or a virtual recorded update, but authenticity in your communication helps generate a connection so you achieve that feeling of belonging.

- **Tell the Truth.** People would rather hear the truth—including bad news—than try to work with uncertainty about what's happening. In the face of doubt, fear, and uncertainty, people look to a leader for that steady hand and optimism. You may not realize it, but people will pick up on your energy during these times. Truth-telling inspires confidence and should never be compromised.

- **Use Key Words at Key Times.** People also see leaders as credible and reliable during a crisis when the message focuses on outcomes, provides good direction, and includes the right words. People want to trust that their leader is aware of the impact at the front line and taking the right actions to manage the crisis. They also want to hear a consistent message. Ensure leaders at all levels "sing from the same song sheet."

- **Recognize People for Good Work.** Share specific examples of front-line staff making a difference. Great leaders learn to tell stories. Stories move and encourage people, helping them to see purpose more than any graph or scattergram ever will. People will feel proud, revitalized, aligned, and connected, especially in stressful times when they hear examples of "making a difference." As we have said before, recognized behaviors are often repeated.

- **Be Mindful of Employee Needs.** Select the best time of day to do a virtual broadcast. It may work best for some organizations to do it at the same time each day. For 24-hour organizations, producing some virtual broadcasts during the day, some during the evening, and some on weekends makes sense. Regardless of the scheduled time, send it to all employees. Some organizations even create 2–3-minute employee-access-only weekly videos that provide updates, manage ups, brief connections to purpose, exciting things coming down the road, and even the cafeteria menu. You are only limited by your imagination and staff expertise!

VIRTUAL BROADCAST OUTLINE

ITEM	TIME
Share wins by highlighting something a person or team did that had a tremendous impact.	2 min
Present the outcomes for the time frame/day and progress made on outcomes to date. Celebrate accomplishments and why that is important for the organization.	2 min
Address specific areas that are not working as well as needed and actions being taken to address these areas.	3 min
Communicate why the employees are essential to solving the critical issues identified. Give specific examples of actions they should take and ways to share their ideas for addressing the issues.	2 min
Express your confidence in your leaders and employees to get the job done. End with gratitude for the work that people are doing.	1 min

Figure 8.6: Sample Virtual Broadcast Outline

Employee Forums

> Employee Forums are senior leader-led employee meetings that occur three to four times a year and are attended by all employees. They allow senior leaders to communicate a consistent message to all employees and learn about and celebrate their workplace.

The CEO/president should do a minimum of 75% of the speaking at these sessions. That ensures not only visibility but the consistency of messaging. These sessions should be about information sharing and be fun and engaging.

Most of the thoughts for virtual broadcast and recording apply to forums. They should occur at set intervals with a predetermined agenda. They are usually built on a theme that ties together the session, supports the mission, and creates an enjoyable opportunity for team-work. All employees should attend these sessions, with leaders setting this expectation.

It is not uncommon to have guest speakers. Let the "creatives" on your team loose on these. Key things to remember are these **three phases** of creating and executing an employee forum:

PHASE ONE: PLAN	PHASE TWO: IMPLEMENT	PHASE THREE: EVALUATE
Create a plan for all to attend. Use a theme and build out the theme and agenda to reinforce your pillars and strategic direction.	Implement the plan and ensure participation with real-time questions/surveys to make it interactive and fun. All sessions should be mandatory, and it is the responsibility of all leaders to get their staff to the sessions.	After every forum, employees should complete evaluations. The results of these evaluations should be used to improve the following forum.

Phase One: Plan

An effective employee forum starts with thoughtful and intentional planning, just like any gathering.

- **Theme:**
  Choose a theme or key concept. Connect fun activities to the theme to make the session engaging and fun for onsite and virtual attendees. Guest speakers, contests, door prizes, posters, costumes, and music are excellent ways to make the session memorable. Drinks, snacks, candy, fruit, or whatever your team likes are also suitable for in-person gatherings. One organization shared news about completing a major re-insulation project of some older buildings by handing out bags of cotton candy branded as "fluffy stuff," to acknowledge the fluffy pink insulation that was now packed into the walls and keeping everyone warm.

- **Logistics:**
  Ideally, everyone attends in person. However, talk through virtual components as appropriate for your organization. All-virtual, hybrid, or all-onsite—there is no "one size fits all" with this. It is about what gets the best results for your team.

- **Connect to Purpose:**
  Begin the session with purpose and connection to the heart of the work people do each day. Consider sharing:

- Patient success stories.

- Notes of appreciation from patients and families highlight how they were touched by the care and compassion they received.

- Messages and notes highlighting teamwork and collaboration. Letters that name several people or departments that have worked together emphasize the value of teamwork.

- Short and impactful videos showcasing your team's meaningful work are a powerful way to engage and inspire your audience. These videos can be produced in-house and provide a unique opportunity for viewers to witness their colleagues in action. They can share impactful experiences, celebrate milestones, and showcase the success of your department or team. Whether it's a 20th anniversary, a master's degree achievement, or a retirement celebration, these videos can help to foster a sense of community and pride within your organization.

- Short videos featuring staff members sharing their personal "why" stories. In the past, Huron launched a campaign called #MyInspiredSign, which encouraged healthcare workers to write a brief description of what motivated them to pursue a career in healthcare or who inspired them to do so. The response was overwhelming, with hundreds of organizations participating and thousands of heartfelt photos submitted. Don't underestimate the impact of heartfelt stories and connect-to-purpose moments.

- **Reward and Recognition:**
Plan time to reward and recognize your organization's individuals, teams, and physicians. Highlight departments that have best practices to share. This not only fosters collaboration but also breaks down silos. Additionally, it creates a positive work environment, which is crucial in today's world, and makes things fun. Principle 9: Recognize and Reward Success dives deeper into this concept and provides valuable insights on effectively implementing it.

- **Question Preparation:**
Employee forums provide an excellent opportunity to address tough questions. Anticipate these, prepare answers, and don't be afraid to collect and incorporate answers into the sessions. It is also helpful to make the answers available after the sessions. These forums have a way of "demystifying" things and clearing out rumors.

- **Agenda Development:**
  Connect the agenda to the theme. Add fun items and align the agenda to your organizational pillars, key performance initiatives, and strategic focus areas. Keep the agenda framework the same for each forum to create consistency—only the topics under each pillar/framework change to meet the organization's needs.

Phase Two: Implement

The balloons are inflated, the costumes are on, the music has been uploaded, and the bagels have arrived. It is finally time to implement your careful phase one planning. At Huron, we have found some key strategies that help to execute a successful employee forum:

- **Hold a leader session first.** The first employee forum session should be conducted for leaders only. The agenda is the same for the following forums, but this first forum is usually half an hour longer to allow for questions and answers. This session also ends with key points for the leaders to address in their departments. This leader-only session allows senior leadership to:

  - Educate the leadership team on information to be presented to the employees.

  - Promote ownership by allowing leaders a firsthand opportunity to provide input and feedback to help improve the sessions for their employees. It's a great way to test-run the content and apply any needed tweaks to the message.

  - Prepare leaders to reinforce the information and answer questions after the employees return from the forums.

  - Allow the leaders to know precisely what they must do in their departments. This creates alignment and exactly what it means to "communicate at all levels."

- **Track attendance.** At each session, take attendance, and include the supervisor's name for accountability. Your organization may use an electronic system, a very efficient way to track attendance and other identifiers. Sometimes these can serve double duty in providing important benefits, resources, or other information. Remember that example in rounding about going to the mailbox? If you have an event that everyone will attend, think about what everybody needs to have and get it to them!

- **Connect logistics and themes/create fun.** Buttons, posters, room decorations, and door prizes add to the excitement. Have people at the door to hand things out, and build on the fun by having employees dress in costumes or theme-based clothing. Be sure to have someone take a lot of photos. Pro-tip: these photos and images, gathered over the years, make for great "slide show" images that can be put on screen in the room(s) where these are being held. Staff love to laugh at pictures of themselves and their co-workers from years ago. And, to be very honest, sometimes we have people we love leave the organization—retire, or, sadly, pass away—seeing them again is heartwarming. I have been in the room where these slide shows are playing, and a picture of someone deeply missed comes up. There are hugs, smiles, and sometimes tears, but it is pretty touching. Those moments remind us how extraordinary these gatherings are on so many levels.

- **Schedule to ensure attendance.** Plan enough sessions in enough different locations and at various times of the day so that ALL STAFF CAN ATTEND. Don't be afraid to make attendance mandatory for all your leaders and those who work with them. Be patient, especially if these sessions are new. There will be mistakes, so as always, give yourself and your team grace and view each event as an opportunity to learn from and build upon for the next one.

Phase Three: Evaluate

The forum isn't complete until the evaluation is done! Post-forum employee evaluations allow you to gather information about employee areas of concern, critical information regarding the culture, and questions that still need to be communicated further. This information will allow you to track/trend employee engagement throughout the year and to respond effectively.

Share the results openly at the next employee forum. This will allow you to evaluate whether people were engaged and help plan future content and sessions. Be transparent with this. It will drive you to be better and help the team see this is the real deal.

Consider the following as you plan your evaluation:

- **Method:** Make it easy for people to provide feedback! Evaluations can be done on paper or electronically with SLIDO® or other measures.

- **Results:** Quick changes and adaptions from feedback can help to make each subsequent session better. If evaluations say that the team loved the music at the first forum, pump it up for the next one! If you noticed no one ate the bran muffins, but everyone ravaged the blueberry muffins, order more blueberry! (Unless you have a large G.I. practice/department—they usually eat ALL the bran muffins... they know things.) Little changes can make significant differences.

- **Engagement:** Choose one to two critical questions from your standardized employee engagement survey and place them on the employee forum evaluation. This creates an excellent opportunity to "take the temperature" of your organization throughout the year. This will allow you to pivot, refocus on certain things, and ensure that what you're doing as a leader and as an organization is being communicated and, more importantly, felt by your team.

- **Consistency:** Keep the questions chosen for the evaluation consistent from forum to forum to allow for comparable results and data trends.

- **Anonymity:** Keep the evaluations anonymous but ask respondents for the name of their leader. This helps leaders create action plans for their departments based on what employees truly want.

- **Analytics:** Prepare, review, and calculate the data to provide a summary after the sessions.

Once the evaluation results have been received and reviewed, the organization's leaders need to act:

- **Senior Leaders:** Meet with their direct reports to communicate the results, identify the wins, confirm what teams are doing right, and review any areas of concern. This should also be discussed at leadership meetings. Highlight the departments that have the highest attendance and have received positive feedback or accolades. Talk A LOT about what went well to recognize high-performing leaders and departments and to help build better leaders.

- **Department Leaders:** Determine what issues must be fixed and incorporate them into their 90-day action plans. This is a great group exercise because the department leaders can learn from each other and figure out ways to support their peers while also picking up new tricks and shortcuts to improve their teams.

Once the forums are over, you all need to take a minute, reorganize, and rest, but this is not the time to disconnect. Use the questions and comments gathered from the evaluations to provide continuous feedback to the staff via emails, newsletters, and staff meetings. Make sure leadership at all levels is responsive across all media.

Worthwhile and Productive Meetings

How many times a week do you leave a meeting and ask yourself why you just wasted an hour of your life in that setting? As noted, you have two precious and limited resources: your time and energy. Wasting them on ineffective meetings is frustrating and a tangible loss to the organization regarding "lost hours" and the resulting monetary cost.

Here are a few ways leaders can make significant improvements in the meetings they lead:

- **Define the purpose:** Communicate it to all participants in advance. For example, "We have one hour to review our current scoreboard results and key action items to be taken over the next 30 days." Or "We will review the rollout plan for the new EMR and highlight areas of concern." When participants have clarity on purpose, they are more likely to come to the meeting well-prepared to meet the goal and less likely to try to address off-topic subjects that are not the primary focus of this gathering.

- **Define the audience:** Carefully consider who is invited and whether their attendance is required to achieve the meeting's goal. While it is good to have "everyone at the table" for some things, too many chefs can ruin the soup for many meetings. If someone who is not invited wants to attend, let them know why and when or if they might be later. It is not only respectful, but it creates transparency and elevates trust.

- **Have a clear agenda that supports the purpose:** An agenda is critical to staying on topic. Even a "troubleshooting meeting" or a "brainstorming meeting" needs an agenda. Prepare and distribute it in advance. You can always set aside some time on the agenda for "other" items but remember your overall goal. The discipline of an agenda will serve you well. Don't minimize or overlook it.

- **Begin on time:** It shows respect to those in attendance and sends a message to those who are late that you expect promptness. Do not recap for late arrivals. Set an expectation that they get the information they missed after the meeting. This may shock some, so let the team know beforehand that this is how meetings will be run.

- **Ensure participation:** Ask for input and encourage sharing different opinions when appropriate. Be aware of the introverts on your team; you may need to give them the space to speak to achieve as much equity as possible. You've already established that the attendees of this meeting are "essential," so show that by ensuring their voices and input are heard.

- **Assign critical roles:** A scribe should produce and distribute a follow-up meeting summary with the next steps to ensure that agreements are followed. The timekeeper helps keep the meeting moving forward so you cover essential topics in the allotted time. It is always helpful for the timekeeper to announce milestones like, "We are at 30 minutes!" or "We are about 10 minutes from our scheduled end time" so participants don't get too wrapped up in discussion or risk being late to other commitments.

- **Review critical decisions and next steps:** Confirm actions have owners and a timeline for completion. I used to have a "WHTDWABW" section on my meeting agendas. This ridiculously long acronym stood for "Who Has To Do What And By When." That ensured things didn't end up hidden or forgotten.

- **Ask for feedback:** Did we accomplish the goals of this meeting? Was it a productive use of your time? What would have made it more effective? You can even have people do a quick 1-10 rating of the meeting in their notes and hand it in as long as they give you a "why."

- **End on time:** This is another way to show respect. Do not assume participants will stay over to complete the discussion; negotiate an extension or plan a follow-up meeting if necessary. Try to have some "10,000-foot view" of organizational meetings or a "primary meeting list" so there is sensitivity to the schedules of most participants. Consider walking distance and time of day when scheduling. Many leaders also "bake in" a 5-10-minute "early end" to allow humans to do human things.

Great meetings do not just happen. They take thoughtful planning to be most effective. Putting some of these ideas into practice will create the disciplined habit needed to succeed.

Virtual Meetings

The best practices for worthwhile and productive meetings also apply to virtual meetings, with a few additional tips:

- **Connect strategically** by keeping virtual meetings fast, frequent, and focused.

- **Recognize, don't run from, shared spaces**, and use meetings to get to know your colleagues and build upon workplace culture. I have had amazing conversations based on some artwork in the background of someone's at-home workspace or shared a funny moment when a child ran into the room making funny faces, or a cat jumped onto the table. Look for these moments and use them to make connections.

- **Test your camera and audio** beforehand to ensure your face is visible and the audio is clear.

- **Eliminate distractions** but do not stress if a dog barks or a room-mate or family member comes on camera. Use the "blur background" or "virtual background" setting when it makes sense.

- **Do not multitask** because while answering emails or tackling chores during the call is tempting, one Harvard Business Review article on battling Zoom fatigue indicates it costs you as much as 40% of your productive time.

- **Mute when not speaking.** This is a must since few working from home have a perfect and serene environment. Whether it's a loud coffee shop, delivery service at the door, or aircraft overhead, muting background noise is a friend to everyone.

- **Practice self-care and take breaks**, as concentration fatigue may start 30-40 minutes into a virtual meeting. Where possible, limit video meetings to 30 minutes. For long meetings, take short breaks and take longer breaks every two hours over the day.

The Power of Storytelling

❝ Tell Your Story.

Storytelling goes back to ancient times. Stories about great battles, storms, events, and people help us know who we are and where we came from and point to our identity. They were etched on cave walls, written on papyrus, carved in stone, and passed down through the generations in tales told at countless firesides under an eternity of stars.

We often say that great organizations are known by their stories. How true that is!

We could sit down and share our stories for hours. We could cry together and recall the significant loss and pain we witnessed during our healthcare journeys. We could also laugh until our stomachs ached at some ridiculous things we had seen and heard.

Tell your story.

Excerpt from Chapter 14, Inspired Nurse; *Author Rich Bluni, R.N.*

Nothing is more "healthcare" than a bunch of people sitting around trying to outdo the others with "You won't believe this one!" Our stories are the happiest, funniest, most heartbreaking, and yes, sometimes the most inappropriate. If there were an Olympics of storytelling, we would get the gold medal every time!

Stories are how people learn about each other, bringing together families, friends, communities, and even nations. Stories are extraordinary ways to share wisdom. They help us learn and expand as humans, leaders, and organizations.

Some of the best employee forums are the ones in which stories are shared. They might be told by the leaders, as pre-prepared videos, or even told directly by patients or loved ones of patients about their emotional or special experiences or moments. It may be a departure from what you usually do, but departures often lead to incredible destinations, don't they? As sharing stories becomes a cultural norm, you may be surprised at how easy it is to harvest more.

Stories are where inspiration is born, which is at the core of who we are in healthcare. As writer Mia Couto once said, "Listen, and you will realize that we are made not from cells or atoms. We are made from stories."

Principle 8 Summary

Communicate at all levels. It sounds like a lofty goal when you think of it, but as we said in the introduction to this book, we are striving for nothing less than "bodacious." To achieve excellence, we must use inspired communication to level up and move forward.

Effective communication requires several essential elements—leading with the why, communicating with compassion, managing up, taking ownership, and fearlessly wielding the shield of transparency. It is also crucial to keep communication boards relevant, visible, and engaging and to conduct staff huddles, meetings, and virtual sessions with heart, mind, and even a touch of humor. Employee forums, effective meetings, and storytelling can make deeper connections and foster a sense of community.

This may all be challenging to implement, and as we've said here already, the good things rarely come without some difficulty, some stretch, and some challenge. But I urge you to move forward with empowering and "leveling up" your communication no matter how hard it may be.

Don't give up on this.

As the fantastic performer Ella Fitzgerald once said, "Just don't give up on what you're trying to do. Where there is love and inspiration, I don't think you can go wrong."

That should be music to our ears.

PRINCIPLE 9: RECOGNIZE AND REWARD SUCCESS

Value and appreciate people working together to get results.

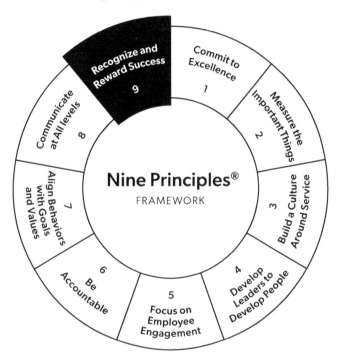

"The sweetest sound someone can hear is their own name spoken with appreciation."

African proverb

66 TIME AFTER TIME...

As I strolled through the food service department hallway, I stumbled upon a wall that was a sight to behold. It was as if Mardi Gras had exploded onto it, with an abundance of glitter, colorful borders, and tinsel that made it impossible not to smile. A message in shiny purple letters at the top of the board read, "GRATITUDE IS THE ATTITUDE." The wall was adorned with greeting cards and note pages, pinned up for all to see.

The department manager, James, noticed me admiring the wall and approached me. "This is where all the love we receive comes to stay," he explained. "Whenever anyone gets a thank you note or a card, we all post it here. I catch my team standing with their morning coffee, reading these notes."

As I examined the board, I was drawn to a letter framed with shiny gold hearts and musical notes. James noticed my interest and said, "Oh, that's a letter we received about Esmie."

I knew precisely who Esmie was. She was a cherished employee who had recently passed away unexpectedly. She was one of those rare individuals who could make you feel better by being in her presence. It was no surprise that she had a special place on this board.

James stood quietly as I read the letter.

To whom it may concern.

I am writing to express my gratitude for the exceptional care your employee, Esmie, provided. My daughter, June, was recently a patient at your facility, and Esmie's kindness and compassion significantly impacted our family.

June has a complicated medical history; my wife and I have been her full-time caregivers since birth. She is visually impaired and has limited speech, making her agitated, especially around strangers. After her surgery, June was placed on a special diet, which she refused to eat. The doctor suggested a feeding tube, which we dreaded as we knew it would cause her further distress.

However, everything changed when Esmie arrived with June's tray last Sunday. We explained the situation to her, and she nodded in understanding and said, "Let me give it a try." Esmie spoke softly to June as she set up her tray, and we watched in amazement as June responded positively and began to calm down.

Esmie asked us about June's favorite song, "Time After Time," by Cyndi Lauper. Esmie gently began singing it to her. June smiled and nodded her head, and Esmie started feeding her. She ate the whole tray! Esmie even agreed to sing the song again and recorded it on our phones so we could play it for June during her next meal. We now call it "The Esmie Song," which calms June whenever she gets agitated.

Esmie's kindness and compassion were remarkable; we will never forget her. She was an angel to us that day, and we will always be grateful for her impact on June. Please tell her to thank you for us.

Sincerely,

William Jones

Upon finishing the letter, James reminisced about the time they read it to Esmie during a staff meeting. The heartfelt words had moved her to tears, and the entire department had cheered. James even recalled how they had convinced Esmie to sing the song for them, a moment they all remember.

As we stood in silence, gazing at Esmie's letter on the board, I couldn't help but feel a sense of awe. It was a powerful reminder of one person's impact on the lives of many. James looked at me through misty eyes and said, "I miss her. We all do. Sometimes when I feel the loss, I open this card and read this to myself, and I swear I hear her singing in my mind, isn't that wild?"

I leaned in and whispered, "No, James, it is not wild."

This experience stays with me as I think about the importance of recognizing and celebrating the great work of others. We all have our own Esmies, those individuals who make a difference in our lives and those around us. By sharing their stories, we not only honor their contributions but also inspire others to make a positive impact as well.

When we talk here in Principle 9 about recognizing and rewarding others, we don't just say, "Recognize and reward." We add the word "success" to the mix, and that's an important distinction.

If you ask the average person walking down the street to define success, they might go right to "being rich." While there is nothing wrong with having a little extra money to spend (and I wish financial security for all of us), as the Beatles reminded us, "money can't buy you love."

Note that we end with this principle and weave recognizing and rewarding people into every principle throughout this book. This concept is the keystone to building a place where people want to do the meaningful work that moves an organization from good to great and great to greater.

As leaders, there are multiple practical and heartfelt reasons for reward and recognition.

Let's start with the practical. You strive to ensure that you reward behaviors, performance, outcomes, and results. If the reward and recognition are connected to those, the message across the organization is clear: "This is the stuff that matters, and this is what we are all about."

People place value on what is shown to be valued. Conversely, people generally disregard what is done out of obligation or expectation if there is no value behind it. No meaning or nothing connected to a deeper "why," and the message gets lost.

Principle 9 is about inspiring excellence through reinforcement—recognition, and reward. We already talked a bit about the "practical," but what energizes me most about Principle 9 is the "heartfelt" part.

Recognize and reward for excellent work. Appreciate people's hustle, dedication, and effort. Honestly, we don't achieve success without work. As Vidal Sassoon wisely reminded us, "The only place where success comes before work is in the dictionary."

So, when we recognize and reward behavior, we're not just being nice. We're ensuring that the behavior gets repeated, not just by the employee who initially performed the behavior but also by those who witness the impact and feel the drive to "be that." Recognizing people encourages others to do the right thing and promotes the consistency we need to inspire a culture of excellence. Maybe more importantly, feeling appreciated is an essential aspect of our emotional well-being, and research has shown that it can profoundly impact many areas of our lives.

A study from *The Journal of Applied Psychology* found that employees who felt appreciated by their leaders were more engaged, leading to lower turnover. A study in *The Journal of Social Psychology* found that individuals who felt appreciated experienced decreased symptoms of depression and anxiety. Also, a study published in *Health Psychology* found that individuals who felt valued and appreciated at work have better sleep and overall physical health. Lastly, a study from the *Journal of Marriage and Family* found that individuals who feel appreciated by their partner have better communication and stronger relationships.

We all want to feel connected to purpose and understand how our work fits the bigger picture. As I've said, people get into healthcare for "big reasons." Sometimes we need to be reminded of that, especially when we've done something that makes that connection. A leader committed to inspiring excellence in their team makes recognition and reward for success a fundamental part of their leadership.

Why Recognition Matters

When things are going great, recognition is always easier. That's an almost universal truth. When you are fit, exercising is easier. When you are in the newness of a relationship, romance is easier. However, much like when you need an antibiotic when there's an infection, sometimes recognition shines brightest when we experience barriers, setbacks, trials, or even dark times. Especially in times of high stress and turnover, recognition becomes even more critical to create an excellent place for people to work, grow, and prosper. It is worth reemphasizing that recognition done well is proven to:

- Attract and retain top talent.

- Grow and develop talent.

- Increase employee engagement.

- Encourage high-performance behaviors.

- Create a sense of teamwork and community.

Let's look at some more compelling evidence.

In the "2023 Global Culture Report," O.C. Tanner Institute collected and analyzed the perspectives of over 36,000 employees, leaders, H.R. practitioners, and business executives from 18 countries worldwide. The report states, "Nearly 74% of employees say recognition is crucial to workplace community. When recognition happens regularly in teams, the odds of having a strong community increase by 508%. When it's integrated into the organizational culture, the odds increase 387%, and the strength of that community increases 19%."

Those are good odds. Like, really, good. But, if you ask workers if they feel "overly" rewarded and recognized, the answer would most likely be "no." The same report states, "Regrettably, only 21% of workplaces worldwide have highly integrated recognition."

O.C. Tanner also asked, *"What is the most important thing that your manager or company currently does that would cause you to produce great work?"*

Unsurprisingly, autonomy, pay, and training appeared as themes, but "recognize me" was the most common theme that surfaced. **Thirty-seven percent of respondents said that more personal recognition would encourage them to produce better work more often.**

The Science of Recognition

The book *Wonder Drug* by Stephen Trzeciak, M.D., and Anthony Mazzarelli, M.D., references "The Fantastic Four." These four hormones deliver messages via the bloodstream to trigger specific responses.

The book states, "Four particular neurohormones—endorphins, dopamine, oxytocin, and serotonin—can work together independently to turn any day into Valentine's Day, essentially stuffing your body/brain mailbox with messages of love and happiness. Activities that increase the Fantastic Four boost mood and well-being." Recognition can do its part to ramp up all four hormones' production. Something positive happens in our brains when we receive recognition.

Another article, "The Science Behind Employee Recognition," says, "Human beings are wired to crave connection, belonging, and acceptance. When we experience appreciation and gratitude, our brains release dopamine and serotonin. These crucial neurotransmitters make us feel 'good,' regulating our emotions and responding to stress. Gratitude catalyzes these neurotransmitters, and actively experiencing gratitude and appreciation allows us to manage our stress levels better."

Practicing consistent recognition in the workplace improves employees' mental well-being and increases their motivation to contribute value to their organization. Verbalizing our appreciation and gratitude alters how we see the world and ourselves. So why don't we do this more often?

Recognition Blockers

It is safe to say that many leaders have not been as good at reward and recognition as they need to be. Remember, only 21% of workplaces worldwide have highly integrated recognition, which means 79% do not! If we are to take this data as fact, we all might need a "mirror, mirror, on the wall" moment.

Here are a few common excuses and associated leadership archetypes that we have heard over the years:

1. **The Cantankerous Curmudgeon:** "No one ever told me I was special... do they need a participation trophy too? If I can survive, so can they. They'll want a raise if they get told how good they are!"

2. **The Hateful Grateful:** "Shouldn't they be grateful even to have a job in this market?!"

3. **The Miserable Miser:** "I bought a ten-pack of thank you cards out of my own pocket from the dollar store and ran out a few months ago, so they know I appreciate them. How many times do I have to say it?"

4. **The Pinnacle of Cynical:** "No one needs this fluffy stuff. They all think it's childish. What's next—gold star stickers and lollipops?"

I know some of you just pictured someone when you read the above descriptions. The good news is that if recognizing your team makes you uncomfortable, you embark on a growth journey. Getting comfortable with being uncomfortable is what makes an excellent leader. Embrace it. It's like diving into ice-cold water. Wading in will be brutally painful. Diving in will hopefully be refreshing.

Don't think of this as something happening "to" you; this is happening "for" you. It will make you a much better leader and will make your team a much better team. We have seen this proven time and time again. If you're a little anxious about it, reframe it:

"This isn't what I've done in the past, but to do what I've never done can lead me to what I've never achieved. I will embrace this discomfort. This will empower my leadership and lift my team."

Criticism Versus Compliments

Recognition matters to people. Yet many might think that giving one compliment to every criticism will balance and make a person feel optimistic about a relationship. It is quite different. Take a look at the research summarized in this chart:

1 to 1	1 compliment - 1 criticism	Negative
2 to 1	2 compliments - 1 criticism	Neutral
3 to 1	3 compliments - 1 criticism	Positive!

Figure 9.1: Criticism to compliment ratio
3 compliments to 1 criticism ratio, p. 232 "How can you keep a positive relationship with an employee? Inside the Magic Kingdom: Seven Keys to Disney Success" by Tom Connellan

Some studies recommend a more significant amount of praise, reporting that five-to-one and seven-to-one ratios are necessary for achieving and maintaining a healthy and productive feedback relationship.

Emily Heaphy and Marcial Losada conducted one compelling study. Heaphy and Losada examined the praise-to-criticism ratio in 60 business units within a large company. These teams were categorized as high-performing, average, or low-performing based on objective measures such as financial performance, customer satisfaction ratings, and 360-degree assessments by individual team members.

The researchers discovered that the most significant factor differentiating the most successful teams from the least successful ones was the ratio of positive and negative comments. The praise-to-criticism ratio for each cohort was as follows:

- High-performing: 5:1

- Average: 2:1

- Low-performing: 1:3

This is not "fluffy stuff." It's based on the science of how our hormones regulate behavior. The effect of the oxytocin boost wears off more quickly than the arresting impact of cortisol, making the experience of more frequent positive interactions important for continuous motivation.

There is nothing to lose here. We all know, deep down, that human beings crave appreciation and recognition. We are wired for it. Whatever the ratio, why not go for the higher one? Even in our relationships. How often are we quick to point out when our kids mess up, or our partner lets us down, and yet we allow the many more times our kids did a great job or our partner was amazing to slip through our fingers?

At the end of the day, as I say in some of my talks, I'd rather "apologize" for being too kind than regret not being kind enough.

Recognition sounds like...	Appreciation sounds like...
	"Thank you. I know it was hard work, and I value you and your team's continued commitment to the quality and safety of our patients. You need to know that you may have saved a life for every fall you prevented. That's powerful."
"Congratulations on achieving your departmental goal for a 70% reduction in falls."	
"Thank you so much for staying late tonight."	"Your commitment to your co-workers and our patients is evident. This evening would've been much harder for everyone if it wasn't for you. I am so grateful to have you on the team."
"It was great to see your department's employee engagement numbers increase to 93% this quarter. "	"You are a valued leader here. Your employees are communicating how they feel about you. I am hearing that many of them feel lucky to have you as their leader. Thank you for being a difference maker and a great example to the other leaders here."
"Your presentation went very well. Congratulations on an audience score of 9.88! That's incredible!	"Whenever you present, your authenticity and soul shine through! Your personal story was moving, and it was obvious you put a lot of hard work and yourself into that talk!"

Figure 9.2: Recognition and Appreciation

The Wonder Twins— Recognition and Appreciation

The words "recognition" and "appreciation" are often used interchangeably. They may look alike, but there is a big difference between them, and the truth is that we all need both.

> Recognition is about giving positive feedback based on results or performance (what you do).

> Appreciation, on the other hand, is about acknowledging a person's inherent value (who you are).

Of course, there are times when both can be applied to a situation, and there are times when one or the other makes more sense. Let's say a department hits a goal they have been working to achieve. If you only praise the outcome, consider the opportunities you miss to connect, value, support, and appreciate each team member.

In contrast, let's say a department missed the goal by a decimal point but showed their heart and spirit in the striving. Yes, you want them to hit that mark, but you don't want to discourage them when they get so close. Maybe there isn't as much to "recognize" as far as a metric, but there may be an opportunity to appreciate their character, integrity, and teamwork.

It's essential to make sure you are doing both.

66 The Red Plate.

Let me tell you about my friend Margaret and her awesome family tradition called "The Red Plate." This tradition started when her kids were little and it's still going strong today.

So, here's how it works. Every so often when Margaret's family gets together for a meal, someone at the table may get a surprise of the special "red plate." And let me tell you, this plate isn't just for show. It's placed in front of someone who deserves some recognition and appreciation.

Back when the kids were little, the red plate could be given for all sorts of reasons. Maybe it was for making an "A" on a test or for working hard during a tough semester at school. It could even be for just being an awesome son, daughter, or friend. As adults, the red plate might be for landing an internship or for just being home for the holidays and showing how special their being home is to the family.

But here's the funny thing. Margaret's kids are all grown up now, but they still get excited and competitive about the red plate. Even today, when they gather for holidays or other celebrations, you will surely hear the sibling who has been bestowed the red plate crowing about it to the others.

Although the reasons for the red plate may have changed over the years, its meaning and purpose have remained the same. It's a beautiful way to show appreciation and recognition for someone's hard work and who they are as a person.

What a great idea! Think of how to carry this "Red Plate" concept into the workplace. Consider creative ways to embed recognition and appreciation into everyday work processes. Allow recognition to be inherent to the way you communicate and share appreciation.

So, who deserves the red plate at your worktable today? Serve it up!

The Power of Thank You Notes

Research by the Duke Center for Healthcare Safety and Quality shows that writing a letter of gratitude helps to improve emotional exhaustion, happiness, and well-being in healthcare workers. The study invited participants to write an appreciative letter to someone who has positively affected their lives.

Of the 1,575 participants:

- 75.4% reported that it was easier to think of things to be grateful for since writing their letter.

- 63.9% requested and emailed a copy of their letter to reflect on and share with the intended recipient.

- 56.7% answered they have other people in mind for whom they might write a similar letter.

- 45.1% talked to someone about their letter.

No one says that a gratitude note makes every problem disappear, but it might make some problems easier to work on.

Effective Thank You Notes—Who, When, What, Where, and How

Like baking a cake or recreating your great-grandmother's famous potato salad, there is a recipe or formula to express gratitude. Something more than just scribbling "thanks!" on a card and tossing it like a frisbee at someone as you run toward your next meeting. Here are some things to consider:

- **WHO:** Thank you notes can create a win for more than the recipient. Acknowledge them by name, include who identified the behavior, and tell them how much you appreciate them. It's a three-way win: the recipient, the person who recognizes them, and you. Gratitude is like that "stone creating a ripple in the pond" effect we hear about.

- **WHEN:** You know how they say, "Don't let the moment pass you by?" It is true of gratitude. Don't wait. Reward and recognize quickly. The impact will be felt more when the moment's emotion is still warm. It's like driving past a Krispy Kreme and seeing the "hot now" light on. We all know that is the time to get those donuts—"hot now" is better.

- **WHAT:** Write the note specifically and not generally. You want the recipient to know how much you value what they did. "Hey, great job" is okay, but it's just "Okay." You are here to create inspired excellence, not "okay excellence." It shows respect to your recipient when you acknowledge them expressly. Remember, rewarded behavior gets repeated.

- **WHERE:** Send the note to the employee's home whenever possible. When an employee receives a thank you note at home, it feels more personal than one laid on a desk, along with a stack of reports and memos. Notes delivered to the home often are talked about with family at dinner, hung on the refrigerator door, and kept to remember. Our homes are our sanctuaries, and that note becomes part of that.

- **HOW:** Handwrite the notes if possible. Countless individuals have told us they'd rather receive a three-sentence, handwritten note than a two-page typed letter. In this age of texts, emails, and social media D.M.s, there is something authentic and special about someone taking the time for a handwritten note. Coco Chanel once said, "Don't be like the rest of them, darling."

August 3rd

Dear Juan,

Christina shared with me this week about the number of positive comments you have received from your patients. She said your patients know you by name, and she consistently hears comments about your compassion and that they know when and what to expect. This means so much to our patients and the families we serve. Christina also told me how you are helping to interview and onboard new staff. Thank you.

You certainly live our values of integrity and excellence and continue to be a vital part of this team and the organization. We are so grateful to you.

Sincerely,
Amanda

If you want to increase the cadence of your written thank you notes, consider ways to make it easier to instill this practice into your work. Save time on your calendar weekly. Use a reminder app to send you emails. Stock up on cards or notes, gain access in advance to staff addresses if you can, or plan how you will distribute them if mailing them to someone's home is not an option.

Don't get too hung up on how many. You can have a reference like "X notes a month," but it need not be a hard rule. This is one of those moments that calls for common sense. Tolerating zero cards a month is as "ridiculous" as mandating 30 cards monthly. If you run a 12-bed critical access hospital, there might be a different "expectation" for the cadence of thank you notes than an 800-bed hospital. Same with a clinic or medical practice versus a mobile care van or a level-one trauma center. So, take a deep breath and focus on the "why" over the "how much."

Over time, sending thank you notes will become an ingrained habit. You will find they are a valuable tool in your leadership toolkit.

Individualizing Recognition

Each person is unique in their desire to be recognized. It is important to connect with your employees and demonstrate your appreciation, giving them recognition in a way that feels good. We are fortunate to have the gifts of our introverts and extroverts on our teams. But while a tiger and an elephant are powerful animals, what feeds them differs. For example, one person on your team may love to be recognized publicly, while another might prefer to hear praise privately.

I recall learning a hard lesson along these lines as a leader. One of my staff, Olivia, went above and beyond, and I wanted to go all out to recognize her. I gathered people together, got some balloons and a gift card, and we all hid in the break room. I had a lookout call the breakroom as soon as she clocked in. When the door opened, we all yelled in unison as loud as we could, "You rock!" Olivia's eyes widened. She screamed, dropped her lunch bag, and ran out of the room in terror.

Not exactly what I expected.

When we caught up with her, she was crying, and I was mortified. I meant well—we all did—but I found out later that Olivia hated surprises. Her older sister always used to sneak up and scare her as a little kid, which completely unsettled her. She wasn't mad at us; she was very gracious and forgiving and found it funny after her heart rate came down. But we all learned a few things. One, don't sneak up on Olivia. Two, not everyone likes the same type of recognition.

As leaders, we need to give individual, meaningful, and lasting recognition. Consider asking:

- How do you like being recognized, acknowledged, and rewarded for a well-done job?

- What type of recognition or praise do you prefer (public, private, written, verbal, or something else)?

- From whom do you most like to receive recognition or praise?

- What is the most outstanding recognition you have ever received?

- What makes you feel most valued at work?

EMPLOYEE RECOGNITION QUESTIONNAIRE
Preferences

Each employee is unique in their desire to be recognized, so ask your employee about their preferences. To connect with your employees and demonstrate your appreciation, it's important to give recognition in a way that feels good to them. Complete the following assessment with new employees, as well as current employees, to ensure meaningful and lasting recognition is given and received.

Employee Name:

How do you like to be recognized, acknowledged and rewarded for a job well done?

What type of recognition or praise do you prefer:
public, private, written, verbal, or something else?

From whom do you most like to receive recognition or praise?

Figure 9.3: Recognition Questionnaire

Delivering Appreciation in Unique Ways

There are many ways to ensure your team feels rewarded and recognized. Group settings, one-on-one conversations, and written thank you notes are all effective ways to recognize and reward success in all the ways we experience it in healthcare.

Some of the organizations Huron has coached have blazed the trail and come up with many unique ways, both big and small, to get creative with recognition and reward. Here are some you may consider:

- "Monarch Monday:" One organization would buy a crown from a costume shop, and if someone gets a special letter of praise or significant manage up, they get to wear the crown for the whole day on the next Monday they work. All their co-workers call them "your highness" for the day. They get a special meal/snack served to them, pictures taken, and a royal proclamation scroll to keep. They go all out to make them feel like the royalty they are.

- "Let's Go PTO:" Some organizations allow vacation/personal time off to be awarded to an employee that doesn't count against their "limit." When someone goes above and beyond, there's nothing like a day off to make them feel well-rested and loved.

- "Gift Bag Swag:" One organization I worked with allowed a budget for employee reward and recognition per department. One department chose to buy gift cards for places that were popular with the team, and when it was time for someone to be recognized, they pulled out what they called the "magic bag of swag." It was a satin purple Santa-type bag, and the team would gather around, clap their hands, and chant "swag! swag! swag!" progressively louder as the awardee reached into the bag and pulled out a card.

- "Better to Give than Receive:" Another organization that gave each department a budget for recognition and reward took great pride in their service to their community and charitable giving. It was a big part of their culture. Their team asked that the equivalent dollar amount that would've been given to the person being recognized as a gift card, bonus, or time off would instead be donated to a charity of that person's choice and that the organization would match that donation. This example started to catch on with a few of my partners, who made it an option for their teams. Not surprisingly, many chose to forgo their rewards in favor of charitable giving.

- "A Gain in the Neck:" An organization partnered with a nearby school of massage, and on scheduled days, the student therapists who were nearing graduation would come in with their tables and set up in the break room. The person being recognized would get covered by their manager so they could get a 20-minute back and neck massage. This one was a big hit!

- "Knocked it Outta the Park:" One town had a beloved college baseball team, and the college worked closely with the hospital on many things. So, their form of recognition was free tickets to the baseball game for a family of up to seven people, with vouchers for hot dogs, too. Some people love their sports (and hot dogs), so this may be a home run for your organization!

As a healthcare organization, you work with many community members and maybe have some on your board who can offer things like free classes at community colleges, car wash gift cards, restaurant vouchers, airline miles, flowers, or dog sitting. People love healthcare workers, and you'd be surprised at how willing your community might be to offer up some love.

It can also be internal, like a meal, coffee shop vouchers, or gift shop "dollars." It may not feel like much, but sending cards of thanks home to partners and kids of employees to thank them for the sacrifice of time their parent or partner made doing an extra shift—especially if it meant they performed some amazing deed—often means more to the employee than you'd think.

I have seen many examples of ways to make people feel valued and appreciated. There are thousands of variations. Be creative. You are only limited by your imagination (and maybe your organizational policies)!

66 SEMPER FI:

As a frequent traveler, I have had many opportunities to watch people at their best and, yes, their worst too. However, in all my travels, one moment on a plane to Atlanta has left a forever lesson of kindness and appreciation in me.

I had completed a speaking engagement, and I barely made my flight. I desperately hoped to get upgraded to first class—mostly because I was looking forward to a meal. Yes, I was that hungry!

I was thrilled that I was number one on the upgrade list. However, my excitement was short-lived as I watched the upgrade screen update, and suddenly there were no first-class seats left. I resigned myself to my seat behind first class, where I would eat my sad airplane peanuts.

No "winner, winner, chicken dinner" for me.

At first, I thought this was the travel angels taunting me. However, I soon realized that my vantage point behind first class was a blessing in disguise.

As I was boarding, I noticed several U.S. Marines waiting. As the boarding continued, one woman from first-class stopped the first Marine and said," I'd be honored if you would switch your seat for mine so you can relax, eat, and drink a little bit. I want to thank you for your service."

The young Marine politely replied, "I appreciate the offer, but I'm flying with three other Marines, and we need to stick together. But thank you so much for the offer."

Just as I thought the moment had passed, a gentleman sitting nearby raised his hand and offered to trade his seat for one of the Marines. Two young women also spoke up, offering their seats so all four Marines could sit together. The four first-class passengers gathered their belongings, chatted with the Marines, and then took their new seats in the rows behind me.

The young Marines were overwhelmed with gratitude and thanked the four passengers profusely. The pilot shared the heartwarming story over the intercom, and the plane erupted in applause.

I can tell you those amazing young Marines made that first-class cabin glow. The pilot even took the time to chat with them and snap some selfies. These brave men and women would have a story to tell for years.

And you know what the flight crew did? They returned first-class meals to the four original passengers to thank them.

During my next connecting flight, I had the good luck and pleasure of sitting next to "Vickie," the incredible woman who first offered her seat. Vickie shared she was a business owner in the financial field. She had about 80 employees and firmly believed in the power of gratitude. She explained that when gratitude is unleashed, it often takes on a life of its own.

She shared that while the pay was fair at her firm, some employees could make more money in a bigger town. They chose to stay because they loved where and who they worked with. They felt appreciated.

Vickie said, "To create a great workplace, put your team first and ensure your company overflows with appreciation. Kindness is contagious."

She continued, "Look what happened when I offered that young Marine my seat. I didn't know any of those other people. I have never met them in my life. Look how fast that man and those two young women offered their seats to those other Marines! That's the power of kindness. I'm no saint or anything, but I wanted to show my appreciation for that Marine's service, and from that, there was a cascade of goodwill."

As we landed and said our goodbyes, I couldn't help but think we needed more Vickies. Her leadership style and belief in the power of gratitude were inspiring. It reminded me of a quote from William James, who has often been called the "Father of American Psychology." He said, "The deepest principle in human nature is the craving to be appreciated."

Principle 9 is precisely that. It reaches deeply into the essence of what William James spoke of. If a leader can get that and make it part of their process and their being, there is no way they can fail.

And quite candidly, it is so simple. We love to make simple things complicated because I think, especially in healthcare, where there are so many brilliant minds, we feel that if something is simple, it can't possibly be significant or valuable or "true."

But I have found, and continue to learn, that the closer you get to the truth, the simpler the lesson becomes. Recognize and reward success. It's impactful, it's simple, and it is the exemplar of a first-class leader.

Principle 9 Summary

Now more than ever, recognizing and rewarding success matters. People need to know what they do counts. They want to feel valued, respected and acknowledged.

Create a great place for people to work, grow, and prosper. Prioritizing recognition can revolutionize the performance and success of individuals and teams. It attracts and retains top talent. It also grows and develops that talent, increases employee engagement, encourages high-performance behaviors, and creates a sense of teamwork and community. Studies report that we need to hear three to five positives to every one negative to feel positive and achieve a healthy and productive relationship.

Combining recognition and appreciation can have a tremendous impact on individuals. It's not enough to provide positive feedback based on results or performance. It's equally important to show appreciation for who people are as individuals. This powerful combination can create a ripple effect of gratitude and emotion.

One timeless and impactful way to show appreciation is by sending a handwritten thank you note to an employee's home. Personalized and individual notes can significantly impact and create a three-way win for the recipient, the person who recognizes them, and you. Reward and recognize quickly for the most significant impact, and when writing, be specific about the behavior and the person being recognized. Remember, rewarded behavior gets repeated.

Creating a culture where gratitude, recognition, and reward are commonplace is, well, let's say, uncommon. That's why it is so memorable when we witness, partake in, or receive it. Our work can be tough at times—we give so much of ourselves in healthcare. What we see and what we do daily is not common. Therefore, people who do the extraordinary deserve to be treated in extraordinary ways.

This quickly catches on as the more we recognize people, the more they begin to recognize others, creating an inspiring, magnetic, and even joyful workplace. Before you know it, you've created a trend that will never go out of style.

As Khalil Gibran once shared: "There are those who give with joy, and that joy is their reward."

The gift of reward and recognition is one where the giver and recipient share equally in the joy.

CLOSING

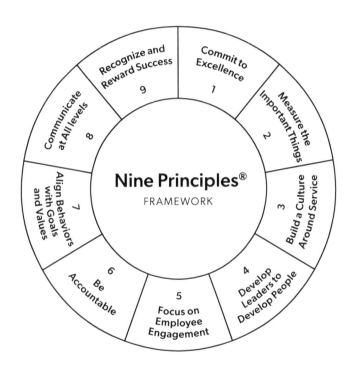

"If you want to build a ship, don't drum up people to collect wood and don't assign them tasks and work, but rather teach them to long for the endless immensity of the sea."

Antoine de Saint-Exupery

We are building something far greater, far more impressive in scope and magnificence than a ship. Yet the quote above reminds us that creating something truly excellent happens when the human imagination is awakened. Our eyes and hearts are fixed on the grandeur of something that pulls at us and calls us to not only do more but also be more than we once were.

Our journey together throughout this book is more than "gathering wood" or "assigning tasks." Instead, it's been about moving and inspiring others to long for the endless immensity of the inspired excellence of healthcare. The most massive ocean cannot match the depth and breadth of what we do, and the most audacious of ships cannot come close to taking one on a more meaningful voyage than healthcare as an extension of the boundless human spirit.

We started this book with a simple premise that my dad Jack, the healthcare maintenance foreman, taught me: The excellence we seek does not necessarily dwell only in our "jobs" but lives solidly in our "work." Our work, our deeper "why," is tied to our "big reason" for being in healthcare in the first place. And maybe, just maybe, that is connected to the greatest of all things on this earth.

Love.

For what else truly drives healthcare but love for others? A desire to make manifest healing and comfort and peace—gifted from the hands, minds, and spirit of one human being to another. All of this comes from the best part of us, fulfilling the powerful desire to leave the world a little better than we found it, one human interaction at a time.

Hopefully, as you've read this book, you have had moments of reflection and introspection. Hopefully, you remembered someone you cared for, worked for or led and flashed back to your own moments of "big reasons."

My greatest wish is that you not only learned something but that you felt something. Maybe something that you have always felt but now feel more distinctly. Maybe something that you once felt long ago that had faded, that you now feel again, like a long-lost friend. Maybe something that you never felt before but have been awakened to.

I hope you underlined and highlighted. I hope you shared a quote or a story with someone else that you thought might need it. I hope you laughed and maybe even teared up as you saw yourself in the stories I've shared with you. (They are not really "my stories" anyway; they are collectively "our stories" as we all have so much in common in health-care, don't we?)

There's a great parable I want to share about Michelangelo. The great artist found himself at a granite quarry looking for the perfect boulder. He stopped before a piece of rock that, to anyone else, would appear to be a boulder like all the rest, but Michelangelo appeared mesmerized by it. He immediately called for the quarryman to load the boulder on a cart which he then insisted on pushing through the streets to his studio by himself.

An onlooker called out, "Michelangelo! You are one of the greatest artists alive! What are you doing pushing a rock on a cart? Do you not see how foolish you look fumbling along? What could be so special about a rock that you would do such a thing?"

Michelangelo is said to have stopped to mop his brow and take a sip of water. With great reverence, he slowly placed his hand upon the boulder and answered, "When you look upon this cart, all you see is a boulder, but when I look upon this rock, I see within it an angel that is calling out to me to set it free."

The uninspired can only ever see the boulder. The great artist is not bound by what they are given; they know that they can turn even a boulder into something inspiring with their hands.

As I said at the beginning of this book, at this moment, you are two leaders: The leader you are now and the one you are becoming. I hope you see the masterpiece inside of you longing to be set free. I hope you see the potential that lies inside the very foundations of your organization. I hope you hear its voice calling out to you. Most importantly, I hope you will answer.

You are no longer bound by what you once were. You are becoming something far more. I hope you feel that deep within yourself. And as we come to the end of this book (but certainly not to the end of our journey), I hope you feel encouraged. I hope you feel empowered. I hope you feel excited.

Above all, I hope you feel inspired. Inspired to lead. Inspired to mentor. Inspired to create. Inspired to grow. Inspired to shine. Inspired to be bodacious.

Inspired to be excellent.

ACKNOWLEDGMENTS

To Dawn, my awesome wife, who never doubted, always lifted me up and was my biggest cheerleader, coach, and trusted advisor. What a lucky man I am to have such an incredible, brilliant, and beautiful woman in my life. You are my inspiration every day and always. Love and gratitude to you and our kids, Rhett, Luke, and Ava, for bringing me too much coffee, reminding me to eat, giving me hugs, leaving me notes of encouragement stuck to my laptop, listening, and giving me thumbs up or thumbs down as I read out loud story after story, and forgiving me for the endless hours of pacing, talking to myself too loudly, staying up later than I should have, and waking up earlier than you all wished I had! I owe you all big time. I love you with all I have.

To Huron's CEO, Mark Hussey. Thank you for being the very best CEO I have ever known or had the pleasure of working with. Your heart, humility, and kindness are all evident in what you do, what you say, how you lead, and, most importantly, who you are. We are all so truly fortunate to have you as our leader. I am grateful to be a part of your team. Thank you for everything.

To Jim Gallas, thank you for your support, authentic leadership, tenacity, and steadfastness. You help make us all better every day in every way. Working with you is an honor and a pleasure. I am very grateful to you.

To Curt Whelan, words cannot express how highly I regard you. This book would not have been possible without your unwavering support and commitment. I will always be humbled and honored that you brought me on board for this project. I have learned and continue to learn so much from you. You are a beautiful example to me and many others, professionally and personally, of what an inspired leader is. I only hope that one day I can be the man of grace, understanding, spirit, and patience you exemplify. You are one of the most amazing people I have come to know in my life, and I am so grateful and blessed to work alongside you.

To Tonia Breckenridge, Jennifer Malatek, and Jennifer Miller for providing your time, expertise, sharp eyes, brilliant minds, and committed support to elevate this book and ensure it could be the best it could be. You are great leaders, authentic to your core. I am fortunate to call each of you a friend. Thank you from the bottom of my heart for your contributions and for inspiring me to be my best.

To Stacy Fenimore, Amanda Smith, and Carrie Thornton. Thank you for keeping us on track and clearing the path. Please know you are so appreciated. We could not have done this without you.

To all the Huron team who contributed their ideas, thoughts, feedback, stories, words, and concepts to this book early on and throughout the process. Thank you so much for helping lay the foundation and create a platform to launch this book from. You are all awesome. Thank you to this team of wonderful, hard-working, and committed people who care deeply about who they serve and work with. You are all awesome. I am grateful to each of you.

To Michelle Mellon for your kindness, amazing editing, and word-smithing to help take this book to the next level, and Nathalie Rock for your artistic skill and bright energy that made this book a joy to see come to life.

And finally, to Margaret Stanzell. Every once in a while, a person comes into your life, and you know it was for a big reason. Margaret, where do I start? Not one word, graphic, or paragraph of this book would've been possible if it wasn't for you. I wish the world truly knew how much you've contributed to healthcare, how much you've done for so very long, all behind the scenes, without fanfare, spotlight, or even sometimes, credit. My name might be on the cover, but let it be known far and wide, your fingerprints are on every page. It is humbling to work with someone like you who cares so much about making a difference and could care less about the pat on the back for it. (But gosh, do you deserve all the pats on the back, and accolades, parades, and fireworks in the world!) I truly am so grateful to you for bringing me onto this project, always believing in me, and deeply caring about my family and me. Healthcare is a better place because of you. Our company is a better place because of you. I am a better person because of you. Thank you, my sister, for ALL this, from the bottom of my heart.

ABOUT THE AUTHOR

Rich Bluni, R.N. is the bestselling author of several award-winning books: *Inspired Nurse, Inspired Nurse Too, Oh No... Not More of That Fluffy Stuff!: The Power of Engagement* and *Inspired Excellence.*

Rich has been a Registered Nurse since 1993 and joined Huron initially as a coach in 2007 and is presently an International Speaker and Senior Director with Huron.

As an internationally renowned speaker, Rich has presented to tens of thousands across North America and Europe, frequently keynoting major conferences, individual hospital organizations, medical practices, and universities. As a Registered Nurse, Rich has over three decades of front-line healthcare and leadership experience across a broad range of areas, including pediatric oncology, pediatric intensive care, trauma intensive care, flight nursing, behavioral health, emergency medicine, risk management, patient safety, and quality.

Rich is passionate about healthcare and inspiring those who chose this sacred path as their profession.

HURON LEARNING SOLUTIONS

In the fast-paced world of healthcare, it's crucial for leaders and staff to adapt their skills to keep up with the present and future challenges. That's where Huron's Nine Principles® Framework comes in. This framework, extensively discussed in our book, plays a vital role in driving success. It empowers organizations to achieve top-notch performance, foster growth, and encourage innovation.

Here at Huron, we understand just how important it is to equip your workforce with the tools and resources they need to thrive. That's why we offer a wide range of tailored options to meet your specific needs.

Whether you're looking for speaking engagements, flexible virtual and on-demand learning, personalized coaching for your entire organization, conferences, or books to guide you, Huron is here to support you and guide you on this transformative journey.

Speaking

Huron speakers are sought after for their ability to motivate diverse audiences, provide practical strategies on healthcare's most complex issues, and deliver field-tested solutions for immediate improvement.

From online executive training to large-association learning and development programs, our experts deliver the perfect balance of inspiration and education for every audience.

Online Learning

The Huron Learning Digital Platform offers convenient and engaging education courses for employees at all levels, delivered virtually, on demand, and accessible from anywhere. Designed to promote individual, department, and organizational priorities, our education training provides the foundation to make goals more achievable than ever.

Conferences

Address change head-on with innovative solutions and inspired leadership at a Huron conference. Our events feature keynote speakers delivering industry-leading perspectives, as well as opportunities to network with other healthcare leaders. After attending an in-person or virtual conference, you will leave with practical tools and tactics to turn your challenges into opportunities. Continuing education credits are available for most events.

Huron Books

Develop the skills needed to deliver results across organizations with Huron's purpose-driven books. Authors provide insights for every healthcare leader, ranging from leadership development, patient and employee engagement, and more.

Learn More

To learn more, visit https://www.huronconsultinggroup.com/expertise/organizational-transformation-healthcare/learning-development